MS/FKV6   1966   10.00 hm

W9-BBI-699

GOLD FEVER

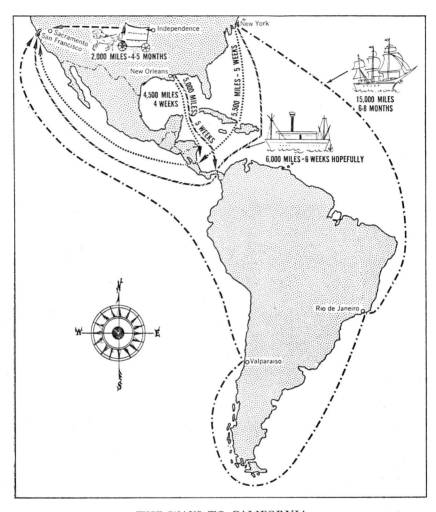

Independence

Sacramento
San Francisco
2,000 MILES - 4-5 MONTHS

New York

New Orleans

4,500 MILES
4 WEEKS

5,000 MILES - 5 WEEKS

5,500 MILES - 5 WEEKS

15,000 MILES
6-8 MONTHS

6,000 MILES - 6 WEEKS HOPEFULLY

N
W   E
S

Rio de Janeiro

Valparaiso

THE WAYS TO CALIFORNIA

GEORGE W. GROH

GOLD
FEVER

Being a True Account, Both
Horrifying and Hilarious,
of the Art of Healing (so-called)
During the California Gold Rush

610.9794

6701323

WILLIAM MORROW & COMPANY, INC.

NEW YORK

1966

Copyright © 1963, 1966 by George Groh

A part of this book has been published as an article in *American Heritage*.

All rights reserved. No part of this book may be reproduced or utilized in any form or by any means, electronic or mechanical, including photocopying, recording or by any information storage and retrieval system, without permission in writing from the Publisher.

Published simultaneously in Canada by George J. McLeod Limited, Toronto.

Printed in the United States of America.

Library of Congress Catalog Card Number 66-22111

To Lynn

FOREWORD

———————

The casual reader of this book might get the impression that in the gold rush nearly everyone died.

That would be very wide of the mark. There was a lot of lusty living—so much so that in less than two years the gold rushers transformed California from a lonely frontier outpost to a vigorous new state.

But there was also a lot of dying. This book is a special report on the ills which beset the adventurers and on the physicians who ministered to them. It could be compared to a battlefield communiqué as written from the particular vantage point of the first-aid station.

It is like an aid station report, too, in that the action is necessarily fragmentary. The casualties come and go amid scenes of general disorder. Often one catches the beginning of a human drama, but not the end. Or the end, but not the beginning.

As a random example, one encounters in these pages a thirteen-year-old boy who stowed away on a ship for California. The vessel ran into a lot of trouble, including starvation and threatened mutiny, and through it all the lad bustled around serving as a cheerful and competent cabin boy.

No doubt the reader would like to know what happened to that boy. The writer would like to know too. There is, however, just that one brief glimpse of him and then he passes from view, lost in the swirling confusion. One can only hope that his luck was as good as his nerve.

There are a lot of scenes like that, and in the end the individual fates are not really significant to the story. Rather, the collective experience merges into a common stream. In the mingled adventures we see what it was like to be alive in that boisterous, exuberant time that was also dangerous and demanding.

CONTENTS

—————————◆—————————

PART I—THE FEVER

1. If they have not a sweeping pestilence . . .   3
2. . . . and one went on a litter.   13

PART II—THE VOYAGE

3. Nine men occupied a space of but six feet square.   23
4. He implored us, amid his groans, to hasten forward.   32
5. . . . you can judge my situation.   45
6. The bread was full of worms . . .   55
7. I think my nervous system has become deranged.   64

PART III—THE TREK

8. Our ignorance of the route was complete.   79
9. During all this time I could hear poor Lyon groaning.   88
10. What the devil is this?   112
11. My mouth fairly watered, for a piece of an indian to broil!   122
12. They look heaven-sent!   150

PART IV—CALIFORNIA

13. The buildings of this Sitty are generally rather poor . . .   167
14. In this land of gold no law governs the art of healing.   176

ix

15. . . . if we are swept away, we will all go together.   195
16. Our cemeteries look like newly ploughed fields.   207
17. I like this wild and barbarous life.   227
18. He was jerked up and down several times to
     break his neck.   242
19. Hang the Sheriff!   261
20. . . . I quit even.   281

Chapter Notes   293

Acknowledgments and Bibliography   321

Index   329

MAPS

———◆———

The Ways To California   *Frontispiece*

Across the Isthmus of Panama   *35*

By Way of Nicaragua   *57*

The California Trail   *80-81*

Rocky Mountain Cutoffs   *113*

The End of the Trail   *123*

PART I

THE FEVER

CHAPTER 1

If they have not a sweeping pestilence, it will not be for want of material to provide it.

—Dr. Joseph Middleton at San Francisco.

When the first great wave of California gold rushers swarmed through Sacramento it cost the community more than $1,000 a week to bury the casualties.

It didn't cost San Francisco very much. Forty-niners who died broke and friendless there were cast out on a beach which became a field of skulls.

The fortune hunters succumbed sometimes to gun, knife, or rope, but more often they died of "California fever." In their own ironic parlance the term embraced both the gold mania itself and all the hardships which the adventure entailed.

The fever took many forms. Thus the gold rushers were ravaged time and again by fearful outbreaks of cholera, malaria, yellow fever, dysentery, all the contagions of the period. That was a predictable, almost inevitable result of mass migration at a time when epidemic defenses consisted largely of soap, water, and prayer.

Still other hardships resulted from the frenzied excitement which swept the migration along. It was an immense movement of people, over vast distances, conducted under conditions unique in the nation's history.

The previous pioneers had gone west by slow stages, estab-

3

lishing strings of settlements each a little farther out than the one before. A few scouts and trappers had ranged far afield, but they were a small band of skilled professionals. The gold rush was another affair entirely. In the first year alone more than 50,000 people spanned the wild continent in a frantic surge. They did it suddenly, on impulse, with almost no organization or planning, with scarcely a thought as to how they would sustain themselves at journey's end.

That, moreover, was but the beginning. The stampede continued through the early 1850s, more than 300,000 people being caught up in the rush.[1]

They went by a variety of routes, all of them arduous. Some risked a storm-tossed 15,000-mile seagoing passage around Cape Horn. Another contingent took a short cut, sailing to the Isthmus of Panama and slogging through a fetid jungle to resume the voyage on the Pacific side. And still others went overland, trekking by pack train and covered wagon across 2000 miles of plains, mountains, and deserts.

Along the way the gold rushers experienced burning heat, numbing cold, starvation, scurvy, fearful accidents, and myriad diseases. When they descended on California they were already the grizzled survivors of nearly every obstacle that relentless nature could place in their path. And then, promptly, they proceeded to devise some new afflictions for themselves.

In the gold camps they existed under conditions which would have made prisoners rebel. Living in such crude shelters as they could throw up in a day, neglecting food, clothing, and sanitation, they clawed the earth for the gold they had come so far to get.

The settled communities were in some respects worse. San Francisco burgeoned in two years from a hamlet of about 800 people to a raucous, ungovernable horde of some 25,000. According to Dr. Joseph Middleton, the immigrants transformed the town into one vast garbage heap. Spoiled food and the intestines of slaughtered animals were tossed into streets and yards, "sending out a smell that I have never experienced the like before." The wharves and the waters of the bay were littered with rotting debris of every description. The tent encampments surrounding the city Dr. Middleton described as filthier still.

"This," wrote the physician, "is the most abhorrent place that man ever lived in. If they have not a sweeping pestilence, it will not be for want of material to provide it."

They were to have, of course, not one pestilence but many.

The total effect was a casualty rate like that of a war. One knowledgeable gold-field physician, Dr. J. D. B. Stillman, estimated that among gold rushers who went out in 1849 about one out of five died within six months of reaching California.[2]

For those who escaped such disasters there were still tribulations enough. A great many found themselves in the peculiar position of enjoying more wealth, and less comfort, than they had ever known before.

The general state of affairs was summed up by forty-niner Horatio Blennerhasset who wrote home from San Francisco to say he'd struck it rich. He added that he was sleeping under a porch, because in the San Francisco of those hectic days mere money wasn't enough to insure a warm bed and dry roof. In fact, Blennerhasset couldn't buy even a sheet of clean, unused paper on which to announce the news of his good fortune. He solved the problem by taking an old letter, turning it sideways, and writing over it in crisscross fashion.

Another wry commentary on life in the gold fields was the rags-and-riches complaint of miner Melvin Paden. To his wife Paden wrote, "I do not like to be apacking a thousand dollars about in my coat pockets for it has toar my pockets and puld the Coat to peaces."

It could be said that all of California was pretty much in

Paden's shape. The gold, and what went with it, tore apart such crude social fabric as existed in that pioneer land.

There was no lack of physicians to treat the stricken adventurers. Borne along in the rush were some 1500 doctors or, anyway, men who called themselves such. They were a colorful lot, representing some of the best and the worst in the medicine of their day.

The physician participants ranged in knowledge and training from almost illiterate backwoods practitioners to graduates of the finest medical schools in Europe and America. They espoused numerous diverse and contentious systems of medicine, at a time when one theory had about as much standing as another. There was, in fact, only one thing they had completely in common. They were gold rushers all. Like the patients they treated, they too had California fever.

In California's community of strangers a physician was any man who hung out a shingle, and so the assorted healers were all equally at liberty to present their claims. It was a wide-open system sanctioned both by law and by custom. California had no regulations at all on who could practice or under what conditions, and beyond that there was no real agreement as to what constituted professional standards.

The medical anarchy was not confined to the gold fields but only most rampant there. It was a time of general upheaval in medicine, a period in which old concepts were being cast aside while new ones were struggling to emerge. Spawned in the process were numerous highly unorthodox, sometimes decidedly eccentric schools of healing. The decades immediately preceding the gold rush had produced a full flowering of such groups as the botanics and Thomsonians, the homeopaths, hydropaths, and eclectics. The phrenologists even had claimed scientific status. And California got them all.[3]

Amid such a plethora of systems it was necessary to have a

separate label designating the disciples of orthodox medicine. They were known as the regulars, though some of their practices look irregular enough to modern eyes. They approached disease as though it were a toxin to be flushed out of the system, and they went at it with vigorous measures of bleed, blister, and purge.

Bleeding in particular was a remedy prescribed for almost everything. Some physicians doubted its efficacy but found themselves almost forced to resort to it because the patients expected it. Dr. James Tyson, for instance, reported that many gold rushers requested regular seasonal bleedings for the presumed tonic effects. In the spring especially one could almost always find several prospectors squatting around Dr. Tyson's tent hospital, draining away the "bad blood" supposedly accumulated in winter.

Bleeding was a simple procedure, requiring only a jack-knife thrust into a vein. Usually, however, it was accomplished with a certain professional flourish. A preferred instrument was the lancet, designed sometimes like a small dagger and sometimes like a knife with a cleaver tip. For stylish practice there was a small brass box with slotted ends concealing as many as a dozen knives; when released by spring action the knives flashed out to scissor the patient's flesh. Or then again it might be done with leeches. The parasites were starved until voracious, then applied to skin temptingly anointed with cream, sugar, or blood.

Generally physicians confined the bleeding to ten or twelve ounces at a session. Some, however, became more sanguinary in desperate cases. At times gaunt, fever-wracked patients were literally bled to death.[4]

Purging was pursued with similar misguided zeal, the patients being scoured out with harsh laxatives, powerful emetics, and drugs calculated to incite a flow of sweat and saliva. The sweating and purging were both induced with jalap, a drug derived from a tropical root. Another root derivative, ipecac, obtained the emetic effect. Most favored of all was calomel, a mercury compound which purged and salivated with demonstrable thoroughness; when administered repeatedly and in large doses it had the unfortunate side effect of causing the teeth to fall out.[5]

Blistering was sometimes applied to wounds and infections, the idea again being to flush out the toxins. A horsehair threaded under the skin or mustard spread over it would both produce satisfactory blisters, but for really first-rate results there was nothing like the slow burning of a piece of cotton on the infected site. More painful still, but more useful, was the practice of cauterizing infections with a hot iron.

A majority of the gold-rush physicians adhered more or less to the regular system. There were, however, militant minorities of the other persuasions. Thus the homeopaths opposed all the heroic therapies and went to extremes in the opposite direction. They developed the odd, almost metaphysical notion that medications became ever more potent when administered in increasingly infinitesimal doses. With grave earnestness they discussed the desirability of prescribing one-millionth of a grain of drug.

The homeopaths achieved their minute doses through a process of attenuation. A grain of medication was first mixed thoroughly with a hundred grains of sugar of milk, alcohol, or other diluent. One unit of the resultant product was then remixed with another hundred-unit batch of the buffer material, yielding a theoretical strength of one part in ten thousand. The third such mixing brought it to one in a million. They could, and did, go on and on, arriving at dilution figures that were both astronomical and absurd.

The contrasting extremes of the rival medical systems gave rise to a mordant jest. It was a saying of the period that the patients of homeopaths died of the disease, while the patients of regulars died of the cure.

However, the homeopaths were not without their virtues.

They made major contributions in stressing the importance of public sanitation, personal hygiene, and proper diet. And in the matter of medication they were sometimes right for the wrong reason; their prescriptions at least didn't drain away the vitality of a man already exhausted by the ravages of disease.

A third group was known as eclectics. They had emerged from earlier systems of herbal healing, like the botanics and the Thomsonians, and they had gone on to borrow freely from everyone else in sight. It was the eclectic claim that they abjured orthodoxy in order to incorporate everything useful in healing technique. Put another way, they practiced on the democratic principle that in medicine, as in politics or religion, one man's opinion was as good as another's.

And then there were others. The hydropaths, for instance. They held that almost all illness yielded to water internally or externally applied. The hydropaths were then much in vogue in Europe, and there they promoted the rise of gracious spas which provided comfort and entertainment, if little else. But in the gold fields hydropathic practice too often came down to dunking a sick man in the chill waters of a mountain stream.

Compounding the confusion of systems was a general breakdown in the standards of professional training. Even the regulars had lost effective control of their training procedure. Altogether it's a reasonable guess that at least half the gold-rush physicians were men who never set foot in a medical school. Many had learned by the preceptor, or apprentice, system, and some were self-taught, self-appointed healers with no credentials at all.

The difficulties of distinguishing between who was or wasn't well qualified is perhaps best illustrated by a tale of two gold-rush doctors. They represented exact opposites, though not quite in the way one would expect.

One of them was Dr. Felix Paul Wierzbicki. He was the

son of a Polish nobleman and he had grown up in an atmosphere which embodied all the culture and learning of Europe. He fled Poland after a revolution that failed; when he
came to America he quickly established himself as a teacher,
a writer, a physician of note. In gold-rush medicine his is one
of the highly respected memories. He was a hydropath—a
water-cure man.[6]

As opposite number there was Dr. Luther M. Schaeffer.
He was a regular. Dr. Schaeffer represented classical medical
traditions which could be traced back through the corridors
of time, back to the ancient Greek physicians, Hippocrates
and Galen. He was also a very typical country doctor of nineteenth-century America. With entire equanimity he could
describe meeting a medical colleague "who graduated at the
same college with myself—that is nowhere!"

The question of credentials, then, couldn't be reduced to
the tidy terms of what theories the physcians subscribed to
or how much formal training they had had. In truth, all of
their theories were horribly inadequate, and none of them
were really equipped for the challenges they had to meet.
Their limitations can be summed up in what they didn't
know about medicine.

They didn't know about bacilli and viruses. They talked
of "invisible animalculae" which appeared under the microscope, and some suspected such organisms of a cruel sting,
but in gold-rush times that was still just a tenuous theory.

They hadn't mastered sanitation, though here they were
on better ground. The best minds among them assumed an
important relationship between filth and disease. But even
the best were a long step away from such crucial refinements
as sterilization of bandages and instruments.

In general, it can be said that they didn't know what caused
disease, or how it spread, or how to cure it. In most cases the
best they could do was to treat the symptoms, reducing the

pain, controlling the spasms or fever, so that the body would have a chance to marshal its own defenses.

The good ones were those who surmounted such limitations with qualities of intelligence, practical observation, and devotion to their task. They needed the devotion, and courage to match it, each time they entered a room where danger hovered in the mysterious form of contagious disease.

They had at their command a few great wonders of medicine. One was a vaccination for smallpox. It was not the refined vaccine that we know today, and it was by no means universally applied, but still they had it, and it worked. It spared them from runaway outbreaks of that particular affliction.[7]

They had quinine. That was the miracle drug of its time. It was a specific for malaria—in fact, it was the first medication that was really specific for anything—and it was useful generally in alleviating fever and pain. It was also expensive. In San Francisco one lot of quinine sold at auction for precisely four times its weight in gold.[8]

The last and greatest of their wonders was anesthesia. Ether and chloroform had both appeared in the years just preceding the gold rush. Those boons, however, were not always available when needed on the far frontier. In the early days of the rush especially, surgery and bone setting at isolated mining camps sometimes had to be performed with the old stand-bys of whisky and opium. The patient was tied down then or held down by the strong arms of friends. It was the pride of good surgeons that they worked very fast, doing what had to be done with quick, bold strokes of the knife, so that there would be only one long moment of agony.

Such, then, were the conditions of life and death which prevailed in the gold rush. Given the circumstances, it seems scarcely surprising that as many as a fifth of the participants may have perished in the first, most chaotic year. The wonder really is that so many lived.

The adventurers had some things in their favor, of course. In California they found a fair and pleasant land, one in which men could sustain themselves if they even half worked at it. Historian John E. Bauer has observed, "Nature seemed to counterbalance mankind's foolhardiness. In few other parts of the world could so improvident a gathering of humanity have survived so well."

The other chief asset of the gold rushers was their marvelous *élan*. They were vigorous, resilient men who went storming across a continent in the confident expectation that they could handle anything they encountered along the way. The qualities that got them into trouble sufficed, sometimes, to get them out.

Gold rusher Lorenzo Sargent expressed the spirit as well as any. He was a mill hand from Massachusetts who went out the first year. When he sailed through the Golden Gate he saw spread before him the garish spectacle of San Francisco. It was a town of makeshift tents and ramshackle shanties, perched along streets knee deep in mud. The inhabitants looked as though they had escaped from somewhere, as in a sense they had. Sargent took it all in with eager eyes and pronounced it grand.

"Of all the cities in the world," Sargent wrote, "this is the greatest one, composed of all nations and colors, and the hairiest set of fellows that ever existed."

They were hairy fellows for a fact. And they got hairier as things went along.

CHAPTER 2

All were off for the mines, some on horses, some on
carts, and some on crutches; and one went on a litter.

—Alcalde Walter Colton, describing
the gold fever at Monterey.

The gold was there, richly seeded through the earth, and so
the gold rush was bound to occur. There was, however, a
particular sequence of events which helped to determine
when and how it came about.

The discovery itself was not confined to a single dramatic
episode. For years the Mexicans in California had been picking up stray pieces of gold. At least a dozen finds had been
made. Each time there was a little flurry of excitement, and
then it subsided and nothing much happened. The times
weren't right for the big rush.

The Americans came then, pushing in among the Mexicans, settling under the Mexican flag, but wanting the territory for themselves. Presently they took it. California
emerged as the newest and most distant outpost of a restless
nation that saw its future in the West. The times became
just right for a rush. It needed only another discovery to
touch it off.

The catalytic events came close-paced together. On January 24, 1848, James Marshall plucked from a mill race the
dime-sized nugget that started it all. And less than two weeks

later, in the Treaty of Guadalupe Hidalgo, the United States claimed California as booty from the Mexican War.

Even then the big stampede did not begin at once. Rather there was a period of build-up, of mounting excitement which went on for nearly a year. In the interim half a dozen small-scale rushes rippled across the Pacific frontier.

The little rushes were themselves instructive. They afforded a preview of the turmoil to come, and they helped to forge a chain of events that was soon to engulf more than a quarter of a million people.

When Marshall saw that first nugget gleaming in the water he guessed immediately what it was. He resorted to a rough test, placing the specimen on a hard rock, and banging it smartly with another stone. It didn't shatter.

At his camp the same day he made a second test, dropping the little yellow pellet into a kettle of boiling lye. He soaked it for hours in the steaming kettle; when he took it out he found the color still untarnished.

Marshall collected a handful of nuggets, wrapped them in a rag, and took them to his employer, John Augustus Sutter, at Sutter's Fort. The two men got out an old encyclopedia, turned to a section on the specific gravity of metals, and together "ciphered out" a crude assay. When they were through they were quite certain. It was gold all right, and fine-quality ore at that.

Sutter didn't like it much—he didn't want strangers swarming all over his little wilderness domain—and he tried to keep the lid on by swearing his men to secrecy. But that kind of secret couldn't keep. A drunken teamster was apparently the first to talk.

Within weeks San Francisco had heard of the strike. People there took it pretty calmly at first; then gold dust from the diggings was displayed in the streets and suddenly the town went wild. The first of the little rushes was on.

Legend avers that a canny operator named Sam Brannan helped to stampede San Francisco by running through the streets, waving a bottle full of gold dust, and crying, "Gold! Gold! Gold from the American River!" Whether it happened just that way or not, Brannan was certainly around, talking it up. He had his reasons. He operated a little trading post not far from the discovery scene.

Another who played a role in San Francisco's eruption was a young physician, Dr. Victor Jean Fourgeaud. In the atmosphere of heady talk his was an informed voice confirming the news.

Dr. Fourgeaud was that rather rare individual, the well-educated frontiersman. He had graduated from a medical college in his native South Carolina; later he pursued advanced studies in Paris, then practiced for a time in St. Louis where he edited a pioneer medical journal. In 1847, at about age thirty, he went on to San Francisco, trekking across the continent with his wife and young son.[1]

When the ore samples were passed around, Dr. Fourgeaud acquired a nugget and subjected it to an assay more sophisticated than that conducted at Sutter's Fort. The specimen proved to be almost pure gold, .926 fine. Dr. Fourgeaud promptly closed his office, purchased a shovel, and set out for the diggings, thereby becoming the first gold-rushing physician.

San Francisco's other physician, Dr. John Townsend, caught gold fever too. Dr. Townsend was a foot-loose type, a robust, black-bearded man who had wandered West from Pennsylvania. He had been a bit of everything, a doctor, rancher, trader, soldier, real-estate speculator, and politician. He was also an old-timer by California standards, having arrived four years earlier with the first party ever to push covered wagons across the Sierra Nevada Mountains.

Dr. Townsend had become the alcalde, or mayor, of San Francisco, and he used the town as base for a horseback medical practice which extended for some five hundred square miles around. It was as close as he ever came to settling down. Of course, he couldn't stay settled when he heard the great news. He closed not only his medical office but also the town hall as he hurried off to the gold fields.

It should be added that Alcalde Townsend did not so much desert his town as move out with it. Between the middle of May and the end of June more than 80 per cent of San Francisco's population decamped for the mines.

At Monterey, California, the gold fever ran a very similar course. Again people heard and doubted, then saw and believed.

According to Alcalde Walter Colton, the first word of the strike reached Monterey on May 29. Reactions were skeptical, but a week later, after hearing a second report, Colton dispatched a horseman to find out. The mission involved a four-hundred-mile ride through rough country, and it was late in June before the scout reported back. In the meantime fresh rumors had circulated and a stranger had drifted through town displaying a piece of gold. Then Colton's messenger returned with pockets full of ore.

Colton described the town's reaction thus: "The blacksmith dropped his hammer, the carpenter his plane, the mason his trowel, the farmer his sickle, the baker his loaf, and the tapster his bottle. All were off for the mines, some on horses, some on carts, and some on crutches; and one went on a litter."

There was a warship stationed at Monterey, and three of the seamen deserted at once, forfeiting four years' pay apiece. Deserting also was an entire platoon of soldiers.*

* In the first eighteen months following the gold discovery army desertions in California totaled 716 men. Observed one soldier: "The struggle between *right* and six dollars a month and *wrong* and seventy-five dollars a day is rather a severe one."

Colton found himself presiding over a ghost town. He reported wryly that one morning he met in a kitchen with an army general and the warship commander, the three of them peeling onions and grinding coffee for breakfast because the servants who saw to such matters had all departed.

"These gold mines," prophesied Colton, "are going to upset all the domestic arrangements of society."

All up and down the California coast other settlements became caught up in the rush. It spread quickly to San Diego, Sonoma, Benicia, San Jose, Santa Cruz, Santa Barbara, Los Angeles.

By July the word had reached Oregon. Men there had only recently refused military duty because they could not leave their families unprotected in the wilderness; now the threats to hearth and home were seen in a new perspective as Oregonians kissed wives good-by and hurried off to the gold fields.

A month later Mexico was in the grip of the fever. At least five thousand Mexicans went streaming north before summer's end.

Hawaii heard too. In four months nineteen ships left Honolulu for San Francisco, carrying with them almost all of the island's white population and a sizable delegation of the native Kanakas.

In all some 10,000 fortune hunters descended on the gold fields in 1848. Fanning out from the scene of the original strike, they made fresh discoveries, opening a belt of mines that stretched for 150 miles through the Sierra foothills.

At the hub of the swirling action was Sacramento, a tent city sprung suddenly to life at the confluence of the American and Sacramento rivers.* A young army officer who was des-

* With typical ebullience the gold rushers called their new town *Sacramento City*. Much later it became just Sacramento.

tined for later fame described the boom-town atmosphere which pervaded both Sacramento and nearby Sutter's Fort.

"People are arriving and departing daily and hourly," reported Lt. William Tecumseh Sherman. "They usually camp for a day or so near us, look about, swear at the high prices, and disappear in the grand vortex."

Lieutenant Sherman added, "It is impossible to get at anything like the truth, but that the amount of gold in these mountains exceeds any previous calculation, I have no doubt. Men have and are still making fortunes, and that Brannan & Co. have cleared $100,000 is certain. His daily sales do not fall much short of $3,000, of which $2,000 are clear profit over and above all expenses."

Such were the little rushes. The big rush still showed no signs of starting. Most Americans had heard of the strike by late summer, stray travelers spreading the word, but the nation as a whole took it very much in stride. California was a long arduous journey away, and besides, the West was a perennial source of tall tales which level-headed men did not accept at face value. When newspapers picked up reports from the diggings they often treated the subject with a Bunyanesque air. And so, for a brief season, the fever remained confined to the Pacific outposts.

Meantime a horseman was pounding across the continent on one of the wild rides of history. His route took him through northern Mexico and he was disguised accordingly as a Mexican peon, but darkened skin and straggling beard could not entirely conceal an Irish mien. He was, in fact, Lt. Edward Fitzgerald Beale, United States Navy, and he carried official dispatches informing the President of the United States that the gold strike constituted a major discovery. He brought also the kind of convincer that had set one settlement after another aflame. Tucked in Lieutenant Beale's saddlebags was $3,000 worth of California dust.

Meantime also there was a quite fortuitous stir in the offices of two shipping firms which had just contracted to provide mail service to California. The companies were setting up a makeshift transport system which would soon be converted into a major conveyor belt for California traffic.

The arrangement called for a shuttle service, with the United States Mail steamship line to run between New York and Panama, while Pacific Mail conducted a similar operation between Panama and California. The routes were connected by an overland crossing through the Panama jungle; the isthmus transit depended on conveyance by pack mule and dugout.

The shipping operation began early in October 1848 when the steamer *California* left New York to take up her station on the Pacific run. The gold discovery was by then more than nine months old, and it had still aroused no real interest in the East. The *California* carried only six passengers, none of them booked for through passage to the Pacific coast, when the vessel departed on what was later termed "the voyage of innocence."

On December 1 another steamer, the *Falcon*, sailed from New York to inaugurate the Atlantic side of the service. Public indifference still prevailed. The *Falcon* carried less than thirty passengers, most of them bound for such way ports as Savannah and New Orleans.

The *Falcon* was just five days at sea when California fever erupted all over the nation. It started when President Polk announced from Washington that the gold strike was indeed a rich discovery. A travel-stained Lieutenant Beale was introduced to the United States Senate, that body responding with a standing ovation to both his deed and his news. Newspapers which had scoffed at the reports before now broke out huge headlines crying GOLD! GOLD! GOLD!

The excitement was immense. Men went charging down the coast, wearing out relays of horses in a desperate effort to catch the *Falcon* when she docked at New Orleans. Nearly two hundred tried to get aboard there, demanding passage, offering almost any price. Those who missed the connection jumped on any ship that would take them to Panama; all at once a fleet of vessels was being rescheduled for that destination.

The hordes that flocked to Panama were heedless of the fact that so far there was only one ship, the *California,* to transport them on the Pacific leg of the journey. Indeed, that vessel had not arrived on station yet. She was chugging up the coast of South America, still pursuing her voyage of innocence. When she reached Panama City she was greeted by 1500 clamorous adventurers, all of them beseeching berths on a ship that could not possibly hold a third of their number.[2]

The big rush was on.

PART II

THE VOYAGE

CHAPTER 3

———————◆———————

Nine men occupied a space of but six feet square.

—Dr. William M'Collum on
a ship for Panama.

The big rush began in winter, at a time when the overland trails were impassable, and so those in the first wave all went by ship.

It was a movement so sudden and frenzied that whole towns were depopulated as though by mobilization for war. In the case of Plymouth, Mass., one-fifth of the adult males were at sea for California before the rush was a month old.

Ninety jam-packed ships cleared east-coast ports for California the second month, and seventy more posted sailing dates. In New York one vessel sold out accommodations within three hours after its first advertisement hit the streets.

At the end of the first year the sea migration had swollen to a human tide of more than 20,000.

By ill chance the movement coincided with a calamitous event. It was an accident of history dramatically symbolized by two ships that passed in a harbor.

One ship was the *Falcon,* an inaugurator of the new Panama route, and the first vessel to be caught up in the excitement. She cleared from New York City on the same day that another ship, the packet *New York,* arrived from France. This vessel was not involved in the rush, but her appearance marked the beginning of a scourge that would have terrible impact on the migration. The packet brought cholera.

Cholera had invaded the nation once before, in 1832, and so its effects were all too familiar. The previous epidemic had raged for two years, sweeping the country, claiming such toll that the dead in some places were given mass burial in trenches.[1]

There had been ample warning that a second attack was coming. The contagion was on the march almost all over the world; it had spread from the Ganges to envelop India and China, the Middle East, then Europe. It rolled across Russia in the summer of 1847; a year later it was laying waste to Germany; in the fall of 1848 it broke out in France and England. As it passed through Europe the pandemic took a million lives.

The mortality rate was dreadful even by the harsh standards of the times. In severe outbreaks cholera killed at least half of those stricken.

An added element of terror was the speed with which cholera destroyed its victims. A man might set out in the morning in seeming health and vigor and be stricken by noon. In the next few hours he might suffer diarrhea, spasmodic vomiting, painful cramps, burning thirst, and complete prostration. That same night he might die in convulsions.

Finally, there was something fearful in the mysterious way that outbreaks came and went, without apparent cause or reason. A scientist would explain it one day by identifying the little comma-shaped bacterium which produced the disease, but that discovery was still thirty-four years away. In the interim men could only flail about blindly, attempting to ward off whatever evil, unseen thing it was that brought death among them.[2]

To the beleaguered populace the danger seemed something that was simply in the air. Medicine could offer no better explanation; indeed, many physicians of the day merely embraced the popular fallacy and cloaked it in pseudo-scientific terminology. A common medical opinion attributed cholera to a "miasma," a noxious emanation which suppos-edly arose from the earth or fermented in the atmosphere.

Some thought the miasma was virulent only to the drunken and intemperate whose resistance was lowered by dissolute living. This, naturally, was a view most frequently pro-pounded from the pulpit, but the attitude pervaded much of society. When cholera began to ravage New York in 1849, the *New York Herald* reported with an air of astonishment that deaths were occurring "among the respectable, including even ladies."

The moralistic and miasmatic theories were based alike on the one solid fact then known about cholera outbreaks. It had been observed time and again that the pestilence flourished where filth and squalor prevailed. To some that made it an affliction which degenerate people brought on themselves. The more enlightened physicians drew another inference, suggesting that, whatever the cause, the remedy lay in cleaning up. But the times were not ready for that.[3]

New York in particular was too steeped in filth to offer effective defense. The crowded tenements of the city were, quite literally, hog wallows. The poor harbored pigs in their dwellings, feeding the beasts on swill and garbage, in order to maintain a cheap source of meat. When civic officials fi-nally roused themselves to rout out the animals it was found that one tenement building alone housed 106 hogs.

Sanitation services existed in name only. Street-cleaning contracts were political plums awarded with the understand-ing that only token performance would be required. If tene-ment dwellers took the trouble to clean their infested quar-ters, the only result was to transfer the refuse to rotting piles which lay for weeks in the streets.

New Yorkers had a sardonic byword for the street situation. The city government was known in those days as the municipal corporation, and so the heaps of uncollected garbage were called "corporation pies."

The extent of both physical and political corruption was neatly capsuled in a barbed proposal made by one New York journalist. He suggested that a civic cleanup be financed by a public fund drive, the fund to be used in bribing office-holders to perform their duty.

Generally, however, there was no clamor for reform. Many asserted that a hue and cry over sanitary conditions would create needless alarm and drive business away. After all, it was argued, the city was no dirtier than many others, and there was no proof that dirt bred epidemic diseases. Authorities were produced to certify that the real threat was not filth but fear; according to this convenient theory, anxiety produced physical and mental reactions which made its victims all the more susceptible to any unfortunate miasma that might be about.

So successfully was fear resisted that New York's port officials and health officers failed even to plan quarantine arrangements for infected immigrants who were sure to come.

Thus a great city awaited the approaching epidemic. There remained only the inevitable incident that would set cholera loose in the streets. It came in the form of political refugees fleeing from Germany after the revolution of 1848. One group of them passed through France and sailed for America, carrying the contagion with them as they boarded the ill-fated packet *New York*. The disease broke out when they were well at sea and spread quickly through crowded steerage quarters where more than three hundred passengers huddled. Seven died before the voyage was done; about forty more were to perish soon after reaching their destination.

The stricken vessel arrived on December 1, 1848, and with its appearance the city stirred at last to belated action. The passengers were herded into a makeshift quarantine camp on Staten Island, the camp facilities consisting of cots hastily set up in customs warehouses. At the quarantine station the epidemic raged on, two or three new cases appearing among the terrified immigrants almost every day. Even then, however, the officials in charge took only routine precautions. They regarded the quarantine as an administrative gesture, useful chiefly in preventing panic; the weight of medical opinion was quite firm in declaring that cholera spread of its own accord and was not transmitted by its victims.

The immigrants for their part were not interested in learned opinions as to precisely how or why the contagion spread. They knew there was death in those warehouses, and they wanted out. Within three weeks half of them had fled, escaping from the island in small boats to lose themselves in the city. Shortly thereafter two local cases appeared in New York's crowded tenement district.

The first spasm of the epidemic was cut mercifully short when freezing temperatures checked the spread. In spring, however, it flared again. By summer's end it had claimed five thousand New York victims.

Meantime the contagion had established another beach-head in New Orleans. And there conditions were even worse. New Orleans at that time was a pesthole so plagued by disease that it lost a third of its population in one four-year period.[4] Cholera was added to the city's afflictions in December of 1848, German refugees being again the carriers, and an epidemic broke out at once.

And so the stage was set for history. All over the country men were setting forth on a tumultuous journey, while in two great embarkation ports a deadly contagion was loose. The gold rushers would pick it up, suffer terribly from it, and spread it wherever they went. The contagion as a result would last longer, travel farther, and take more lives than any previous epidemic in American history.

The gold rush, of course, was not the sole agent in such

disaster. Given the conditions of the time, the epidemic would have scourged the nation in any case. But there was nonetheless a fatal conjunction in the circumstances which brought the two events together.

The gold rush was to cholera like wind to fire.

To those caught up in the events the connection between migration and epidemic was not so apparent. One of the few to sense even a casual relationship was Philip Hone, New York's onetime mayor and a peripatetic observer of the city's affairs. In a diary entry dated December 16, 1848, he noted that "California gold and the cholera are the exciting topics of the day. These two diseases are equally infectious; both interfere with the honest pursuits of industry, and, though the former does not so immediately affect the health and endanger the lives of its subjects, its injurious effects may be of longer continuance."

Among the hurrying argonauts there was a different view. They were optimists, all of them, or they wouldn't have been going; it was in their nature to believe that they would get the gold and not the disease. Some did give passing thought to the danger of traveling in epidemic times, but only as one more hazard to be prepared against. There was, for instance, Robert Hutchinson, who placed his trust in a homespun prescription when he departed his village in Maine to catch a ship for the gold fields. On the flyleaf of his diary, handy for quick reference in time of need, Hutchinson inscribed in bold letters: "Recipe for Cholera, one tablespoon salt, 1 teaspoonful red pepper, mixed in ½ pint boiling water."

Most of the gold rushers ignored the contagion. They regarded cholera as something they could not really do much about, and so they simply hoped it would go away. And, indeed, for a time it appeared that it might. During that interval of reprieve the argonauts gave their attention to the more pressing problem of which route they should take. As it happened, that question was directly related to whether or not they would soon encounter the epidemic again.

For the seagoing argonauts there were basically two choices. They could go the old established way, by sailing ship around Cape Horn, or they could take the new short cut through Panama. The latter was considerably cheaper, about four times as fast, and decidedly more hazardous. The spirit of the times was such that a third of the voyagers braved the jungle-choked isthmus the first year; within two years it had become the route of choice for three-fourths of those going by sea.

Not the least hardship of the isthmus route was the character of the ships. Only the most foolhardy attempted Cape passage in a poor vessel, but on the Panama run almost anything went. The leakiest old derelict could command full booking, and the better ships were often packed to almost double the assigned capacity. Some ships went so far as to bed down surplus passengers in the lifeboats.

Accommodations on a Panama steamer were described by Dr. William M'Collum of Lockport, N.Y., who sailed on the side-wheeler *Crescent City* in February 1849. Dr. M'Collum was a country doctor of pioneer stock, a man inured to hardships and accustomed to making do, but even so he evinced distinct surprise when he got his first look at what had been advertised as a "noble and favorite" ship.

"Our introduction to the ship," Dr. M'Collum wrote, "gave us a glimpse of the 'elephant.' * The deck was covered with coal, dust, snow and mud; California baggage in all its profusion, uniqueness and variety, was piled up in massive layers, or strewed about as if tossed on board with a pitch-

---

* "Have you seen the elephant?" was a phrase used by P. T. Barnum in ballyhooing his gaudy show. The expression was converted into a national byword, men asserting they had seen the elephant by way of saying that they'd been taken in.

fork." When he inspected his steerage quarters he found that "Nine men occupied a space of but six feet square." The ship carried 160 steerage passengers, all of them dependent for ventilation on a single hatch opening.

It was Dr. M'Collum's opinion that "The farmers in bringing into our village dead hogs for market dispose of them with as much regard for comfort as dictated the arrangements of our sleeping quarters."

Dr. M'Collum's vessel was no worse than the average. On the typical Panama steamer the best possible accommodations consisted of a tiny cabin containing two to four berths, a washstand and mirror. Second class was more gregarious, twelve to fifty berths being closeted together. In steerage the berths could run to any number, limited only by mathematical laws. Steerage bunks consisted of canvas stretched over wooden frames six feet long and eighteen inches wide; they were usually stacked in cells of nine, three wide and three deep, with about two feet of air space separating each passenger from his next neighbor above. Sometimes the steerage lacked a toilet facility. Usually the passengers provided their own linen and eating utensils. At mealtimes they formed long lines and filed past the galleys, filling their plates and cups, then retired to bunks or crouched in passageways to consume their food.

Vociferous complaints from passengers eventually forced some reforms. The ship lines began to boast of little niceties, one steamship company advertising that curtains would be installed on request for the privacy of unescorted ladies. (Escorted ladies apparently continued to rely for privacy on the vigor and vigilance of their consorts.) The feeding arrangements were also revised, plates being provided and mess tables set up. The improvements were meager, however, as evidenced in the journal of Dr. Isaac Reed who went out two years after Dr. M'Collum. Dr. Reed described mess conditions thus: "Horses have stables and hogs have styes but the sons of men are crowded in an aisle 5 by 60 with a trough on either side 18 inches wide lined with zinc; here your food is thrown, pewter plates and tin cups, hard crackers, strong tea and coffee, pork and beef well seasoned with dirt and sweat." He added that he had to bribe the ship's steward to procure food fit for sick passengers to eat.

Such dirty, crowded ships were a natural breeding ground for disease of every kind. Dr. Reed's diary makes poignant reference to a resultant casualty on his vessel.

"Witnessed a funeral at sea today," the physician wrote. "A child. Corpse was placed in a box, weights attached and dropped into the fathomless deep. The Bell was tolled, the wheels stopped and the burial was aft the wheel house; when the wheels again revolve we move forward to our destination and perhaps our end." *

A scene of burial at sea appears often in gold-rush memoirs; as in Dr. Reed's report, the cause of death frequently was not specified. Indeed, the particular cause, if known, must have seemed rather incidental. The circumstances were such that the weak or unlucky could be expected to perish.

Fortunately for isthmus travelers, the first leg of the voyage was short, lasting only two weeks on the average. There was scarcely time for a full-fledged epidemic to develop. That came later, at Panama.

* For Dr. Reed the gloomy forebodings were borne out. The rigors of gold rushing were too much for him, and he died in California the next year.

CHAPTER 4

He implored us, amid his groans, to hasten forward.

—Bayard Taylor, nursing a
stricken companion through
the Panama jungle.

The Panama crossing was a sixty-mile passage through swamp
and jungle, with a mud-hut town at either end.

Once this crossing had been a trade route of empire, a
vital link in the vast colonial network maintained by Spain.
But Spain's power was long vanquished, and the encroaching
jungle had all but swallowed up the old Spanish installa-
tions. There remained only decrepit forts and some clusters
of half-ruined churches and dwellings.

A new kind of empire was in the making, a Yankee one,
but it was not yet established. The Yankee presence was typified by bustling, hastily contrived enterprise in transport and
trade. Thus the gold rush had scarcely begun when a newly
formed company undertook the strenuous task of laying a
railroad across the isthmus.

One gold-rush party commandeered a Panama work train
and insisted on riding it to the end of the rails. That, however, took them less than ten miles. They had to make the
rest of it the hard way.

For most it was the hard way all the way. They landed at
the squalid little town of Chagres, at the mouth of the broad

and muddy Chagres River.* From there it was some forty miles upriver, by whatever conveyance they could manage, to the tiny jungle settlements of Gorgona and Cruces. The rest was overland, across the high, narrow spine of a mountain system, with Panama City at the end of the trail.

A steamer service was installed eventually for the river passage, but in the early period the travelers relied on native dugouts called bungos. Often there weren't bungos enough to go around, and so men found themselves stuck in Chagres with no feasible way to get through the jungle. Gold rushers were nothing if not enterprising, however, and they came up with some ingenious solutions.

One group bought the ship bunks on which they had slept and knocked the planks together to form a raft. It was hailed, proudly, as "the first American bottom launched on the Chagres River." It served well enough for the purpose, and when they were through with it they sold it for a tidy profit.

The man who bought the raft put it to a quite different use. He hauled it ashore, turned it upside down, stuck some poles under it, and called it a hotel. In the Panama of those years one could do pretty well offering such accommodations to the passing stranger.

Some other equally picaresque hotels sprang up to meet the travelers' need. They varied colorfully in detail, but in essence they were all alike. Invariably they were verminous establishments, run usually by seedy and malarial tropic castaways. The innkeepers looked, in one gold rusher's apt phrase, like men who had been "steeped in water for a length of time."

One typical hostelry was the Half-Way House, described as "a miserable little tent, not more than 12 feet square," with total facilities consisting of "three cots, one table, two plates, two knives and forks." It was an establishment con-

---

* As the rush progressed the port of entry shifted to Aspinwall, now called Colón.

siderably overtaxed by a traffic which averaged about twelve guests a night. The house rule on cots was first come, first served, with belated arrivals consigned to the dirt floor. The meals, of course, were served in shifts.

Another Panama inn was most memorable for the fact that it lacked a coffee grinder. A gold rusher discovered that when he asked for coffee and was told that he'd have to wait a bit while a fresh supply was made up. Presently he glanced out the window and saw a native girl squatting on the ground, chewing coffee beans and spitting them into a pot. That particular traveler decided to dispense with his morning coffee.

Still other discomforts were experienced from a tropic climate which alternated between torrid heat and drenching rain. The rainy season was a particular hazard, transforming the final overland stretch of the crossing into a swampy morass.

Most of the travelers negotiated the trail stretch with pack trains rented from natives. A few made it unaided, their camp gear and luggage piled high on their backs. And a very few, either poor or parsimonious, eschewed the boat service and walked the whole way from Chagres. That was described by one who tried it as constituting "one hell of a week."

Finally there was the experience of sweating it out in Panama City, waiting for ships. Often the delay stretched out for weeks. As a consequence a continual floating population of two to three thousand gold rushers thronged through a town of some eight thousand native inhabitants.

Panama City became a boom town, raucous with bars, brothels, and gambling houses. Inevitably some who had withstood other hardships now squandered their health in injudicious revels. And some squandered their money, which was almost as bad. It was a poor place to wake up broke.

It was also a filthy town. Many gold rushers described that, but none better than Dr. M'Collum. In detached, professional fashion he observed simply that in Panama City it was

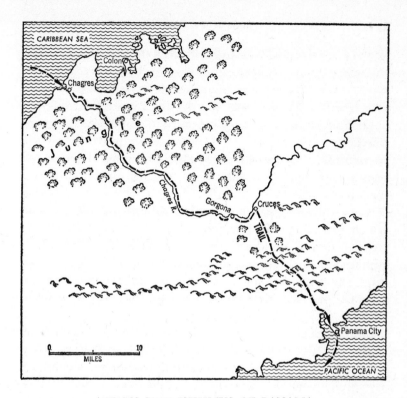

ACROSS THE ISTHMUS OF PANAMA

against the law to shoot at vultures. The birds performed an indispensable service in street sanitation.

Panama conditions created an omnipresent threat of disease. The migrants were exposed to all the native ills, and they soon introduced some new afflictions of their own. As a result the isthmus was swept by one epidemic after another.

Cholera appeared early in 1849. Gold rushers brought it in from New York and New Orleans, and the hot, wet country provided an ideal breeding ground for the disease. The first outbreak devastated the area, killing a fourth of the native population, and taking heavy toll among the adventurers. A second, less severe attack followed the next year. Thereafter new outbreaks flared sporadically throughout the rush.

Another scourge of the isthmus was yellow fever. It was so prevalent, and so virulent, that it came to be known as "Panama fever." That was a misnomer—the disease was common enough throughout the Caribbean and southern regions of the United States—but the isthmus again provided all the prerequisites for fearful outbreaks. The mosquitoes which transmitted the yellow-fever virus swarmed thickly all along the Chagres River.

The incubation period for yellow fever was about a week, which meant that it fitted with deadly precision into the traveling schedule. The victim who picked it up while boarding at New Orleans was about due to experience the first symptoms when he landed at Chagres. And the man who got it at Chagres would know about it by the time he reached Panama City on the other side.

Another kind of cycle fitted it into the larger scale of the migration. By chance the yellow-fever outbreaks reached a peak just when the worst danger from cholera was beginning to pass. The most severe yellow-fever epidemics came in 1853, 1855, and 1856.

A third major hazard was pernicious malaria. Gold rushers called it "Chagres fever," and it was definitely an affliction native to the region. Other forms of malaria were then widespread in the United States, but the isthmus variety was far worse than anything known in northern climes.

Gold rusher J. M. Letts had Chagres fever in mind when he wrote, "Chagres had the name (and it undoubtedly deserved it) of being the most unhealthy place in Christendom." Many argonauts had their lives insured before starting, Letts said, and there was a clause in each policy stating that all benefits were forfeited by travelers who remained in Chagres overnight.

A surgeon of the Panama Railroad, Dr. Chauncey Griswold, added, " 'Chagres fever' is usually spoken with an emphasis that strikes terror to the timid. Although the name is not, by any means, a classical one, yet it has the advantage of being correct in a general sense; for I do not believe there is another place in the world where the causes of disease are developed and fostered to a greater extent."

Dr. Griswold believed that Chagres fever was due to a foul emanation which arose from the surrounding swamps. He thought the emanation was particularly dangerous at night, and he warned travelers that despite the oppressive heat they must sleep with doors and windows tightly closed against the pestilential air.*

For therapy the railroad physician recommended fifteen grains of quinine, a staggering dose. He added somewhat inconsistently, "The native remedy is limes, the juice of which they suck, with slices of the same placed upon the forehead and temples, and with this simple treatment, and abstinence from food and water, they readily recover."

Dr. Griswold was undoubtedly too sanguine about the state of native health. Much later a medical survey disclosed that Panamanians had an average life expectancy of about twenty years, with malaria being one prime factor in the high mortality.[1]

From another physician on the scene, Dr. F. N. Otis, we learn that the work crews of the Panama Railroad were plagued by assorted epidemics all through the gold-rush period. The worst disaster occurred when the railroad brought in a thousand Chinese laborers. Dr. Otis asserts almost plaintively that "every possible care was taken which could conduce to their health and comfort. Their hill rice, their tea, and opium in sufficient quantity to last for several months had been imported with them—they were carefully housed and attended to—and it was expected that they would prove

* The emanations theory was a very old one, and it had been applied to malaria more than to most ills. In fact, the name malaria derived from an Italian term for "bad air."

effective and valuable." But within a month "disease broke out among them, and raged so fiercely that in a few weeks scarcely two hundred remained."

For the casualty rate among gold rushers we have no comparable estimates. They stampeded through in wildly disorganized fashion, leaving their dead behind in graves uncounted and often unmarked. But there remains evidence enough of the price they paid.

Panama City acquired two new landmarks which testified to the general travail. There sprang up an American hospital, always crowded, which was staffed at times by up to five physicians. And before long there was also a big new American cemetery.

Like everything else at Panama City, the burial arrangements were casual in the extreme. One argonaut who viewed the cemetery saw "Cart loads of boans and sculls, some with the hair on."

The various afflictions were bad enough in themselves, and they became a good deal more trying when combined with the sheer physical ordeal of traversing the jungle. A vivid human view of that experience was provided by Bayard Taylor, a correspondent for the *New York Tribune*, who made the trip in 1849.

Taylor's party got off to what seemed a fine start at Chagres. Brawny Negroid boatmen sped them up the river, poling tirelessly with rhythmic strokes, and keeping time to such songs as "Oh! Susannah" rendered in Spanish patois. Then, nearing the river town of Cruces, the boatmen picked up news from the shore and swung into a different chant. "Mucha cholera," they cried, applying their poles to the water. "Cruces—mucha cholera."

Taylor thought at first it was a dodge to get out of working the boat the last few miles, but it didn't take much of that unnerving wail to deter him from finding out. He and his companions left the river at Gorgona, a few miles short of Cruces, and struck out overland on rented horses. At that point they were joined by a stranger, "a lank Mississippian" of cadaverous mien who quit his own group and attached himself to them without explanation.

The Mississippian had evidently sized them up as the right sort to be with in a time of trouble. As they rode through the jungle he revealed that he had felt the first stirrings of cholera the night before.

It was about the worst possible place for such an announcement. The trail which had been rough at the start had quickly deteriorated into a series of swampy ravines deep mired in mud. They begged the ailing Mississippian to turn back, but he refused, declaring he was "bound to go through."

As they pressed on they encountered another cholera victim, a stricken argonaut who lay writhing on the ground. A friend who was attending the man "seemed on the point of taking the epidemic from his very fears." Taylor's party didn't stop; they had their hands full by this time with their own invalid.

The Mississippian had become so wracked with convulsions that he could scarcely go on. "We were alarmed," Taylor wrote. "It was impossible to stop in the swampy forest, and equally impossible to leave him, now that all his dependence was on us." That statement, incidentally, wholly vindicated the Mississippian's judgment in his choice of traveling companions. Some others on the trail wouldn't have found leaving a stranger impossible at all.

Aside from holding the afflicted man on his horse, however, there was very little they could do to help him. Taylor at one point offered him a drink from a bottle of claret, but that was a mistake. The Mississippian swigged hard and was worse as a result.

The trail grew worse too. "Scrambling up ravines of slippery clay," Taylor wrote, "we went for miles through swamps and thickets, urging forward our jaded beasts by shouting and beating." In places the horses sank into mudholes up to their bellies and had to be hauled out by violent effort. In places, too, they had to pick their way around the rotting carcasses of horses, mules, and oxen which earlier parties had left strewn along the way.

By dusk they had put the hardest going behind them, but they were still four hours' travel from Panama City. Said Taylor: "We pitied the poor horses, but ourselves more, and determined to push forward."

The Mississippian entirely concurred in that decision. "Leaning over the horse's neck, he writhed on his saddle in agony, and seemed on the point of falling at every step." And yet "he implored us, amid his groans, to hasten forward."

The tough and determined Mississippian made it to Panama City. Whether he survived is not recorded.

Many another Panama traveler was forced to suffer through illness without a physician's aid. For men in such circumstances Dr. M'Collum offered some sound advice.

Dr. M'Collum took a restrained view of medication, believing that the argonaut's medicine chest was amply stocked if it contained "a small quantity of calomel, quinine, Dover's powders, soda, rhubarb, some adhesive plaster, a little lint, and a small flask of brandy." In lieu of massive treatments he urged the importance of proper rest and diet in maintaining the body's natural defenses.[2]

"If you remain long upon the Isthmus," he advised prospective argonauts, "avoid exposure to the heat of the sun in the middle of the day; eat light food; indulge in fruit but moderately, especially if you have the least tendency to diarrhoea. Unless sick enough to require treatment under the advice of a physician, take no medicine except from five to ten grains of quinine, daily.

"Excitement and fatigue should be avoided."

It was a sensible regimen, but it was seldom followed. Avoiding excitement and fatigue, in particular, was difficult advice for a gold rusher to take. Most of them were men like the Mississippian in that, sick or well, they were "bound to go through." And most of them were sure that alcohol and strong medicine would help them do it.

J. D. Borthwick, a gold-rushing Englishman who went out via Panama, commented at length on the "American characteristic" of imbibing quack remedies in huge quantities. Almost every argonaut, he said, was a walking apothecary, laden with boxes of pills and bottles of vile liquids for every known disease.

"The moment they imagined that there was anything wrong with them," Borthwick wrote, "they dosed themselves with all the medicines they could get hold of, so that when they really were taken ill, they were already half poisoned with the stuff they had been swallowing. Many killed themselves by excessive drinking of the wretched liquor which was sold under the name of brandy."

Borthwick described one victim who "while the doctor was treating him for fever, was at the same time treating himself to large doses, taken frequently, of bad brandy, of which he had an ample stock. About a day and a half settled him."

While sailing up the Pacific from Panama, Borthwick was stricken with a fever himself and fell into the hands of a purging physician. The experience reinforced his conviction that in matters of medicine the Americans were a reckless lot. As Borthwick told it, "I could have cured myself very easily, but there was a man on board who passed for a doctor, having shipped as such; he had been physicking the others, and I reluctantly consented to allow him to doctor me also. He began by giving me some horrible emetic, which, however, had no effect; so he continued to repeat it dose after dose, each dose half a tumblerful, with still no effect, till, at last he had given me so much of it that he began to be alarmed of the consequences. I was a little alarmed myself, and putting my finger down my throat, I very soon relieved myself of all his villainous compounds. I think I fainted after it.

"I took my own case in hand after that, and very soon got rid of the fever, although the emetic treatment had so used me up that for a fortnight I was hardly able to stand. We afterwards discovered that this man was only now making his *debut* as a physician. He had graduated, however, as a shoemaker, a farmer, and I don't know what else besides; latterly he had practiced as a horse-dealer, and I have no doubt it was some horse-medicine which he administered to me so freely."

Concluding on a slightly more charitable note, Borthwick observed, "We had only two deaths on board, and in justice to the doctor, I must say he was not considered to have been the cause of either."

Obviously Borthwick was a man who didn't undertell a story. Even so, his account may well have been pretty close to the mark. There were doctors like that, and some of them had learned their trade in a barn.

Some other gold rushers registered the same complaint in briefer form. There was, for instance, Mrs. Betsy Gordon, who traveled the Panama route late in the rush. On the last leg of the voyage an epidemic struck. "We buried 5 on the passage across the pacific," Mrs. Gordon wrote. "Death occurred in every instance in which the Physician was called. I very much doubt whether he understood his business."

And then there was George Cornell, who wrote of a physician under similar circumstances: "He gave me something that almost killed me. I never suffered so in my life. He charged me $1.50 and it done me no good."

Of course, the physicians were cast in no easy role. They did what they could, given the times and the circumstances, and there were some who served splendidly by any standard.

One who made a simple but very useful contribution was Dr. John Frederick Morse, of Brooklyn, who made the Panama crossing in 1849. On the Pacific leg he caught one of the bad ships; it was a vessel so dirty and disease-ridden that the regular ship's physician simply gave up on the job and asked to be relieved of duty. At Acapulco, Dr. Morse took over as a volunteer.

Dr. Morse wrote that his first act was to descend into the steerage and there "lead off in the noble function of scraper and cleaner." He commented that while "the steerage was occupied by men of excellent minds and standing, yet it was singular to see them daily vitiating their constitutions by breathing the most fetid air, rather than to do themselves what was obviously the duty of the stewards. The moment, however, I took my position as a sweeper, I was joined by more than were needed."

Another who served well was Dr. Albert Ball, who was confronted with some shipboard epidemic while sailing up from Panama. What the disease was, or what he did about it, we do not know. Probably he was one of those physicians who by his mere presence provided comfort and encouragement. We can imagine him spooning medicine and nourishment into the sufferers, and bathing them when they wallowed in filth, and wrapping them in blankets when fever was followed by chills. When they reached San Francisco they took the highly unusual step of expressing their gratitude in a paid newspaper announcement.

The announcement, signed by seventeen people, was published in the *Alta California* on March 11, 1850. It read: "We the undersigned, passengers on board the ship *Kingston*, from Panama to San Francisco, having been compelled to employ the services of Dr. Albert Ball, surgeon of said ship, take pleasure in thus conveying to him our public acknowledgement of his skill and kindness. To the citizens of San Francisco, we can safely recommend him as a skillful physician."

CHAPTER 5

———◆———

I had a high feavor and only three pints of water and no
one to take care of me you can judge my situation.

—George Blanchard, reporting
an epidemic at sea.

For those who took the Panama route the last leg of the journey was very often the worst. On the voyage up the Pacific
the hardships and dangers accumulated with telling effect.

The passengers were worn down at this stage with fatigue
and ill-nourishment, and they had suffered repeated exposure to all the afflictions that racked the isthmus. When
they left Panama behind and took to ships again they frequently carried with them the seeds of continuing epidemics.

An added hazard was the fact that the Pacific voyage extended for thousands of miles along nearly uninhabited
coasts. When disease appeared at sea there was almost no
recourse but to go on, accepting whatever casualties might
occur.

A few cruelly stricken vessels were transformed into virtual death ships. Public attention focused on the spectacular
cases, while the general problem of floating epidemics became
so commonplace that it was reported in only sketchy detail.
Thus the San Francisco newspapers would announce from
time to time that a newly arrived ship had lost a dozen or
more passengers at sea. Occasionally the human story of such

tragedy can be half glimpsed from some scrap of the surviving record.

One otherwise unrecorded shipboard epidemic is known for its effect on a single family. The evidence consists of a private death notice published by a San Francisco newspaper in 1850. The commemoration was written in the sentimental style of nineteenth-century bereavement, but from the florid prose a few stark facts emerge.

The subject was John R. Baker, a forty-niner who left wife and children in New Orleans when he joined the rush. Apparently he prospered, for a year later he sent for his family. Knowing the hardships of the isthmus crossing, he went to meet them at Chagres.

The Baker family crossed Panama safely and boarded a steamer for San Francisco. Then some unidentified illness broke out. In the death notice it was described as "Isthmus fever." Whatever it was, John Baker died of it in mid-voyage. Three days later his wife, Sarah Ann, was fatally stricken. The Baker children, aged two and three, survived to reach San Francisco as gold-rush orphans.[1]

Other shipboard epidemics were chronicled by men who lived through them. There is, for example, the account left by P. J. Barber, an Ohioan, who crossed the isthmus in 1852. On the Pacific run his vessel was subjected to the combined tribulations of food shortage and double epidemic. The contagions were measles and yellow fever. The ship was beset also by angry quarrels, half a dozen fist fights breaking out among men who were so sick and weak that they could scarcely drag themselves around deck. Barber put it all down in dry detail, giving equal emphasis to a death and a black eye. Here are some representative entries from his diary:

"March 20: This morning at 3 oclock a man from Indiana died with the Panama fever, was buryed at 7 oclock A.M."

"March 25: Today at 12 oclock Barnns F. Ives commited suicid by jumping over board, he was deranged, having been sick with the measles—the 2nd mate hurt in trying to save him."

"April 3: Hopkins sick with fever. Pike getting better. A dead calm all day. Passengers look *down* in the *mouth.*"

"April 15: A fight between two passengers—*one* got a black eye. Passengers half starved. Many of them sick."

"April 22: Man died of measles."

"April 27: A fight at the breakfast table for coffee."

Barber went on in that laconic fashion, setting down the little trials and large tragedies. When his diary entries are tabulated, they add up to a sick list of more than fifty persons, of whom fourteen died.

While Barber scratched his diary entries another group was enduring almost identical hardships on the same run. They too were stricken with both measles and yellow fever. Again there was an acute shortage of food. The results, however, were even more devastating. James Chelton gave the main outlines of the story in a letter to his brother, Valentine:

"We left Panama the 7th of March on the bark *Emily,*" Chelton wrote. "We had not been out long when disease and Death made its appearance among us. There was from 30 to 50 sick at one time, myself among that number. There was from 2 to 3 shoved overboard some days, some of them before they had fairly breathed their last. There was seventeen died before we got half way."

Chelton's fellow passenger, George Blanchard, added some vivid details. According to Blanchard, the *Emily* was old, slow, almost unseaworthy. It was also a foul ship, even by gold-rush standards.

Wrote Blanchard: "The cook was so dirty as you may judge as he one day boiled a piese of his shirt with some rise. This and other things I could mention made it go hard."

As to the epidemic, Blanchard said it broke out the first week and continued almost all the while they were at sea; half the passengers and crew were incapacitated at times. Meantime supply shortages heightened the crisis. The food ration was cut again and again, being reduced finally to a daily allotment of a half pound of bread and a quarter pound of flour per man. Water was doled out at a rate of three pints a day. For the sick the latter deprivation was particularly hard to bear.

As Blanchard put it, "I had a high feavor and only three pints of water and no one to take care of me you can judge my situation."

The voyage was interminable. They were scheduled to complete the passage in thirty-five days, but at the end of two months they were still less than halfway. Finally the passengers braced the captain and demanded that he make for the nearest shore at whatever risk. The plan was accepted, but even that took some doing; they had been blown well out to sea, and it was the eightieth day before they raised the coast of Mexico.

They put in at a little Mexican village but could obtain no supplies except sugar and water. They subsisted largely on that for eleven days more while sailing up the coast to San Blas, Mexico. There the captain announced his total disinclination to continue the voyage. He offered a cash settlement to anyone who would get off the ship and more than half the passengers promptly accepted.

The rest feared being stranded and sent a delegation sixty miles overland to consult the nearest American consul. There were protracted negotiations back and forth and threats to seize the *Emily* for failure to fulfill its obligations. Eventually the consul put up $5000 to get the migrants going again on another ship. And then, incredibly, they were plunged into a second voyage of terror as bad as the first.

Again there was a critical shortage of food and water. And again, fever. It may have been a continuation of the earlier afflictions, or they may have picked up something else at San Blas. In any case, it was extremely virulent. Blanchard described one scene:

"Mr. Batchelor and Mr. Cathring were pardners and died within five minutes. They were put on 2 planks side by side and the ship hove to and buried both at once. I tell you it was a dreadful sight."

As the epidemic progressed the scant decencies of the burial service were increasingly neglected. Sometimes the corpses were simply picked up and tossed over the side. There was something about it, something that went beyond the mere fact of death, that disturbed Blanchard deeply. He made it his business to record the name, age, and home state of each man who died. Later, writing his parents to describe the voyage, he appended his list of names as a kind of memorial to those who might otherwise have vanished without a trace.[2]

Blanchard's list revealed a death total of thirty-seven, out of an original party of about one hundred. The voyage had lasted seven months.

Despite the grim details Blanchard's letter contained a touch of the gold rusher's indomitable optimism. He ended by saying, "Tell all my friends I have seen hard times but expect to see better." And then, lest friends be misled, he felt constrained to add, "if they will take my advice they will stay home."

Another memorable account was left by Frank Marryat who crossed the isthmus with his wife late in the rush. He too experienced a double ordeal, surviving yellow fever in the jungle and outlasting a second, unidentified epidemic on the Pacific voyage.

Marryat's bout with yellow fever began during the last

stretch of the isthmus crossing. He had an agonizing time of it, slogging over the Panama trail while so weak and delirious that he fell repeatedly from the back of his mule. Soon the contagion spread to his traveling companions. Marryat does not give the toll, but he records the fact that among those who were infected in his party he alone survived. Then he and his wife boarded a steamer for San Francisco and a fresh horror ensued.

"I had secured a dog-hole of a cabin," Marryat recalled, "and was no sooner on board than my wife, worn out by fatigue and anxiety, was attacked by a violent fever." Two doctors were aboard, but they could offer no help, being ill themselves. Then a general epidemic broke out among passengers "crowded as thick as blacks in a slaver"; the victims "gave way to fear, and could not be moved from the lower deck, and so lay weltering in their own filth."

"From the scuttle hold of our small cabin," Marryat wrote, "we could hear the splash of bodies as they were tossed overboard with very little ceremony."

As they sailed up the coast another threat appeared when the ship sprang a severe leak after being pounded by storms. Oddly that was probably a stroke of luck. Marryat thought that "this new danger drove the epidemic out of the passengers' heads." What may have happened is that the storm drove the infection off the ship. They received a thorough dousing from the sea, and they got rid of a lot of contaminated effects when they lightened the foundering vessel by dumping baggage over the side.

For two days and two nights they bailed for their lives, every passenger who was able working with tub and bucket to empty the grimy water that sloshed through the hold. Finally, battered and exhausted, but triumphantly surviving, they steamed into the way port of Acapulco. The Marryats got off there to rest and recuperate, concluding that even in a gold rush there was such a thing as pressing one's luck.

More dramatic still were the adventures of Dr. R. Beverly Cole. He was a man destined for a big role in gold-rush medicine. It was, however, sheer luck that he reached California at all.

Dr. Cole was a young physician, only three years out of medical school, but even so he was no stranger to calamitous events. When he was just beginning practice, at Philadelphia in 1849, he found himself in the midst of a city-wide cholera outbreak. He responded by turning a delapidated building into an emergency hospital; there he lived and worked for three months, hardly venturing outside the walls until the crisis abated.

Ironically, he later joined the gold rush at least partially for reasons of health. He had become tubercular, a condition aggravated by overwork and frail physique, and he decided that his condition might improve in California's already well-advertised climate.

He went in 1852, taking a steamer to Panama. The run coincided with another flare-up of cholera. On the first night ashore fifteen of his fellow passengers died.

Dr. Cole got through that outbreak unscathed, but he had rough going across the isthmus. He assumed responsibility for two women travelers, and they proved to be genteel, dependent types who took it for granted that someone would see to all their needs. Dr. Cole for his part was a dapper gentleman of very elegant air; he appeared unsuited to the rigors of jungle travel, but there was stuff in him that always rose to the occasion. On the river passage he repeatedly waded chest-deep in the water, pushing the dugout through obstructed channels. Along the way he was forced to relinquish his baggage, including changes of clothing; when he reached

Panama City he looked and felt like a man who had wallowed in mud the whole length of the crossing.

At Panama City he got rid of the encumbering women and joined forces with two friends who had preceded him from the steamer. The three of them took lodgings in a room where fifty men stretched out on a floor covered with grass mats. Dr. Cole was exhausted and so slept heavily. When he awoke the next morning he found his friends on either side of him lying dead on their pallets. Cholera again.

About a day later the young physician was felled by a severe attack of dysentery. He found a place of refuge and lay recuperating for several weeks, sustaining himself largely on ice cubes because he didn't trust the local water and food. It was a prudent regimen, but expensive and hard to maintain; such ice as was available in Panama City had to be imported by sailing ship all the way from Cape Horn.

Finally, gaunt and weak, Dr. Cole boarded the steamer *Golden Gate* for the Pacific voyage. And then the great disaster struck. A regiment of United States infantry clambered aboard, bound for California, and brought with them more cholera. They turned the steamer into the most tragic ship in Panama's gold-rush annals.

The soldiers were already badly infected when they joined the ship; the first night aboard thirty-two of them died. Thereafter the epidemic continued to rage with such violence that the steamer's captain feared to put to sea. He could find no relief on shore either, for there was no one with either the facilities or the inclination to take the troops off his hands. As a despairing solution an old hulk in the harbor was transformed into a military hospital ship and the *Golden Gate* hove to nearby, waiting for the epidemic to subside. It did eventually, but not until the death toll had reached eighty-four.

One of the soldiers involved was Ulysses S. Grant, then a lieutenant. There was an apocryphal tale that he stayed drunk the whole time, but actually he performed in very creditable fashion. When enlisted men who manned the hospital ship began to desert Grant stationed himself there as a guard. He personally nursed many of the sick, acting, as one soldier put it, "like a ministering angel to us all." Another witness said Grant was "one of the coolest men in all these emergencies I ever saw." *

While Lieutenant Grant manned his station on the hospital ship, Dr. Cole was attending to his duties on the *Golden Gate*. He converted the ship's saloon into an emergency clinic for the civilian casualties. Though close to exhaustion he worked incessantly, snatching only brief hours of troubled rest.

Dr. Cole's other and more memorable contribution was a morale measure which he ever afterward regarded as an inspired idea. He organized the regimental band into shifts and persuaded them to play from morning to night. For days on end a cacophony of martial and sentimental airs blared from the stricken ship. Then the music stopped. Cholera had ravaged the band.

All the while men were dying at the rate of five or ten a day. The bodies were buried over the side, wrapped up in canvas, and weighted with cannon balls. Some of the corpses came loose from their moorings and washed up on Panama City beaches, creating panic in the town. It was the corpses which forced a resolution of the situation. Settling for what seemed the lesser danger, Panama authorities permitted an

* In his *Personal Memoirs* Grant added some details of the epidemic as seen by the soldiers. His unit of the regiment (the Fourth Infantry) was first stricken at Cruces. They experienced several terrible days in that pesthole town while bogged down because transportation arrangements had gone awry. Grant got them out of Cruces by throwing regulations away, buying mules at twice the authorized prices, but the epidemic pursued them as they floundered over a swampy trail. Grant estimated that he lost a third of his detachment between Cruces and Panama City. A regimental surgeon said of the same march that sometimes he went back along the trail to bury casualties and couldn't find them because the bodies had sunk into the mire.

island in the bay to be used for hospital and cemetery purposes; the troops were allowed to disembark on the island
also in order to facilitate a thorough fumigation.

Dr. Cole got off when the crisis abated, rested a bit, then
resumed his voyage on the sailing ship *Columbia*. His trials,
however, were not quite ended. On the *Columbia*'s Pacific
passage five died of yellow fever.

CHAPTER 6

The bread was full of worms . . .

> —Roger Baldwin, experiencing
> a pioneer's discomforts on
> the Nicaragua route.

As the gold rush gathered momentum another sea route emerged. This one involved a short cut across Nicaragua. Like the Panama crossing, it was an old Spanish trade route which had been neglected for centuries.

Nicaragua offered some quite favorable conditions. The crossing was longer but the transit was easy, the San Juan River and broad Lake Nicaragua permitting boat passage for all but the last few miles. Nicaragua was also closer than Panama, reducing the round-trip distance between New York and San Francisco by nearly five hundred miles. Most important of all, Nicaragua provided a healthier climate.[1]

Set against these advantages were chaotic transport arrangements which made the Panama trip seem by comparison a well-ordered affair. The forty-niners who first attempted Nicaragua discovered that ship service ran to the place but not from it; they wound up stranded for months on a jungle shore.

The first Nicaragua expedition was promoted by George Gordon, a fast-dollar operator from Philadelphia. It was Gordon's optimistic theory that facilities and accommodations would almost automatically arise as needed once demand was created by setting people in motion. Accordingly he formed a company, chartered the brig *Mary* for the Atlantic side of the run, and offered bright promises of a quick trip via nonexistent connections.

Gordon held out some then unusual inducements, agreeing to furnish bedding for ship berths and camping equipment for the overland phase of the journey. He made plausible arrangements for the crossing itself. But he left almost entirely to chance the matter of obtaining new transport once the travelers reached the Pacific side. A cautious argonaut might have detected that defect in planning from one line in Gordon's advertisement: "In the *unexpected* event of vessels not being procured, $75 of the passage money and 60 days provisions will be refunded to each passenger."

Caution was not the gold rusher's long suit, of course, and so the Gordon Passenger Line experienced no difficulty in securing full booking. In February 1849 the *Mary* sailed from New York with a capacity load of 136 passengers. They enjoyed an uneventful Atlantic run; then they landed in Nicaragua and their troubles began.

They had brought with them a small dismantled steamboat which they assembled on the spot for the journey up the San Juan River. The boat's engine works proved defective, however, and they had to resort to native bungos. It took them nearly six weeks to cross the isthmus by bungo and mule train. Then for three months more they waited for ships that never appeared.

For a company of castaways they managed quite well, living comfortably enough off a lush country that was not yet overrun with adventurers. A revolution broke out while they waited, but they managed to resist efforts to draw them into the fray. What they couldn't resist was the urge to go on to California at any cost. One group of them became so impatient that they fitted out a bungo and headed up the coast. That party was never heard from again.

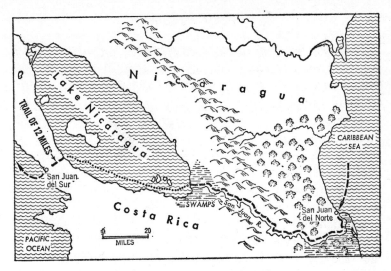

BY WAY OF NICARAGUA

The rest finally made connections with an assortment of tramp ships, all vessels of such disreputable cast that they were out scrounging for passengers at a time when any seaworthy craft was turning business away. The result was a series of grim ordeals on what soon became starvation ships.

About a hundred of the castaways obtained passage on the brigantine *Laura Ann*. She was an overcrowded vessel, ill provisioned and poorly managed; when she was well at sea it was discovered that the water tank leaked and half the food was spoiled. Bad weather brought added hardship, the ship laying becalmed one day and being driven off course the next. Within a month the situation was desperate. According to one of the party, a young man named Roger Baldwin, they were soon reduced to a diet of bread, rice, and beans, with a daily water ration of one quart per man.

"The bread," said Baldwin, "was full of worms and defiled with cockroaches; the rice was half hulls, with as many weevils as kernels; the beans were of a peculiar kind, and the more they were boiled the harder they became. There was no water to be wasted on them."

Baldwin chose the rice as the lesser evil. For two weeks he subsisted on twice-a-day meals of a handful of soggy rice boiled in a half pint of water; the remaining pint of his water had to suffice for a twenty-four-hour drinking supply.

At one period they suffered also from what Baldwin called "a strange sickness." He was sparse on details, noting only that "it was akin to influenza, but with peculiar symptoms." Probably they picked up some tropic fever. They may also have contracted dysentery while eating the last of the spoiled meat. Whatever the cause, it was a wretched, debilitating illness which prostrated almost all aboard for more than a week. The crew members at that point simply gave up, leaving a few sick but determined passengers to work the sails.

The miserable voyage dragged on for some 1,500 miles. Finally, when they were down to their last eighty gallons of water, they put in on the wild coast of Southern California. Then suddenly their luck changed. Landing at evening on a fog-shrouded, uncharted coast, they avoided shipwreck and came ashore within sight of a fresh-water pond. Thirty-six hours later a Peruvian ship came by, bound for San Francisco with trading goods, and they were able to buy provisions. Foraging inland, they also found a ranch thirty miles away and obtained a few head of cattle which they butchered. A run of good fishing allowed them to salt down several barrels of mackerel. Meantime, however, the crew deserted, the two mates and all the seamen striking out overland to reach the gold fields. The passengers manned the ship again, reaching San Francisco about three weeks later.

Hard-pressed though they were, Baldwin's group was the luckiest of the various parties that escaped from Nicaragua on the tramp ships. In letters home Baldwin later reported what happened to his erstwhile comrades on the other vessels.

One party on a small sloop endured a voyage of 132 days, including thirty-two days becalmed in one spot under a blazing tropic sun. "They had," wrote Baldwin, "only a pint of water apiece a day, much of the time almost perishing from want of food. Once they ran on the coast as a venture, as we did, but found no water. They dug for it, and searched the interior for thirty or forty miles, but in vain, and at length were obliged to put to sea with only a bottle of water apiece, their only chance being to fall in with a vessel, or make some port within five days, at the end of which time they expected to perish." But then "a rude still was made out of a tin boiler and a gun-barrel, salt water was put in, and to their great joy, it trickled down fresh. For twenty-two days they lived on what they could thus manufacture, averaging half a pint a day to each man, their only food being three mussels a day."

Baldwin added that some from the sloop "endeavored to walk up the coast, and found themselves in lonely deserts, obliged for days together to live on cactus, and were almost beside themselves for joy when they found a poor broken-down mule that had been left by the wayside."

It is presumed, though not reported, that the wayfarers ate the mule.

Of still other Nicaraguan comrades Baldwin noted briefly, "Others of our company joined a party which came up from Panama in an iron boat. For months they suffered everything. At length speaking a steamer, one leaped into the water, crying that he was perishing. A rope was thrown to him, and he was dragged on board the steamer; the others have never yet been heard from."

The hardships encountered by the first Nicaraguan expedition discouraged mass travel on that route for a time. It remained a perfectly feasible crossing, however, and someone was bound to exploit it. Financier Cornelius Vanderbilt seized the opportunity in 1851, obtaining control of the transit rights, and setting up a ship line to service both sides of the run. Thereafter gold rushers swarmed over the route

by the tens of thousands. The country became so well traveled that when Mark Twain passed through about a decade
later he complained that the natural beauty of the jungle had
been altogether spoiled by the billboards of Yankee merchants.

Once established, the new crossing proved a good deal
safer than Panama. The terrain was more favorable, a system
of lakes and rivers providing a continuous water passage for
all but the last few miles. The climate was comparatively
mild, due to high altitude, and the region less ridden with
endemic disease. As a result it was a preferred route for families going out to join men in the gold fields. Some ships on
the run consigned as much as a fourth of their space to
women and children. There was a brisk traffic, too, in adventurers returning from California. Many a gold rusher who
had experienced Panama going out decided that coming back
he'd try Nicaragua.[2]

The Vanderbilt Line used the health factor as a chief selling point, particularly during periods when Panama was in
the grip of its recurrent epidemics. In one advertisement published in San Francisco the ship company inserted three separate health assurances in the course of a fourteen-line notice:

THE VANDERBILT LINE
FOR NEW YORK AND NEW ORLEANS
VIA NICARAGUA!
NO CHOLERA OR YELLOW FEVER
BY THIS ROUTE!

Passengers are assured that the crossing on this route from ocean
to ocean is in first rate order. The land crossing

ONLY 12 MILES

The route is now in excellent condition and passengers may rely
on being forwarded with speed and comfort, free from epidemics
and

AHEAD OF ANY OTHER LINE!

The steamships *Pacific* and *Brother Jonathan* on their last voy-
ages were free from sickness and did not lose a single passenger.

The advertisement was not entirely candid. Nicaragua was much less pestilential than Panama, but that didn't make it a health resort. The country had its share of tropic conditions, and the travelers soon made matters worse when they brought in their own ills.

The first major epidemic came in 1852, when cholera invaded the route. The outbreak produced at least one death ship, the *S.S. Lewis,* which lost thirty-six passengers during a two-week run from San Juan del Sur to San Francisco. It was the first time Nicaraguan travelers had been subjected to that kind of ordeal. Thereafter cholera and yellow fever appeared sporadically, though usually the depredations were less severe than at Panama. Then in 1855 the situation on the two routes was suddenly reversed. The Panama Railroad was completed in that year, making Panama transit quick, easy, and relatively safe; Nicaragua at the same time was ravaged by its most deadly cholera epidemic.

The 1855 outbreak reached its first peak in July when two death ships sailed from San Juan del Sur, the *Sierra Nevada* losing thirty-one passengers and the *Cortes* twenty. There followed a brief respite, the epidemic subsiding entirely for about two weeks. Beneficiaries of the lull included a large group that sailed from the infested coast about August 1 on the *Uncle Sam.* There were some 750 on the big ship, including more than 200 women and children, and they completed the run to San Francisco without a death or even a serious illness. On its very next run, however, the *Uncle Sam* attained the grim record of being the most devastated vessel ever to sail on a gold-rush voyage. This time the ship buried 104 persons at sea, an average of one every three hours throughout the trip; and nine more of the passengers succumbed after reaching San Francisco.

Another occasional hazard of Nicaraguan travel was shipwreck. That happened on other routes, too, but the Vanderbilt Line was particularly accident prone. In a fifteen-month period, from February 1852 to April 1853, the company lost four out of six ships assigned to the Pacific run.

In the first two wrecks the ships ran aground without loss of lives. In one instance a steamer piled up on the Mexican coast, stranding 900 people, including about fifty women and ninety children. They had to make a fifty-mile forced march through the wilderness, and when they reached Acapulco they were stuck there for weeks, dependent on what food they could beg while they waited for another ship to complete their journey. That, however, was mere difficulty. Another group met disaster when the steamer *Independence* caught fire after striking a reef off the coast of Lower California.

The fire started in the damaged engine room and swept swiftly through the doomed vessel. The ship was stuck fast on jagged rocks in the midst of heavy surf, and there was wild confusion in attempts to escape. Some of the lifeboats proved almost useless for lack of oarlocks. And some boats reached the safety of a nearby island, then remained there, the boat crews ignoring cries for help and refusing to brave the surf a second time. Out of 300 passengers, 125 died by fire or drowning.

The survivors were marooned for a time on a barren island without food, water, or shelter. They became so demoralized that the living began to loot the dead. According to one witness, "Men were stripping the bodies of clothing, and actually quarreling, yea fighting, over a corpse to plunder."

Two months after the *Independence* disaster the Vanderbilt Line lost still another ship, the *S.S. Lewis*. The wreck of the *Lewis*, however, was anticlimactic. The ship missed the Golden Gate in a fog and piled up high and dry on a beach at Bolinas Bay, a few miles to the north. The *Alta California,* a newspaper unfriendly to the shipping line, took this tart note of the vessel's demise:

"As there were no lives lost and no distress occasioned by the disaster, other than the temporary inconvenience to the passengers and the anxiety of their friends, this loss may be considered as rather beneficial to the traveling public, as the *S.S. Lewis* could not be considered wholly seaworthy."

CHAPTER 7

I think my nervous system has become deranged. Satan is again in a supremacy. It is most mortifying.

> —Rev. James Wood, wrestling with
> flesh, the devil, and scurvy
> on a voyage around Cape Horn.

The other great sea route to the gold fields was the long voyage around the tip of South America. That was by far the slowest way, but it was usually the safest and most comfortable.

The safety and comfort were relative, of course. The passengers suffered tropic heat and freezing cold; they had to endure months on end of scorbutic diet. Frequently enough such hardships produced a death or two. There were, however, no hell ships strewn with the dead and dying.

The epidemic danger, in particular, was immensely reduced, because there was less opportunity for contagion to get aboard. Once a company had cleared the embarkation point it became an isolated, self-contained unit, safe from exposure except for those brief intervals when the vessel put in for fresh provisions.

Another element of safety came from the nature of the ships. Cape Horn traffic was carried by clippers, converted whalers, and windjammers, the best of the merchant fleet. The crews were of like quality; they were men accustomed to living on their vessels almost the year around, and they knew their business or they didn't last. They ran clean ships usually, and when disease appeared they scrubbed down promptly with lye or other strong disinfectants.

Under such circumstances contagion was reduced to a random, incidental danger which one could expect to encounter now and then. The annals of Cape passage often treat the problem quite casually. One example is a ship's log in which the captain embellished the navigational record with occasional brief comments on events of the vogage:

"Ice gone, poultry spoiled"; "Spree in forecastle—the Devil to pay"; "Saw whale"; "Passengers in Midship have a row"; "Small pox broke out on board"; "Fruit cake raffled for, and a drunk amidship"; "Another drunk amidship"; "Expect to be in San Francisco in 10 or 12 days."

There remained the hardships of long and uncertain voyage. Most of the Cape ships depended on sail and so were subject to all the vagaries of weather. A swift ship blessed with favorable winds might complete the run in five or six months, but the average was nearer eight. Some vessels were driven as far off course as the coast of Africa. Many lost a month or more wallowing around wind-whipped Cape Horn or threading their way through the treacherous Strait of Magellan. One storm-tossed little ship was a year en route from New York to San Francisco.

Along the way the passengers experienced almost the full extremes of climate. Crossing the equator, they flopped about on the decks, seeking such scraps of shade as the ship afforded, for the ill-ventilated holds were intolerable then. Later, rounding Cape Horn, they weathered the bitter gales that came shrieking up from the Antarctic. One gold-rush diarist described off-Cape conditions in a single telling sentence: "About nine last night the captain went to the galley and leaned over the stove to thaw the ice out of his whiskers." And when the chill Cape winds were left behind, there was the equator to cross again.

The most serious problem was maintaining sufficient provisions for all the months at sea. Canning was then in an early, very unreliable stage. Ice, of course, was almost unobtainable. As mainstays of food preservation they had to rely on the ancient, primitive methods of salting and drying.[1]

At best the voyagers suffered the ill effects of a debilitating diet. At worst they got scurvy. That dreaded condition resulted from a lack of ascorbic acid, or vitamin C, an essential food element which is supplied by fruit and vegetables.

Medicine at the time had no knowledge of vitamins, minerals, and proteins. The relationship between food and health was clear enough, however, and the good ships took such precautions as they could. They stocked up heavily on dried fruits, and they called at way ports to restock with fresh produce. Many vessels also carried livestock along, quartering pigs, sheep, and goats on the deck to be slaughtered as needed.[2] But even so the argonauts were reduced much of the time to such maritime delicacies as dandy funk, lobscouse, and salt horse.

Dandy funk was a heavy pudding made from mashed-up navy biscuits boiled in molasses; it was sometimes fortified with fat scraped from the cooking pot. Lobscouse was a hash concocted of salt pork or beef, hard bread, and potatoes. Of lobscouse a connoisseur observed, "It is very greasy, but we eat it."

Salt horse was the last resort. That was plain salt meat, "as salt as salt itself," without the hash and pudding refinements.

There were numerous attempts to supplement such diet with the produce of the sea. Shark, dolphin, porpoise, and albatross all were tried in time of need.[3] Opinions varied widely as to the gastronomic results, but on the albatross there was a clear consensus: no matter how it was baked, boiled, or fried, that tough and oily bird just would not do.

Water presented another problem. It was stored in wooden

casks and over the weeks and months it became stagnant and murky, giving off a foul odor that was variously compared to bilge water and bad lamp oil. It became more inviting, however, as it became more scarce. That happened often when poor sailing weather forced a ship to institute tight water rationing.

The general state of provisions prompted one argonaut to write home offering practical advice to those who might wish to emulate his voyage. "Be sure," he wrote, "to bring a Peil or Bucket to catch rain water . . . also lemons and figs."

The knowledgeable travelers always carried a little something extra to see them through. On the ship *Europe,* for instance, the passengers were no sooner aboard than they began "curing cabbage bought for their own convenience," and "paring onions to put them down in a barrel to pickle." These foresighted domestic preparations were influenced perhaps by the fact that six women sailed with that group.

On another ship Joseph Kendall confided to his diary that he was husbanding a box of quinces which he did not see fit to tell his companions about. "I often take a spoonful or two on the sly," he wrote. "I have a bottom berth, and I have to get down on my hands and knees, and, lying nearly flat, open my little box, and take the quinces. I have to watch some time before I can get this opportunity." [4]

And then there was the argonaut, a Yankee-trader type, who late in the voyage assembled his companions for a shipboard auction of a jar of spiced prunes. He sold the prunes one at a time, averaging better than a dollar apiece.

As the voyage dragged on food became an obsession with some. A case in point was a gold-rush minister, the Reverend James Wood, who was continually reproaching himself for the intemperate cravings of his stomach. He confessed that when his ship reached Rio de Janeiro he was "the *first* in the *first* boat to go ashore"; he rushed straight to the market and there succumbed to a lust for oranges.

"This would seem almost silly," the minister wrote, "but when the stomach has been deranged for six or seven weeks and nothing but salt provisions, or little else but salt provisions, the appetite longs for land foods."

About four months later, and still voyaging, the Reverend Wood found himself in the grip of now more insistent demands of the flesh. "I am becoming more and more irritable," he observed in his journal. "I think my nervous system has become deranged. Satan is again in a supremacy. It is most mortifying."

What had gotten into the minister was not Satan but scurvy. The irritability, the craving for fruit, the chilblains of which he also complained, all were early symptoms of a condition that afflicted innumerable others on the long voyage.

One cruelly distressed voyage was that of the ship *Brooklyn* on a Cape passage in 1849. In repeated attacks of scurvy about half of the 200 passengers were stricken. Some were so crippled that they had to be carried ashore on landing. Several died.

As was often the case, the tribulations occurred through a piling up of mistakes and bad luck. The *Brooklyn* carried too many people, one passenger stating that six men were jammed together in a cabin only six feet by eight. Food was so poorly stored that barrels of spoiled potatoes, beans, and bread had to be thrown overboard. The captain was in such reckless hurry that he passed up a chance to reprovision. And finally, with all margin of safety exhausted, they encountered ruinous weather.

A physician aboard, Dr. J. Praslow, reported that the scurvy began to appear as they sailed down the coast of Patagonia, near the Cape. The cases were few at first, and the symptoms mild, but the condition grew steadily worse during the hard going that followed.

They were battered by storms for seven weeks while rounding the Horn, the vessel being driven far down in the ocean to latitude 64 S., about 250 miles from the Antarctic Circle. By that time twenty-five of the passengers were stricken. Here was a vicious circle, for the bitter cold wore away the vitality of incipient victims, while the scurvy, in turn, made the cold much harder to bear.

They enjoyed the expected respite when they rounded the Horn and stopped for fresh produce in Chile. Then, sailing up the Pacific, they endured a second, much more severe attack of scurvy. This time half the passengers and crew were stricken.

A third onslaught, and one that surprised Dr. Praslow, came at journey's end. He noted numerous cases of "flagrant scurvy *on landing.*" Casting about for an explanation, he surmised that the physical exertion and emotional impact of arrival brought on some latent cases. It was a shrewd deduction at a time when the effects of stress received scant attention.

Dr. Praslow added that when he arrived in San Francisco his first few weeks of practice were almost entirely taken up with scurvy patients from his ship. He couldn't obtain fresh fruit for the sufferers, but he did the next best with vegetables and dried fruit, and he applied a potpourri of other remedies. He doused the patients inside and out, sponging them with vinegar and water, bathing them in malt, and feeding them liberal doses of beer, wine, and port. He prescribed tartaric, citric, sulfuric, and hydrochloric acids, all taken as fluids. He fed them brewer's yeast and used the yeast for a poultice as well. But the most effective remedy of all proved to be scraped raw potato. Like nearly everything else on Dr. Praslow's list the potatoes were administered both internally and externally; they proved excellent as diet and seemed to help when applied as poultice to the bleeding sores.

Dr. Praslow's patients were fortunate indeed to receive

such moderate and generally sensible treatment. Some scurvy
victims fell into the hands of medical doctrinaires who purged
on almost all occasions, regardless of the patient's condition.
Then debilitated men were given harsh laxative doses of jalap
and epsom salts. Dr. Praslow observed tersely that patients
so treated "usually died in a few days."

The food problem and its attendant ills led to occasional
spectacular brawls between passengers and crews. Sometimes
such affairs ended with the captain relieved of command.
And sometimes the captain put the passengers off.

The trials of a hungry and mutinous vessel were epitomized
in the voyage of the *Bonne Adele,* a French bark which sailed
from New York for San Francisco in the first weeks of the
rush. The vessel was badly managed; she was some weeks at
sea before the captain suspected that he had more passengers
than passage tickets. When he conducted a count his fears
were confirmed; the ship harbored not one stowaway but
three. Among the illicit passengers was a thirteen-year-old
orphan boy, a brash little gamin named George Henstis, who
had managed to give everyone the impression that he was
with someone else. For lack of any better solution he was
signed on as cabin boy to work his way the rest of the voyage.

The passengers were vastly amused by the stowaway incident. Later they had some second thoughts about the attrac-
tions of so untidy a cruise. Before the voyage was half done
the *Bonne Adele* was on semi-starvation rations and threatened with armed uprising by the passengers.

The tribulations were recounted by H. A. Scofield, a newspaperman who was aboard. The ship was still beating down
the Atlantic, Scofield reported, when they ran out of such
staples as sugar, molasses, pickles, raisins, and cheese. Then
the water supply ran low; the daily ration was cut to a pint
per man, and they abandoned cooking in order to preserve
the precious fluid.

"We attempted to eat beans and rice cooked in sea water, but could not," Scofield wrote, "and we were compelled to make the most we could of mouldy biscuit and salt meat."

The situation grew steadily worse, the water dwindling to a putrid remnant in a single cask, and the passengers began to talk openly of seizing the ship. According to Scofield, they half agreed on a plan to beach the vessel on the desolate coast of Patagonia; once ashore, they expected to find food and water enough to sustain them on an overland trek across the tip of South America. It was a foolhardy scheme almost guaranteed to turn a dangerous situation into total disaster. Fortunately it rained; as the water level rose in the casks their hopes rose, too, and they decided to stick with the ship. And so for a month more the voyage continued, the captain and passengers now eying each other with open hostility, while the *Bonne Adele* rode out a stormy passage around the Cape.

They stopped for fresh produce at Valparaiso, Chile, and there the captain and passengers denounced each other to the maritime authorities. The captain went to the French consul, filed charges of mutinous conduct, and announced vehemently that he would not sail another mile with men who dared to speak of insurrection at sea. The French consul entirely agreed.

Some of the passengers meantime were in the office of the American consul, pouring out bitter complaints against a sea captain so greedy that he would scrimp on provisions at the risk of life. The American consul agreed too. Unfortunately the matter was outside his jurisdiction. If it were an American ship, he pointed out, he would be empowered to relieve the captain of command. Since it was a French ship, there was nothing he could do. The passengers were not impressed with this fine point of maritime law. They stormed and raged while the harassed consul took refuge in professional patience; finally he washed his hands of them with the suggestion that perhaps they should try another ship.

The protest delegation appealed next to the city's governor and there received unexpected support. The governor stated flatly that under no circumstances could the *Bonne Adele*'s captain go through with a threat to put the passengers off. Quite possibly the governor was influenced by a disinclination to have a party of insurgent and nearly insolvent adventurers left on his hands.

Scofield was in the thick of these proceedings and he left the governor's office with satisfying assurances that they couldn't do this to him. And then he discovered that they had done it. While protests mounted and petitions flew the *Bonne Adele* quietly sailed away, leaving about eighteen of the adventurers stranded. Luckily gold rushers were wont to carry such funds as they had sewn up in their clothes; the abandoned argonauts scraped up $50 apiece and, after some frenzied negotiations, they found a ship that would take them on for that price.

Months later when he reached California Scofield was still raging at the American consul's failure to protect the travelers. Writing to his hometown newspaper, the *Whitehaller,* of Whitehall, N.Y., he berated the official thus:

"I say out with such bloated office holders and sapsuckers of the American people, who assume to be our masters when they are only our servants, and let their places be filled by a better man."

In a more philosophical vein, Scofield conceded that the enforced stay at Valparaiso was not without its compensations. The tropic port he termed "one of the most romantic of all the places I ever saw. It is emphatically a city of hills, of mud huts, and of women—who when they see a stranger take him in. Whitehall is no comparison; it can't begin the same day."

Numerous other argonauts were temporarily stranded at one point or another along the way. Nothing of that sort, however, matched the wildly improbable fate of five men from the bark *Hebe*.

The *Hebe* eschewed circumnavigation of Cape Horn in favor of a run through the narrow and dangerous Strait of Magellan. While threading the strait the ship encountered an unmanageable head wind and was forced to cast anchor. There was the usual urgent need for fresh meat, and three passengers and two crewmen went hunting on a wild island. Then abruptly the wind changed direction and a gale blew up with such force that the anchor cable snapped.

As the *Hebe* scudded into the channel the captain looked at his billowing sails and thought of his opportunity to be out of a dangerous situation. He looked back and considered the probabilities of shipwreck if he attempted to turn about. And then, conveniently, he recalled something he had quite neglected to mention when the hunting party went ashore. The whole area, he announced, was infested with fierce cannibal tribes. It was too bad, but no doubt the fellows on shore were already consigned to a native's pot. So saying, he sailed on, leaving behind five erstwhile sailors and gold rushers who were suddenly cast in Robinson Crusoe roles.

If the abandoned men were picked up by some other ship, the record does not survive.

Of course, not every voyage was beset by disasters. For a truly exemplary cruise one turns to the *Edward Everett*. She was a Boston ship, chartered by patrician adventurers who formed a co-operative and went out in style.*

The tone of the expedition is conveyed by the fact that the *Edward Everett* was named after the president of Harvard University. That worthy in turn presented the ship with a

* New England gold rushers were partial to co-operative ventures, Massachusetts alone sending out 102 joint-stock companies in 1849. The companies almost invariably dissolved soon after reaching the gold fields, but they served a valuable purpose in providing a measure of organization and discipline while en route.

fine library and sent each member of the company off with
a new Bible under his arm.

The undertaking was organized as the Boston and California Joint Mining and Trading Company. That name was
indicative too. These were gold rushers who set forth with
pickax in one hand and trading goods in the other, and they
carried along a good stout safe in the confident expectation
that one venture or the other would surely prove profitable.

The joint company numbered about 150 men, including
eight sea captains, four physicians, a clergyman, a mineralo-
gist, and a geologist, along with numerous merchants, manu-
facturers, farmers, and skilled craftsmen. They were in short
the essence of New England, prudent, pious, substantial, and
shrewd—and yet bold spirited enough to be off with the first
organized party to sail from Boston in the rush.

They made allowance for every contingency, foreseeable
and unforeseeable. Thus the ship was equipped with light-
ning rods against the caprice of nature and with two brass
cannon in case pirates should attempt to impede their passage.

They established a shipboard police force and set aside a
portion of the vessel to serve as brig, in the improbable event
that one of their number should run amuck.

The four physicians in the company were appointed as a
board of health to preside over a dispensary well stocked
with drugs. The physicians were also entrusted with twenty-
five gallons of liquor, a company bylaw restricting the alcohol
to medicinal purposes. Finally they took along a two years'
supply of food, just in case.

For all the careful, well-planned preparations, however,
the expedition was still up against the hard fact that the art
of sailing was much more advanced than the art of preserving
food. Day after day the elite company sat down to a dinner
of "Hushamagrundy," a concoction of parsnips, rutabaga
turnips, and salted codfish.

By the time they reached California they were showing the signs of incipient scurvy. The affliction can be deduced from the report of Reuben Shaw, a Bostonian who declined a berth on the ship and went by wagon train instead. When Shaw arrived at the diggings he looked up his old friends from home and observed with dismay that they were "a very debilitated lot."

"I have many times congratulated myself," Shaw wrote, "that I was NOT one of the passengers on the good ship *Edward Everett*."

That, however, was but one man's opinion. Out on the trail, on the burning deserts and in the high mountains, one could have found sick, hungry, exhausted gold rushers who would have given almost anything to have gone by sea.

PART III

THE TREK

CHAPTER 8

———————◆———————

Our ignorance of the route was complete.

> —John Bidwell, a member of the first
> wagon train to attempt the California
> Trail.

The rush by land brought another great stream of humanity surging to California. It was a movement even larger and more tumultuous than the migration by sea.

Some elements, of course, remained the same. There was again the brave spectacle of people setting forth by the tens of thousands on an incredible journey. Inevitably, too, there was repeated the harsh drama of disease and death sweeping through the ranks of the travelers. But in other respects the two movements were wholly different.

The sea-borne travelers experienced brief struggle at the isthmus crossings, but otherwise theirs was a largely passive adventure. They merely endured for the most part while their ships bore them along. On land the migrants had to match their strength and will against all the demands of the journey.

The trek itself was a formidable feat, especially so for the greenhorns among them. Men who had been clerks and shop-keepers a short time before found themselves traversing immense reaches of wilderness. In the process they forded great rivers, crossed rugged mountain ranges, and stumbled

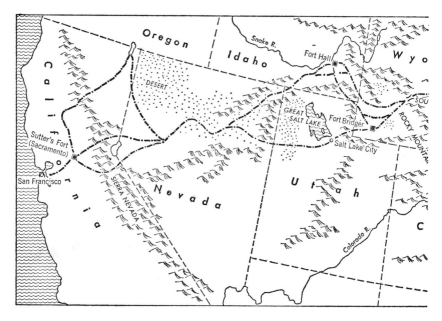

THE CALIFORNIA TRAIL

through deserts which offered not a drop of water or a blade of grass.

They had to do it on an inexorable timetable imposed by nature. The season for travel was compressed into a brief span of about five months, beginning when the spring grass appeared on the prairies, and ending when snow blocked the Sierra passes.

It came down to this: If a man could strike a rough average of fifteen miles a day, and if he could maintain his pace despite illness, exhaustion, and ruinous accident, then he made it with a little to spare.

If he couldn't do that, he was in trouble.

The chief overland route was the California Trail. That was a rude pathway which spanned 2,000 miles, from jump-

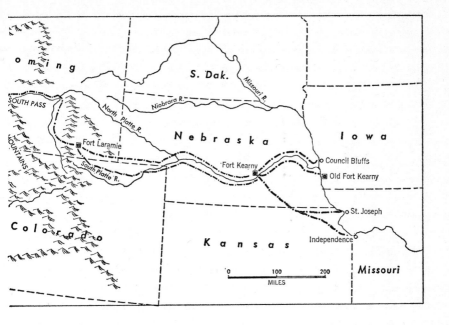

off points along the Missouri River to Sutter's Fort at Sacramento.

A common starting point was the bustling little frontier town of Independence, Missouri. From there the first leg of the trail ran almost straight as a string across the prairies to Fort Laramie. Then it snaked through the Black Hills and looped over the South Pass of the Rocky Mountains.

So far it was easy going. The country was wild but hospitable enough by pioneer standards; for much of the way the travelers had only to follow the banks of the Platte and Sweetwater rivers. In fact, it was so natural a route that along this stretch the line of march coincided with sections of the Oregon and Mormon Trails.[1]

Once over South Pass, the California route broke up into a tangled maze of alternate trackways. From Wyoming to

Nevada there were seven forks in the trail, the branch paths weaving back and forth across a 250-mile front. And that part was hard going. Every alternate course represented some trail blazer's struggle to find a better way across the mountain and desert barriers.

By gold-rush times it was already a storied trail. Little bands of westering pioneers had been moving over it for years, preparing the way for the migration to follow. Built up in that period was a hard-earned knowledge of where to go and how to travel.

The first to attempt it were the fur trappers known as mountain men. They were a wild breed who dwelt in the Rockies and from there pushed out to roam all over the West. In the 1820s and 1830s Jedediah Smith and Joe Walker led fantastic expeditions to California and back; on one trek Smith and two others were the only survivors from a party of more than twenty.

The wagon trains came next, the vanguard appearing in 1841 when a group called the Western Emigration Society formed a caravan for California. They numbered sixty-nine people when they left the Missouri frontier, but more than half of them changed their minds en route, electing for Oregon; the California contingent came down to thirty-one men, a woman, and a baby.

They were a mixed lot, these new pioneers. There was, for instance, John Bidwell, a New York schoolteacher who promoted the affair. He was looking for adventure and opportunity and he found a full measure of both, becoming something of a founding father in the new land.*

Another in the group was Talbot Green, who took some medicine along and acted as the company doctor. Green also

* Bidwell gave his name to Bidwell's Bar and Fort Bidwell. He became a congressman from the new state and was a delegate to the convention that nominated Lincoln. In 1892 he ran for President himself, on the Prohibition ticket.

carried with him a lead ingot, or at least a chunk of something coated with lead, though the core of it may well have been bullion. A decade later he was exposed as an absconded bank clerk named Paul Geddes.

The woman was Nancy Kelsey from Kentucky, eighteen years old, and married since fifteen. She was going out with her husband and year-old daughter, and her motives were straightforward and simple: "Where my husband goes, go I."

The disparate characters shared a total innocence as to the nature of the trek they were undertaking. They didn't even know the way. Bidwell said later, "Our ignorance of the route was complete. We knew that California lay west, and that was the extent of our knowledge."

In Missouri Bidwell picked up some highly imaginative maps which showed Great Salt Lake to be an inland sea some four hundred miles long; it was represented as the headwaters for two rivers, each larger than the Mississippi, which flowed on to the Pacific. Aside from the maps, their geographical information consisted of an approximate idea of the latitude of San Francisco Bay. They thought that if necessary they could just march across that latitudinal line, taking their directions from the sun.

Luckily they met a mountain man who escorted them as far as Fort Hall in Idaho, a little more than halfway. After that they were on their own. Predictably they got lost, endured long hunger marches, and ran fearful risks as they launched across wastelands without knowing when or where they would encounter the next water. In the Nevada desert they abandoned their wagons and converted to pack train, tying what supplies they could salvage to the backs of the oxen. When they crossed the Sierra Nevadas they were reduced to a foot caravan, having eaten the animals. Nancy Kelsey was walking barefoot by then, carrying the baby.

They made it, but just barely, subsisting toward the end on mule meat and boiled acorns. And when they reached

California they found, as others would, that it was only a scene for new struggle. In the case of the Bidwell party they fell into the hands of Dr. Juan Marsh, a physician of sorts and a rascal of parts; he extracted from them almost all they possessed in return for provisions.[2]

In 1844 another, better-organized group proved that it was possible to get the wagons through. In that historic party was Dr. John Townsend, the physician-adventurer and inveterate boomer who later led San Franciscans in the first rush to the gold fields. Just then, however, the ebullient Townsend had visions not of prospecting but trade. He was taking out a wagonload of fine silks to sell to the Spanish ladies in California.

Dr. Townsend traveled with a wagon train composed of twenty-six men, eight women, and about seventeen children. They were guided by mountain men, and they came equipped with some tough competence of their own. The train members included such useful frontier specialists as a gunsmith, a blacksmith, some expert bullwhackers.

One of the things this party contributed was a new technique for fording swollen streams. They learned that they could convert a wagon into a crude boat by sewing rawhides around the frame. Later, when winter caught them still on the trail, they resorted to some of those same rawhides as a substitute for food.

The crisis for the Townsend party came at the final obstacle, a snow-clogged pass in the Sierra Nevada mountains. They hedged their bet there by splitting into three groups. Dr. Townsend stayed with the main body, helping to chain-haul the wagons up the face of a sheer, clifflike granite slope. They went at it with great care, unloading the wagons first, and packing their essential supplies over the mountain hump by difficult and dangerous labor. The children were led and carried across in the same fashion. Then they went back for their wagons. It took a double team of oxen pulling from above, and all available men pushing from below, to hoist one empty wagon up the icy slope. They did it six times.

While the main body labored at the pass a mounted patrol set off in search of other solutions. Dr. Townsend's young wife went with that group. They swung down the flank of the mountains, riding hard, looking for a place where they might break through and summon aid. Meantime, the doctor's seventeen-year-old brother-in-law volunteered for a third contingent which stayed behind to guard some abandoned wagons and supplies. The assignment very nearly cost the youth his life. He wound up alone in the frozen mountains, waging a desperate struggle against hunger and cold. But he hung on, and got through, and so also did all other members of this resourceful party. Indeed, they registered a population gain along the way. At the main body's winter camp, on the Yuba River in California, Dr. Townsend officiated at the birth of their newest recruit, one Elizabeth Yuba Murphy.[3]

Two years later the Donner party discovered how fearful the same journey could be when bad luck and bad judgment compounded the hazards. The Donner train started late in the season and ran into trouble almost at once. They lost a man to disease, another to accidental gunshot, and a third to murder; two others simply disappeared under cloudy circumstances. Finally, late in October, they arrived at the steep pass where Dr. Townsend and his companions had pushed on through. But the Donner party did not push through. Stuck fast in the snow, only a hundred miles from trail's end, they couldn't muster the effort to struggle on. They ate their oxen, and then each other, in the trail's most grisly ordeal of starvation and terror.

There grew up a legend that the Donner party murdered each other for food. The actual facts are gruesome enough; those who were living simply sustained themselves on those who were dead. One man as he lay dying made his wife promise that when he was gone she would eat her share. Out of eighty-seven in the group, forty perished.

Such were the hard beginnings of the California Trail. By 1848 the journey had become a part of the nation's folk experience, upward of a thousand people having traveled the route. Thus when the gold rush began the way west was already established. The great wasteland barriers were known and charted in rough fashion, and the main directions were well enough marked with faint lines of wagon tracks across the land. But still it remained a trail, with all that that implied. Along the entire two-thousand-mile distance there were only four small forts plus the isolated Mormon settlement at Salt Lake City.

Over this wild trail the gold rushers came swarming. In 1849 the movement totaled more than 22,000 people, traveling with 60,000 oxen, mules, and horses. Strung out single file, that year's migration alone would have been sufficient to form a continuous wagon train sixty miles long.

The rush created the first traffic jams in the history of the West. At St. Joseph, Missouri, the wagons were backed up for miles waiting the opportunity to be ferried across the Missouri River. Two teamsters there shot each other to death in a quarrel over who would be next in the line.

At Fort Kearney on the Nebraska plains a newspaper correspondent counted 180 wagons which passed the fort on a single day in 1849. The wagons rumbled past the check point at the rate of about one every five minutes all that long and dusty day.

The second year's migration was double the first. The third year brought an ebb in the human tide, tales of death and hardship reducing the flow to a few thousand, but after that came another surge. By 1855 more than 150,000 people had taken part in the trek.

The crowding changed the whole character of the trail.

The former thin line of tracks became a beaten path through the wilderness. Across the prairies the sod was trampled out in a great swath a hundred feet wide. In places wagon-wheel ruts were ground so deep into the earth that marks of the passing are visible yet.

At once lonely South Pass there was a busy post office where wayfarers could send back news of their progress for the price of a dollar. And in the desert, where sulfurous water boiled up from the ground, a ramshackle trading post soon appeared. This oasis emporium dealt chiefly in raw whisky; the stuff went down as hot as the water but with more satisfactory results.

In their vast numbers the gold rushers found more weakness than strength. True, they traveled in force sufficient to beat off marauding Indians, but that had always represented one of the lesser dangers. Other, more deadly perils were only aggravated by crowding. There was, for instance, the vital problem of maintaining wagon teams. The animals at the head of the procession ate up the sparse grass in arid regions, leaving little or nothing for those that followed; as a result mules and oxen often weakened and died, and that could be a prelude to disaster.

Disease appeared, too, spreading from wagon to wagon, and infesting the camps where the migrants clustered at the end of each day's march. Cholera was the most terrible killer, particularly in the first two years.

As a consequence of such tribulations some new and melancholy markers appeared to point the way to California. All along the trail the route was littered with abandoned wagons, with bleached bones of animals, and with the graves of men.

The first year's migration alone cost nearly a thousand lives.[4]

CHAPTER 9

During all this time I could hear poor Lyon groaning. His moans grew fainter and fainter, till at last I heard the sentinels outside saying he was dead and asking after me.

—Oliver Goldsmith, stricken with cholera
on the trek.

April was assembly time for the great trek. At the frontier towns that served as jump-off points the gold rushers arrived every day by the hundreds, clattering in with their teams and wagons, or pouring off the big steamboats that plied the Missouri River.

At Independence, Missouri, the first year a hostelry called Nolan's Inn was swamped by 400 men who slept two and more to a bed. Around the town there sprang up a chaotic bivouac of people who camped in tents, in wagons, or simply stretched out on the ground.

They had to endure an enforced wait of a month or so until the prairie grass was lush enough to sustain their teams. Meantime there was much to be done. They traded feverishly for supplies, and worked over their wagons, and squatted around each other's campfires exchanging information, and misinformation, about the journey ahead. Many were relying on maps and guidebooks drawn up by writers who had never seen the prairies, much less the wild regions beyond.[1]

88

6701323

As the adventurers shook down for travel a rough sort of organization emerged. They formed into makeshift companies, giving themselves brave names like "Spartan Band" or swaggering names like "Helltown Greasers." On their canvas-covered wagons they emblazoned other bold statements of their character and purpose, the wagon signs proclaiming "Wild Yankee," "Live Hoosier," "Rough and Ready," and "Going for Gold."

They prepared as though expecting to fight off howling Indians every mile of the way. Standard equipment was a rifle in hand, plus a revolver tucked in the belt. One gaudily uniformed Massachusetts company carried sabers as well and mounted a swivel gun on each of their wagons. An Iowa company required each member to take along thirty pounds of lead and 5,000 percussion caps.

The wild West atmosphere elicited wry comment from one feminine gold rusher who wrote to her sister, saying: "Our men are all well armed. William carries a brace of pistols and a bowie knife. Ain't that blood curdling? Hope he won't hurt himself."

While they girded for imagined battles a real danger was coming to meet them. The cholera had been raging all winter at New Orleans; by early spring the epidemic was sweeping up the Mississippi, riding the riverboats, advancing at the rate of a hundred miles a month. Soon enough the pestilence invaded the Missouri, laying a belt of death across the frontier zone through which the migrants were moving.

The crowded camp at Independence was hit hard at just about the time that the early starters were moving out on the trail. In subsequent weeks the disease took such heavy toll at Independence that those who were still arriving almost all shifted to an alternate starting point at St. Joseph. There was, however, no easy escape. As the traffic flowed to new areas, so also did the contagion.

At Fort Leavenworth, about midway between Independence and St. Joseph, Major Osborne Cross reported that "the cholera had spread through every town on the Missouri River." He added that outbreaks "raged with great violence on board several steamers, one of which, after losing nearly 30 passengers, was entirely abandoned and left tied to the shore."

Another observer at Fort Leavenworth was James Collier, a Customs official bound for California on government business. To his superior Collier wrote: "We have had to encounter disease and death, at almost every step. . . . You can hardly imagine the dreadful havock made by the cholera, along the river & on the boats. . . . It has followed the immigrants & the opinion is expressed by the officers here that there will be great distress among them."

At St. Joseph the epidemic caught gold rushers who were jammed up by the thousands at a Missouri River ferry crossing. The situation was described by J. Goldsborough Bruff who attempted to cross a company there. The ferry landing, he said, was "one dense mass of wagons, oxen and people." Bruff estimated that he would lose two weeks getting his wagons across. Meantime cholera was spreading through the encampment and new arrivals were bringing fresh infusions of the infection almost every day. One particularly alarming incident was the appearance of a steamboat which had lost forty-seven passengers to the disease while plying up the river system from New Orleans. On hearing such reports Bruff pulled his company out and marched a hundred miles north to another less frequented ferry crossing in Iowa.* It was a good try but unavailing; the epidemic would overtake him before he had crossed the plains.

There were many accounts of cholera on the trail. Mostly the adventurers described it in terms of their own fragmentary

* About 20 per cent of the forty-niners jumped off from Iowa, following branch paths which intersected the main trail some two hundred miles out.

experience, but here and there one glimpses the larger scene.

Major Cross was again a witness to events. He was moving over the trail with a company of mounted riflemen; they were bound for Oregon, but they accompanied the forty-niners on the intermingled path across the prairies. In a journal entry dated May 24 Cross reported, "The cholera now began to make its appearance along this route. The emigrants were suffering greatly. They were often compelled to travel when it was almost death to be moved."

Two days later he wrote: "It would be useless to attempt to enumerate the deaths that occurred. The graves along the road too plainly told us that the cholera was prevailing to an alarming extent."

In some wagon trains, Cross said, the disease "raged with such violence that nearly whole parties were carried off."

Cross had proceeded only a hundred miles when one of his own troop was stricken. Aid was solicited from a passing physician, a Dr. Browne of St. Louis, who pronounced the case hopeless. Faced with the harsh exigencies of the trek, Cross decided to keep moving, dragging the dying man along in a hastily contrived ambulance wagon.

"The man became entirely deranged," he wrote, "and required the strength of one person to keep him in the wagon. His sufferings were very great, and his cries most distressing, particularly as it was not in our power to render him assistance or relief."

Others testified to the first year's travail in terms of the mute evidence they saw inscribed in the earth. Thus Dr. Joseph Middleton of Kentucky noted, "For five or six hundred miles the roadsides were strewed with fresh graves." A forty-niner named Kimball Webster added, "The cholera followed the immigration to near Fort Laramie, making sad ravages on many companies. Many have left their bones to bleach upon the great plains of Nebraska, with not even a stone to mark their resting place."

The reference to bleached bones was not entirely a rhetorical flourish; there were places where wolves got into shallow graves and scattered the remains about. Dr. Amos Batchelder of New Hampshire told of walking out from his campsite one night to find a man's body spilling out of a half-opened grave with two wolves crouching close by. And in a letter to the Cincinnati *Gazette* a gold rusher who signed himself M. Powell described a place where "the bones and skulls were so numerously torn from the graves and strewn over the prairies that it resembled a field months after battle."

The next year the losses were even worse. In 1850 a correspondent for a Missouri newspaper estimated that along one cholera-ridden stretch of the route the migration was costing more than a man a mile. He saw a wagon train in which only one man was able to sit up; the group had originally numbered twelve people, but when they were encountered six of them were dead, four were dying, and the remaining two were on the point of collapse. A week later the same correspondent saw a party in which sixteen out of seventeen were sick; he met also two men who were each the sole survivor of a train.

Dr. George Davis, a Missourian, was another who described the terrible losses of the second year. To a friend he wrote, "The emigration was immense and very sickly—from 2 to 4 thousand were birried on the Platte River—often from 6 to 9 in a grave." *

Dr. Davis said, "I prescribed for about 300 cases of cholera or diarrhoea only 2 of which died so far as I know." And for those who might come after him he warned that the traveler "must drink none out of the 10,000 little wells or holes dug in the Platte bottom from 1 to 4 feet deep. You should use no water but running water for yourself or stock."

---

* A few of the mass graves reported by Dr. Davis may have been not graves but caches. Some gold rushers reportedly resorted to such hiding places for valuable but encumbering articles, like kegs of brandy. One is left to wonder when and how they expected to reclaim their property.

The Davis letter raises some interesting speculations about the doctor himself. Evidently he was one of those backwoods practitioners who combined shrewd observations with some quite astonishing areas of ignorance.

His spelling and grammar reveal a marked deficiency of academic training. That, however, was not unusual. A more serious shortcoming appears when Dr. Davis speaks of treating "300 cases of cholera or diarrhoea." Apparently he didn't know the difference. We can assume that he prescribed the same opium pill for all bowel conditions and claimed a cure if the patient didn't die. We can take it for granted, too, that if he had only two failures in 300 cases, then he was dealing with diarrhea, not cholera.

An ignorant man, this Dr. Davis, even by the standards of his day. But for those around him in a time of need, he was all they had.

And it just happens that he was exactly right about those water holes.

To the migrants the cholera onslaughts must have seemed as chance-ridden and unpredictable as the misfortunes of war. One company might be attacked again and again, while other outfits close around went through untouched.

As a general rule the parties that started early and moved fast got ahead of the epidemic; if they were lucky they stayed ahead. But the late-comers often suffered terribly. They were exposed at every crowded way stop and even on the empty reaches of trail. They quite literally took their lives in their hands each time they cupped palms to drink from some muddy water hole which all the others had used before. And once they picked up the disease, they were likely to carry it with them for many a mile.

One such ordeal was recorded by P. F. Castleman, a forty-niner who went out with a party of twenty from his native Kentucky. Cholera hit this group early and hard, killing four of them before they set foot on the trail; thereafter the disease followed them across the country, striking three times more. They also endured mountain fever and scurvy, were ridden with dysentery, and suffered a near-fatal casualty from accidental gunshot, and at the end the survivors were harassed by Indians as they staggered over the last stretch of the journey.

An unusual feature of Castleman's group was the presence of nine slaves, all of them owned by a company member named Churchill. Most slaveholders left their chattels behind, suspecting rightly that the gold-rush atmosphere would stimulate escape, but Churchill was a domineering sort who felt sure he could keep his slaves in line. Churchill, in fact, made it his business to keep the entire company in line. He "proclaimed himself wagonmaster," an act that brought still further problems to the ill-fated band.

Most of all Castleman's party suffered from the mistake of starting late. They formed up in Kentucky on May 2, 1849, at a time when advance companies were already out on the trail; when they joined the great procession they were a good four thousand wagons behind. They reaped, as a consequence, all the harvest of troubles the migration was sowing.

Their trials began on the steamboat approach up the Missouri River. It happened that a boat just ahead of them was devastated with cholera, and a survivor of the plague ship got aboard their own vessel when they docked briefly at Jefferson City, Mo. This refugee from contagion must have been greeted as such people always were, with some avoiding him as though he were death itself, while others bolstered their courage by insisting that personal contact had no effect. Castleman did not give his own view of the matter; he simply reported that shortly the stranger was dead and the disease was spreading through the boat. It cost Castleman's company two men, the slaves Joshua and Richard dying on successive evenings.

The fear-haunted river voyage lasted nearly two weeks. Then they spent a week at St. Joseph, waiting at the ferry, and that cost them two men more. The victims were brothers named Pepper. Again the blows fell in quick succession, the first brother succumbing one evening and the other the next morning. Death claimed the second brother just as they were striking camp to begin the long trek. It made for a late start the first morning, the company being delayed almost until noon by the necessities of burial.

Finally they were off and moving on a trail that was by now well seeded with the deadly contagion. Before they were five miles out they began to pass other companies that were laying by on account of illness. They found, too, that their own outfit was marked as one of those stricken, so that fellow adventurers were clearly uncomfortable in their presence. The first trail entry in Castleman's diary noted, "They all appeared to want us to go on and not stop near them, as they seemed to think that the disease was contagious."

For two weeks they rolled on, enjoying easy travel, but seeing all around them the warning signs of stalled wagons and fresh graves. "It gave us a hint," Castleman wrote, "that there was a great deal of sickness on the road." And then it was more than a hint. The sound of retching in one of their wagons announced that cholera was striking at their own company again.

The victim this time was a slave named Ned Red. They pulled off the trail and made camp while the company physician, a Dr. Buckner, did what he could. From what we know of the physician we can deduce that his treatment was opium and mercury, generously applied. We can gather, too, that the company by now was losing faith in such prescriptions. They had no recourse, however, except to wait and see while the stricken man pitted his strength and vitality against the disease. Meantime Castleman made himself useful by roaming the prairies in search of fresh meat. On the third day of the enforced encampment he returned from a hunting trip and saw beside the parked wagons the raw scar of a new grave. Ned Red had lost the unequal contest.

This one shook Castleman. Perhaps the weeks of shared hardship and danger had made Ned seem less a slave and more a comrade. Or maybe it was just one reminder too many of the deadly enemy that rode unseen in their train. In any case, the next diary entry departed from Castleman's usual practice of dismissing death with a bare mention of the details.

"There seemed to be a general rush this morning," he wrote, "with one and all to get away from the place where we had been deprived of one of our company by the awfull epidemic."

He added somberly, "It has become so customary to see fresh graves, and companies laying by on account of sickness, that I seldom speak of them or even think of them, only when I see them."

Four days later the slave Alexander was stricken. It hit them at a bad moment, in the midst of a storm, and at a time when their company was astride a mile-wide river crossing on the South Fork of the Platte River. As luck would have it, the wagon containing the medicine chest had already forded the swollen river when Alexander collapsed in another wagon on the opposite bank. For twenty-four hours the storm held them helpless. Finally Dr. Buckner got across, "gathered up a lot of physic," and returned to take up his discouraging ministrations. The others decided that since they had to lay by anyway, they might as well unload their wagons and dry out their sodden provisions. Before the task was accomplished Alexander was dead.

Alexander's death was very quickly followed by the desertion of some new members of their party. They had fallen in with another small company, the outfit consisting of nine men, a woman, and a boy. Now the strangers eased away, offering an embarrassed excuse. In Castleman's words, "The three waggons that joined our train left us this eavening, saying that they would drive out to the wood as it was reported that there was plenty some two or three miles ahead, but I think they were afraid of the cholera as it has been very fatal at this place."

Another two days of journeying brought a fresh reminder of the peril around them. This time it was an Indian lodge, deserted by all save a pack of dogs that lay howling around the entrance. Castleman, always curious, rode up to investigate. When he pulled back the deerskin flap he saw "two or more corpses, partly wrapped in a blankett." He wasn't sure of the number as it was dark inside and because he was struck with a thought which made him back out of there in a hurry. "It may be posable," he wrote, "that those persons died of the cholera and, fearing that the disease was contagious, they left them in their wigwam."

There it was again—that question of contagion. Castleman kept turning it over in his mind, noting that some people thought so, but he never committed himself on the matter. Perhaps he couldn't afford to. After all, if it was contagious, what was a man to do when his companions were stricken?

Four days beyond the Indian lodge they reached Castle Rock, a towering stone mass that served as a picturesque landmark along the route. To the hard-pressed company, however, it was just a new site for the old ordeal. In his diary Castleman wrote, "Preston More is complaining of a diarea which I feare will terminate in cholera as it has been running on for two days."

Early the next day More collapsed. They stopped the wagons again but not for long; More died the same afternoon. He was their seventh casualty in about that many weeks.

Two days after burying More they saw across the far horizon the first shimmering peaks of the Rocky Mountains. Castleman could not know it, but they had reached a kind of boundary in the fearsome trek. When they got into the chill mountain country they would throw off the epidemic that had stalked them for a thousand miles. But in the mountains, and in the desert beyond, they would encounter other trials almost equally hard to bear.

Struggling along about three or four days behind Castleman's Kentuckians was an equally afflicted party from Michigan. Oliver Goldsmith told of that experience. He didn't put it down until many years later, but some episodes he remembered vividly, for he was himself one of those stricken. He had the eerie experience of lying in a tent, only half-conscious, yet alert enough to hear and understand when his companions discussed whether he was living or dead.

Goldsmith's company was another of those hard-luck outfits that caught the disease early, while steamboating up the Missouri. They had to cope with both cholera and panic, the authorities in terrified river towns refusing them permission to land the sick and bury the dead. Goldsmith does not say how they dealt with the gruesome dilemma of corpse disposal. Perhaps they slipped ashore in uninhabited areas to perform their burials. Or then again they may have been among those who contributed to the spreading disaster by dumping bodies into the river.

At Independence, where they joined the trek, they suffered new losses. Again the chronicle is chary of detail; we know only that fifty of them left Michigan together, and only thirty-seven were still around when they struck the trail. Of the missing thirteen, some died, some were left behind as too ill to travel, and some may have abandoned the adventure.

One recorded casualty at Independence was an unnamed physician who accompanied the party. Goldsmith said of him, "Our doctor was often called upon to attend the sufferers, both among the townspeople and the immigrants. He soon fell victim to the dread disease, and died after a day's illness."

Fortunately two medical students were also along; they were promptly pressed into service as acting physicians.

The trek itself was another gauntlet run. They were moving through Kansas, from a starting line a hundred miles south of that taken by Castleman, but the scenes were identical. Said Goldsmith: "We passed many deserted camping grounds where we saw the sad effects of the epidemic—from one to six graves—and came to several camps with sick ones unable to continue the journey."

In the space of ten days Goldsmith's company lost four men to the epidemic. Then they were hit twice more in swift succession, a man named Lyon being stricken one day, and Goldsmith himself falling ill the next. He described the episode thus:

"The captain called an early halt of the train, the doctor having told him that Lyon would either be better, or dead, before morning. When our tents were pitched mine was so near his that the guy lines crossed each other. It had been raining hard all that day and the ground was very wet. Our company had but one canvas cot and that was placed in Lyon's tent. When he left the wagon to go to it he was vomiting badly. I went to my tent, crawled into my blanket, and experienced the same symptoms.

"The doctor gave me some remedies, but I could keep nothing on my stomach. This continued until midnight, when the doctor told the man who was attending me that if I could not keep the medicines down they must be injected. He gave orders to have a small sheet-iron stove brought from our mess wagon, a fire lighted and a poultice made as hot as possible of corn meal covered with mustard and sprinkled with cayenne pepper.

"During all this time I could hear poor Lyon groaning. His moans grew fainter and fainter, till at last I heard the sentinels outside saying he was dead and asking after me. Then they brought the poultice and placed it on my stomach.

If it had been of red-hot coals it could not have been hotter. They held my hands and shortly after I fell asleep. When I awoke I felt much better."

As one who survived the disease Goldsmith was naturally inclined to credit the medication. Actually the treatment had served at most to damp down the more violent symptoms. His life he had saved himself, by outlasting the attack through sheer stamina. He had further need of that quality as he convalesced on the sun-baked prairie, jolting along in a wagon bed or on the back of a horse:

"Owing to the burial of Lyon we were late in starting out the next morning. They put me in a wagon and fortunately we had but five miles to travel before reaching the Big Blue River. This gave me a chance to rest and recover some of my strength." He added, gratefully, that the river crossing entailed a three-day delay during which he had little to do but lie around.

The river camp proved an added boon for they met some Indians offering ponies for sale. Goldsmith said, "I was advised, if I had the money, to buy a pony as it would be much easier for me to go on horseback than ride in a wagon without springs." At the suggestion of a friend he selected for himself a gray mare, somewhat advanced in years, thin-sided and sway-backed; it was a sorry-looking beast, but it just suited the condition of the rider.

"Different members of the company had purchased ponies," Goldsmith observed, "and my mare was the subject of many jokes among them. They ridiculed her style, doubted her endurance, and guyed me about her every score and occasion. They had chosen younger and gayer animals, but my friend declared she would stand the journey best of all and told me how to take care of her, advising me to rest her whenever I could. This I was able to do very often, as I was too weak to ride more than short distances at first."

The company pushed on and Goldsmith kept pace as best he could, falling behind when he was forced to rest, but catching up afterward by plugging doggedly along. He was in no particular danger, for there were plenty of other travelers about, and if he lost too much time, he just kept moving at night, until he came to his camp. His companions deferred to him in rough fashion, excusing him from such communal duties as standing sentinel and gathering fuel for fires. Then his strength returned, and it became his turn to nurse a stricken comrade.

"Soon after my recovery," he wrote, "one of my mess was taken with cholera. He rode in the wagon which I drove in order that I might attend him. He was a German, named Klimper. He had no confidence in our doctors and said some very uncomplimentary things to and about them, in his queer, broken English. He refused to take their remedies, telling them that everybody died who did so, and that after he had purged all that was in him, he could not purge any more, so would get well without their poisons. He became very weak and emaciated, unable to get in or out of the wagon without my help, and we fell behind the train and were very late in getting into camp.

"I finally told him I had some medicine in my bag that had cured me and he must take it or he would surely die. He was still inclined to be obstinate, but consented at last to try it. I had the doctor prepare a heavy dose for him which I palmed off as something of mine. He eyed it suspiciously and did not swallow it until he had poked out some dark substance, which he said was opium. He got well."

Like Castleman, Goldsmith saw all around him the evidence that others were suffering similar affliction. It became a thing so common that most of it he passed by without paying particular heed. And then, in the midst of the general disaster, he glimpsed one small tragedy so poignant that it ever afterward remained in his memory. It occurred on the

North Fork of the Platte, almost at the end of the cholera zone.

"As some of us went to the stream to bathe one evening," Goldsmith wrote, "we saw a good wagon on the opposite shore. The canvas curtains, flapping idly in the breeze, seemed to invite investigation. Two of the men went over to see if anyone was around and if not, why the wagon was left there. They stumbled first upon a new made grave, then going to the wagon and looking in, saw the body of a poor young fellow who, apparently, died of cholera, alone, without a soul to do him a kind service or say a soothing word. He had evidently buried his wife, unaided, and must have realized that he, too, was doomed, for he had turned his cattle loose."

Described also by Goldsmith was the havoc which the epidemic was spreading among the Indians.

"From time to time," he wrote, "we came across queer looking objects in the trees. On investigation these proved to be the bodies of Indians wrapped, with all their trinkets and belongings, in large buffalo robes and suspended in the branches. The Indians so disposed of their dead, not as some believe to take their souls more easily to the Happy Hunting Grounds, but to keep the bodies from being molested by wolves."

He added that the Indians themselves had the bad habit of molesting the migrant dead. "They opened the graves— no matter how deep they were—to get the clothing. In this way cholera was contracted, causing great fear among them and adding much to their distrust for us—they believed we had poisoned them. A great many deaths occurred among them."

The observant Goldsmith was one of the few to suggest the full dimensions of cholera's inroads among the Indians, for the natives very probably suffered as much as the migrants. The great warrior tribes of the plains, the Sioux, Cheyenne, and Pawnee, were especially devastated, the migration and its attendant epidemic cutting a swath right through their lands. Some observers believe they were so weakened as a result that the climactic Indian wars were put off for a generation.[2]

A dramatic Indian tragedy was recounted by Capt. Howard Stansbury of the United States Army. He was going out on a surveying mission, and he mingled with the forty-niners for about half the trek. Along the way he saw a Sioux death camp which moved him to pity and horror.

As Captain Stansbury reported it, the primitive mausoleum consisted of five lodges, containing nine corpses. Eight of the number had been dead for some time and they were all laid out in like manner, close-wrapped in buffalo robes from head to foot. The ninth was different. It was the body of an Indian girl, about eighteen years old, and only recently dead. She was not muffled like the others. Instead, her robes were laid back, exposing her face and the upper slopes of her breasts. Later Captain Stansbury discovered why. In talking to men who had preceded him he was able to put the whole story together.

It seems that cholera had attacked a party of Sioux and the survivors had fled, leaving the dead behind. Left behind also was the girl, who was not dead, but gravely ill. The tribe despaired of saving her and feared to remain with her in the stricken camp. Despite their terror, however, they postponed flight long enough to pay her the traditional death honors in advance of the event. They dressed her richly, putting fine new moccasins on her feet, wrapping her legs in scarlet cloths, adorning her with buffalo robes beautifully embroidered with porcupine quills. They put her in a separate lodge, set apart from the others who had already perished.

For a day or two she lay there, clinging to a thread of life, while gold rushers passed by and looked in on her and hurried away. Sometimes when a grizzled face poked through the flap of her tent she propped herself up and stoically returned the gaze. Then she succumbed, dying peacefully, it seems; Captain Stansbury said that her features were composed "in quite an agreeable expression."

The thing haunted the soldier, and when he wrote of it he spilled out his anger at all who allowed the girl to suffer alone. The conduct of the Indians was the more forgivable, he thought, because in his view they were heathens and savages. For them, perhaps, there was some excuse. But for Christians? For civilized men? Captain Stansbury didn't think so.

Some Indians joined the gold rush, sharing both the high hopes and hardships of the trek. Conspicuous examples in the first year's migration were Cherokee and Wyandot companies from the Oklahoma and Kansas territories.[3]

An Indian physician, Dr. Jeter L. Thompson, led one Cherokee band that was almost wiped out by the epidemic. The disaster was glimpsed by a passing observer who described the stricken company thus: "A few days ago it consisted of fourteen persons. Since yesterday, six had died with cholera, one was dying at the time they were visited, and the remainder were too ill to assist in burying the dead. Among the whole of this party there was but one man who really was able to render any assistance to the others."

The lone man reported as still functioning was Dr. Thompson. He ministered to his comrades and held his company together, though he himself was so desperately ill that he could barely drag himself around.

When the attack passed the party numbered only five survivors, Dr. Thompson among them. They went on to California.

The presence of so much random disaster presented the gold rushers with a human problem of large dimensions. It was the problem of one man's responsibility to another in the hour of distress.

The migrants who had gone by sea had largely escaped that

dilemma. They were bound together within the tight confines of a ship's deck; when crisis came they might handle it well or badly, but they were forced by circumstances to stick together.

On the plains it was different. They had a choice.

They had to face the question without support from society. For there was in the wilderness no procedure for keeping order, no agency to aid the sick and helpless, no law at all save that imposed by custom and conscience.

The only unit they could count on was the individual company, held together by common consent. Most of them settled for the hard rule that a good company took care of its own.

It made, of course, for cruel choices. There was no room in it for that abandoned Indian girl. Often, indeed, the travelers could afford little enough aid and comfort to those of their own kind.

It was not a matter of being indifferent to human values. Many were glad to share food and medicine, if they had it to spare. Some even would pause for days at a time to aid a stranger, though that decision came harder. Time was crucial, and the trail was choked with strangers who needed help.

The dilemma was well illustrated in the experience of J. Goldsborough Bruff. He was the wagon-train commander who had pulled out of that cholera-infested camp at St. Joseph in an effort to bypass the epidemic. Bruff was a good man, conscientious and competent; he adhered to a sensible policy of avoiding trouble whenever he could, and he kept his outfit moving in smart order across the plains. And then he came hard up against the problem of stray unfortunates who couldn't manage. He was confronted three times in two days with a wretched little one-family party that was overwhelmed with troubles of every kind. It started like this:

"I passed an ox-wagon in the road, without cattle, and a female sitting alone, on the tongue, weeping. I asked her the matter, and she informed me that her husband and son had gone ahead some distance to look for a stray poney, and she was afraid they would not get back before night. On inquiring about her oxen, she said they were below, in the river bottom. I would have left her a guard, but other companies were coming along, and I thought her husband would not be so imprudent as to leave his poor wife alone on the road, in this wild country."

That night he met the rest of the family, the father wandering into Bruff's camp with the boy, a lad of about twelve. They hadn't found their lost pony. The boy was showing signs of illness, and they were not able to make it back to where the woman waited. Bruff gave them food and shelter for the night.

The unfortunate family got itself straightened out somehow and got ahead of Bruff and then promptly broke down again. Late the next day he saw the woman a second time.

"She was again sitting on the wagon-tongue, weeping, and said that her son was sick in the wagon, and her husband had gone back some distance, and the oxen were several miles below, in a bottom, with no watch over them. This poor woman has seen hard times indeed; the son will probably die, the indians or emigrants will carry off their oxen, and finally the husband will take care of himself."

It was a damned shame, but there was nothing Bruff could do about it. Nothing, that is, unless he wanted to scoop up the wailing woman and her sick son and her bumbling husband and carry the lot of them to California. And if he adopted that kind of policy, his train would very quickly become a collection of disasters.

Bruff shook his head in dismay and marched on by.

When misfortune appeared within a company a different set of rules applied. The obligations then were quite plain. The members were bound together by solemn agreement, by the ties of comradeship, and indeed by self-interest. If they could not rely on each other, they were in deep trouble.

The good outfits marked themselves by the way they treated their sick and even, or perhaps especially, by the way they buried their dead. In that last act there was much that symbolized the morale of a company and the esteem in which it held its members.

Bruff's company again provides a case in point. Cholera overtook them on the plains, a death "sudden and astounding," as Bruff put it, and he canceled half a day of his usual hard-rolling schedule to do the proper thing. He selected a gravesite on a hill overlooking the trail and set his men to hewing out slabs of sandstone with which to line the vault. Bruff himself worked for three hours sculpting head and foot stones, lettering the slabs, and blacking the inscriptions with grease from a wagon wheel. Meantime someone remembered that the deceased had once been an army noncom; a messenger was accordingly dispatched up the trail to bring back a nearby squad of soldiers to do final honors.

When all was in readiness the dead man was sewed up in his blue blanket, draped in a flag, and laid on a bier that was made from his tent poles. There was a solemn procession, the men all in clean clothes, marching two by two to the strange funeral music of a bugle, a flute, a violin, and an accordion. At the grave a service was read by "an elderly gentleman"; then the soldiers stepped forward and swung their rifles to the sky for the last salute. It was, without doubt, the most elaborate such ceremony performed on the trek.

Some other companies met the test in simpler fashion but in the same spirit. Thus an Ohio company lost a man named Frank Adams to cholera. They buried him under a stone slab inscribed with his name and state. Afterward the company physician, Dr. Samuel Mathews, wrote a long letter to Adams's brother. Dr. Mathews told of the last moments and described the grave. He announced that the company had

voted to sell the dead man's possessions and hold the money
in trust until it could be sent back to the family. And as a
final gesture he listed possessions that weren't worth selling
but might be desired as family mementos. He offered to send
back a daguerreotype miniature, a pocket Bible, two journals, a gold pen and case, a dozen other personal effects that
had been carefully preserved.

By contrast some companies disintegrated under the epidemic's blows. There was panic then, and desertion, and the
casualties became nameless dead shoveled hastily into shallow pits.

Dr. Joseph Middleton observed one party that was clearly
in the process of coming apart. They were camped at a creek,
at a place where they had lost two men from cholera, and
they were in a great hurry to be done with the business of
losing a third. When Dr. Middleton rode up on them a
stricken man lay moaning in a wagon, while a short distance
away his companions were already digging his grave.

John Nevin King, of Illinois, hinted darkly at even more
unseemly haste in the way his company disposed of a casualty
named Walker. Again the affair occurred after the company
was demoralized by repeated losses. Said King: "We buried
Walker an hour after he died his thumb twitching but pronounced dead by Physician."

Still another company simply deserted a stricken member.
That story was recounted in the gold-rush diary of Alonzo
Delano.

The desertion victim was Joseph E. Ware. Ironically Ware
had joined the trek after writing a popular guidebook on
how to make the journey. It was an honest work in that Ware
claimed no personal experience; he pieced his account together from newspaper clippings and the memoirs of ex-
plorers, and in the process he became so fascinated that he
decided to go and see for himself. Then he got cholera, some-

thing he hadn't anticipated in describing the hazards, and he discovered danger of another kind that no guidebook has ever successfully charted.

As Delano reported it, Ware "was taken sick east of Fort Laramie, and his company, instead of affording him that protection which they were now more than ever bound to do, by the ties of common humanity, barbarously laid him by the road side, without water, provisions, covering or medicine. Suffering with thirst, he contrived to crawl off the road about a mile, to a pond, where he lay two days, exposed to a burning sun by day and cold winds by night."

A party headed by Charles Fisher came along finally and found Ware lying by the pond. "They took him into their tent," Delano said, "and nursed him two days; but nature, overpowered by exposure as well as disease, gave way, and he sank under his sufferings. Fisher was confident that if he had had medicines and proper attendance he might have recovered."

The migrants didn't think of cholera as one of the natural obstacles and yet, in a way, it was. One could almost have marked it off on a map, like a desert. The factors of climate and conditions of the trek created a well-defined epidemic belt which extended out some 600 to 700 miles from the jump-off points. For most of the travelers it meant that the threat hung over them for thirty to forty days. And then, finally, they left it behind.

There was a kind of transition zone which began at Fort Laramie, 635 miles out. Fort Laramie, in fact, marked a double transition. From there on into the Black Hills cholera lingered, but it was not nearly as devastating as it had been before. And over the same stretch the country began to get rough, though not nearly as bad as it was going to be.

The new problem was graphically symbolized by a huge junk heap and garbage dump which grew up around the fort.

Great quantities of equipment, supplies, and provisions were discarded there as men took stock of the terrain and lightened their loads.

One gold rusher estimated that there was at least 4,000 pounds of discarded bacon alone, some of it stacked neatly in piles, and some scattered in random fashion across the ground. In abandoning the food some gold rushers put up signs inviting others to help themselves and volunteering advice on the edibility of the various provisions in the pile. And then there were a few who mixed dirt into the flour and sugar and poured turpentine over meat, lest others should profit from their loss.

Beyond Fort Laramie another new sign of the times took the form of a trail increasingly littered with animal carcasses. In one short stretch through the Black Hills Castleman counted a hundred dead oxen. There would be a lot more of that farther on.

The animal deaths were due partly to hard hauling and shortage of grass and partly to the fact that the water in this area was often heavily impregnated with alkali. At one such pool a migrant erected a board sign inscribed with a scrawled warning: "Look at this—look at this! The water here is poison, and we have lost six of our cattle. Do not let your cattle drink on this bottom."

It was no easy matter, of course, to keep thirsty beasts away from such water. When they got into it and drank copiously, the results were frightening; the saliva would pour from their mouths; they would heave, swell, tremble, drop to the ground, and quickly die. As remedy the gold rushers took fat bacon, attached it to a stick, and shoved it down the animal's throat. The idea was that the fat would counteract the alkali by forming a kind of soft soap in the stomach. Sometimes it worked.

Such were the problems in the Black Hills. Then they

rolled on, into the Rockies, and it became for all practical purposes a whole new trek.

Goldsmith put it precisely: "The cholera left us, but we were never without some drawback. From good roads, plenty of feed for our stock and drinkable water we were now to experience the trials, discomforts, and, finally, the horrors of journeying through a country lacking all three."

CHAPTER 10

What the devil is this?

—A gold rusher, eating
buffalo dung

South Pass of the Rocky Mountains was a broad, grassy slope which rose so gradually that the migrants never knew the moment when they crossed the Great Divide. But when they came down the other side they knew well enough that they were in a new kind of country.

The difference was simply and graphically illustrated by the layout of the trail. Up to South Pass there had been one basic trail, much of it nearly straight, because that was the natural route. But after South Pass there were trails branching everywhere, and none of them straight, because there wasn't any good way to go.

The travelers had to thread their way first through the western slopes of the Rockies. The roughest stretch was a course which zigzagged through river valleys and boulder-strewn canyons for three hundred miles or more. It took usually about three to four weeks.

According to the branch path followed, the adventurers might also encounter a desert within the mountains. That was a barren region about forty-five miles wide, with little grass and no water; it called for a two-day forced march with a dry camp in between.

After the mountain passage came a long pull down the

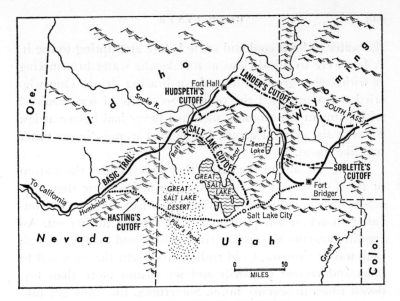

ROCKY MOUNTAIN CUTOFFS

length of the Humboldt River. For 365 miles the river sustained them through a parched, inhospitable land of sand hills and sagebrush. Then the river was swallowed up by the arid earth, disappearing into a marshy bog called the Humboldt Sink.

Beyond the sink stretched the Forty-Mile Desert. Here nothing grew. The sand in places was knee-deep to a floundering ox, and the only water was found at a spot where springs and geysers spewed forth boiling hot and laden with sulphur.

Gold rushers usually paused for a day or two to prepare for the desert. They baled loads of hay from the marshy meadows surrounding the sink and filled every receptable they had with water. Then they launched into the wasteland and made a run for it, moving all day and all night until they got across.

Some tried to make do with what the desert provided. At the boiling springs they scooped holes in the earth, collecting the water to let it cool and settle before attempting to use it. A few were so injudicious as to take the water hot, mixing it with coffee grounds to make a bracing drink. One who tried that chronicled the result: "Soon after I was troubled with pains in the Stomack such as I never had before at last I was in the greatest agony. I thought I would die my water was like blood."

On the far side of the desert they struck either the Carson or the Truckee River, depending on which route they took across the sands. It was a Hobson's choice; the Truckee was easier to get to but presented harder going farther on. Ascending into the Sierras, the river twisted and turned through high-walled canyons. Gold rushers who went that way had to cross and recross the swift and icy stream more than two dozen times in seventy miles. Sometimes, too, they got into canyon turns so tight that to squeeze a wagon through they had to lift it up bodily and hoist it around the bend.

And then, finally, they came to the last great obstacle, the pass across the Sierra Nevada. On the Truckee route the pass comprised a thirty-mile stretch, much of it so steep and difficult that they had to rope-haul the wagons along, snubbing the ropes to trees to keep the vehicles from crashing down the precipitous slopes. A pace of half a mile an hour was considered good going across the pass.

In sum, the western half of the trek constituted about 1,100 miles of brutal terrain. The result was a steady attrition of wagons and animals, and that in turn meant the loss of supplies and provisions on which survival depended. One observer estimated that in the desert alone he saw three thousand dead animals and at least six hundred abandoned wagons. Another said that through the Sierra country wrecked wagons dotted the landscape on the average of one a mile.

There occurred a progression of events which one finds again and again in gold-rush annals. When wagons were wrecked or abandoned the men salvaged what supplies they could by making pack animals of the lumbering oxen. And then, when the beasts gave out, the men themselves took up the packs and struggled on in what came to be known as "Walkers' Train."

Of course, there was an attrition of men too. They stood up to it better than the oxen, better even than the mules, but some of them paid a terrible price.

The rigors of the western terrain coincided with the appearance of some harsh new maladies. Again the ills were closely related to trek conditions, so that the zones of affliction could be charted almost as accurately as the wastelands that had to be crossed.

Encountered in the Rockies, and again in the Sierras, was "mountain fever." Gold rushers used the term loosely, to cover almost any fever they got in the mountains, but modern medical detective work has tracked down the conditions that in all likelihood were chiefly responsible. It appears that the migrants were stricken with Rocky Mountain spotted fever and Colorado tick fever, especially the latter.[1]

Rocky Mountain spotted fever was a disease caused by rickettsia and transmitted by ticks; the symptoms included high fever, aching bones and muscles, and painful headaches, sometimes accompanied by mental disturbance.* Colorado tick fever was a debilitating virus disease. The two ills together were nowhere near as prevalent as cholera, and not as deadly, but for the persons infected they were enough to transform a laborious mountain passage into a grueling experience.

The other great tribulation was scurvy. It began to appear on the long haul down the Humboldt River and from there on it got progressively worse, severe cases developing between the Forty-Mile Desert and the Sierra Nevada. Often enough

---

* Rickettsia are minute rod-shaped or coccobacillary microorganisms; they act as parasites and cause disease in vertebrates.

the scurvy was combined with semistarvation or acute diarrhea, or both; the effect was to rob men of their strength at
the very time when they needed it most.

Of all the ordeals this one should have been the most preventable. The knowledgeable adventurers were well aware
that it was crucial to carry not only sufficient food but the
proper kind. And those who didn't know it were warned as
events unfolded. The newspapers were soon flooded with letters from gold-rush veterans, and many of them offered excellent advice as to trail conditions and travel requirements.

The cautionary advice was well illustrated by a series of
letters signed "M. M." and published in the *Missouri Republican*. The correspondent wrote from Sutter's Fort after
taking part in the first year's trek. In straightforward, un-
dramatic fashion he warned that it was a rough business; he
estimated that among those who reached California about
one-third arrived so sick and spent that they were months in
recovering their health. He noted particularly that "scurvy
has been the poison bane of the emigration." And then, for
those still determined to risk it, he suggested a list of essential
provisions.

For basic rations M. M. advised 125 pounds each of flour
and salt pork, adding that greasy meat should be avoided as
much as possible. He observed that risen bread went down
better than saleratus biscuit, and he noted that yeast kept
well all the way. Finally, with special emphasis, he urged that
the minimum ration for each man should include "a plenty
of pickles, one-fourth bushel of onions and one-half bushel of
beans. Vinegar should be used every day. Apple and peach
fruit and rice are as useful articles as can possibly be taken on
the road. To each man 80 pounds of rice and three-fourths of
a bushel of apple or peach fruit at least are necessary."

It's not clear whether M. M. thought that the rice was antiscorbutic. In any case his list was sound; a gold rusher thus

provisioned could risk the road with the knowledge that at least his own body would not betray him.

There were many, of course, who took thought of such necessity without waiting to be warned. Thus one finds a feminine forty-niner, an Iowa woman named Catherine Margaret Haun, who observed in her journal that she was well provided with "citric acid—an antidote for scurvy." She added, "For luxuries we carried a gallon each of wild plum and crabapple preserves and blackberry jam."

Others concocted salads from wild fruits and vegetables found along the way. Resourceful travelers could avail themselves of such plants as water cresses and lamb's-quarters greens; by diligent forage they could also find wild currants, chokecherries, and service berries. The last named were serviceable for a fact; they belonged to a botanical family which a hundred years later would yield the material for the first synthesis of ascorbic acid.

Altogether it was quite possible for the travelers to eat well enough, provided that they planned for it in advance and worked at it continuously as they went along. And some did just that. One particularly engaging example was Dr. Charles R. Parke, a young physician who found himself being battered by snow and hail as he crossed South Pass on July 4, 1849. Instead of bemoaning the weather Dr. Parke utilized it for a gastronomic coup. He milked two cows that were pulling his wagon, mixed the milk with some peppermint oil from his medicine chest, and processed the concoction by juggling it along in the back of his wagon. The result: ice cream.

"It was delicious," wrote Dr. Parke. He added, pleased as could be, that he was undoubtedly the first man on earth who had eaten ice cream atop the Great Divide.

Unfortunately there were also improvident types who gave but scant thought to preserving health and well-being. They were in a frenzy to get on with the journey, and they fell quickly into a pattern of eating anything that came to hand, under any conditions. The careless attitude was typified in an incident recounted by Oliver Goldsmith.

Goldsmith's outfit gathered one night around a campfire of buffalo chips, or dried dung, while eating steaks provided by the same beast. Presently a diner grimaced in disgust, waved aloft a piece of challenged meat, and turned to the cook, inquiring, "What the devil is this?" The cook inspected the item and acknowledged that sure enough it wasn't a steak but rather a chip that had gotten into the skillet by egregious error.

Said Goldsmith: The cook "made no apologies, but simply remarked 'I wondered what had soaked up all my bacon fat' as he tossed it away."

That was exactly the kind of thing that could lead to trouble—to an entire company being disabled for days by diarrhea.

Other, far more serious difficulties stemmed not from any stray chip in the skillet but rather from the items that weren't there. Those who were careless of diet stocked up on salt meat, flour, and dried beans and let it go at that. Then, in a fit of mass madness, they compounded the error by throwing the beans away. A rumor had got around that the beans were causing the cholera.*

For many the end result was reliance on a diet almost wholly devoid of fruits and vegetables. And once they started on that they were caught up in a deadly timetable. At about ninety days they began to feel the first symptoms in the form of chronic fatigue. If they weren't alert to scurvy, however, they could miss the initial warning easily enough. It usually hit them in the Rocky Mountains, where the going was such that a man could expect to be tired.

---

* One supposes that the migrants associated beans with bowel disturbance, the latter being one symptom of cholera. The first year's migration in particular was notable for discarded beans.

The next critical phase occurred at about 120 days, when the blood ascorbic-acid level reached zero. This time there was no overt warning at all. An all-important metabolic fuel gauge had registered empty, but they didn't know it, and they kept plugging on. They only felt more tired than before.

About ten to fifteen days later they began to break out in ugly skin sores. If they were behind schedule on the trek— and the scorbutic ones were usually behind—then this caught them still stumbling across the Nevada desert. They were cursing the internal affliction and the external ordeal, and all the time they were moving among cactus plants containing juices which could cure their condition. But they didn't know that, either.[2]

At about 160 days the skin hemorrhages began to appear. These were less noticeable than the sores but more ominous. The new scars were pinpoint size, perfectly round, and purplish red.

About twenty days after that the gums swelled, the teeth came loose, the legs became black and swollen. That was the very last warning. If they corrected the condition immediately, they might still return to something like normal with quite surprising speed. If not, they died.

As it happened, most of the afflicted ones just did make it, dragging their lacerated flesh over the last mountain pass in time to beat the double deadline of scurvy and snowfall. There were some hundreds, however, who weren't that tough or that lucky. They contributed to a fresh string of roadside graves.

The scurvy hit hardest at those already weakened by disease. One grave marker near the Humboldt River provides a succinct example; the brief, clinical epitaph described the tribulations of one man, but it might well have stood for the whole migration. J. Goldsborough Bruff reported the inscription:

"W. Maxwell, died Aug. 24th, 1849,
Cholera, Teamster in "Pioneer Line"—
Took Cholera on the Platte, then
Scurvy; from Independence." *

Sometimes scurvy combined also with starvation. The two were not directly related, but again there was a process of one thing leading to another on the wheel of disaster. As men were undermined by scurvy they lost the strength to contend with fate; it became all too easy then to neglect the animals, to abandon broken wagons that might have been fixed, to live from day to day without regard for the stern discipline which the long haul required. And once they adopted that course any accident left them wholly undone.

Starvation was a recurrent problem throughout the rush, but it became most acute in 1850. That was the year of over-confidence, the time when all warnings were shrugged off by those who insisted on believing that the continent was conquered now and the way laid straight. It was, of course, a very natural human response. People all over the country were hearing from friends and neighbors who had gone out before, and very often the reaction was, if they made it, so can I. Thus the trail the second year became twice as crowded; the percentage of greenhorns was higher than ever; the preparations were sometimes inexcusably slipshod. Some foolhardy souls heard about the piles of abandoned food and concluded blithely that they could count on such bounty whenever occasion required. As a result the migration that year very nearly came apart at the seams.

* The Pioneer Line was a commercial organization which undertook to convey gold rushers across the trail for $200 a head. It has been described as the West's first experiment in public transportation and it was, in a word, disastrous. The entrepreneurs were too optimistic; they underpriced the trip, then scrimped and took chances to make it up. The result was a sorry tale of abandoned wagons, lost supplies, critical failures to meet the schedule, all complicated by the ills which so often beset disorganized stragglers. As the epitaph said: "Cholera on the Platte, then Scurvy."

One who took part in the 1850 trek wrote from the Nevada desert, "Footmen, who comprise nearly one-fourth of the numbers now on the road, are reduced to subsisting on the putrefied flesh of dead animals. This has produced the most fatal consequences."

Another participant reported meeting a starving migrant who had lived for six days on a few pounds of coffee. He added that in the Sierra Nevada hunger became so general that ten pounds of flour could be exchanged for a horse.

Still another observed, "It is hard to turn away a starving man 1,500 miles one way, and 300 the other, from any source of supply, but we are obliged to do so."

CHAPTER 11

My mouth fairly watered, for a piece of an indian to broil!

> —J. Goldsborough Bruff, starving in the Sierra Nevada mountains.

The second half of the trek became for some a remarkable test of endurance. For almost all it was rough going. The full cycle of trials was again illustrated in the adventures of P. F. Castleman and his fellow Kentuckians.

Castleman's group was the company that lost seven men to cholera before reaching the Rocky Mountains. Beyond that point new troubles piled up. Mountain fever, scurvy, hunger, Indian harassment, a crippling accident, bad luck in choosing trails, divisive quarrels within the company—all this was their lot.

They had endured the last cholera attack on June 21, 1849, while approaching Fort Laramie. About five weeks and five hundred miles later, in the heart of the Rockies, sickness appeared again. Castleman reported it on July 27, saying, "We finally concluded to lay by the balance of the day, as I was very unwell and had not been well for several days." He added, "H. Buckner and Mr. Porter are boath complaining. Porter has the chronic diarrhea."

The next day: "This morning I felt verry unwell, so I went to Buckner who was our company physician (or pretended to be). He said that I had the Billious fever, which we termed

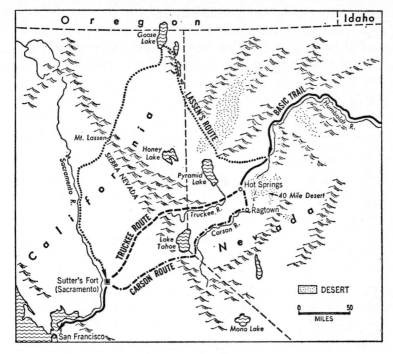

THE END OF THE TRAIL

the mountain fever. He gave me a dose or two of colamel (calomel) which he said would break the feaver if it had the right effect."

And two days after that: "I am verry fatigued, altho I have broken the feaver, but am verry badly Salivated." *

Castleman's party was having schedule trouble, too, falling steadily behind as a result of illness, and that led them to gamble on routes. They came upon Hudspeth's Cutoff, a new, uncharted path which had been beaten out only weeks before, and without having any clear idea of where it would lead they swung off and took it. This time they were lucky enough; the cutoff didn't save them much, but it didn't cost them anything either, and that was not a bad result for an untested short cut through jumbled mountains.[1]

* Calomel caused a free flow of saliva.

Then they were pushing down the Humboldt River, and they gambled again and made about the worst possible choice. Seeking to bypass the Forty-Mile Desert, they took an alternate course called Lassen's Route. Unfortunately it bypassed by altogether too much. Lassen's Route started off in deceptively enticing fashion, seeming to run straight west, but then it swung far to the north, going almost to Oregon, before it angled back to Sutter's Fort. It added two hundred weary miles to the trek and took in terrain as fearsome as that on any route.[2]

The Kentuckians blundered into the long detour in the most haphazard fashion. Some wayfarer informed them that the side track was "a neare way to the mines," and they were desperate enough to clutch avidly at any favorable rumor. Also, they could see in the earth the fresh-cut wagon-wheel tracks which showed that many others were turning off that way. So they chanced it.[3]

Within two days they discovered that they had exchanged one desert for another. Theirs was a white desert, an appalling salt flat that extended for twenty miles; the path across it was littered with dead and dying animals. Castleman wrote, "I do not think I have been out of sight of a carcass, and in many places the road is blockaded up so that you are compelled to leave it or pass over their dead bodies."

After the salt flat it was better but not good; within a week Castleman was reporting, "We left one horse today. He had become so weak that it was almost impossible to get him along, and he would fall every time he passed over a rough place in the road, and then have to be lifted up again. So we left him to perish; which we feared would be the case with all in a short time."

And the next day: "We knew that we must either lose a great deal of our propperty now by throwing it away, or lose all our teams soon, with provisions, clothing and every thing else. We all agreed to throw away everything that we did not actuly stand in need of."

And still again: "Passed more than 50 dead beasts here in less than two miles. Some had been left harnessed or yoked, as their owners would become disheartened and would walk off and leave them."

For two weeks they struggled through desert; then they were out of it and climbing into the Sierras. From atop the divide Castleman gazed back in awe at the place they had been.

"I looked back over the dry and ashy desert several thousand feet below and could, it seemed, trace our wake through the sands of the last terrible days. It looked horrid, and I thought: 'Nothing would ever induce me to attempt to cross it again.' It is an ill-fated country."

Gazing westward from the same pinnacle, he saw a dramatically opposite view. Words fairly tumbled out of him as he tried to describe it:

"I beheld a beautiful valley . . . I could see streams and rich grasses . . . and an immense forrest of pine which seemed to reach to the skyes . . . and Goose Lake glowing in the western sunset . . . the many trains encamped . . . and peaceful smoke seeming to rise and hover over the valley, which was covered with cattle and horses. Truly I thought it was the grandest scene I had ever beheld."

There remained a month's hard pull, to make up the ground lost on the long detour. Their line of march angled across the Sierra's western slopes, traversing mountainous country all the way. That brought new problems.

Through the Sierra region the Indians hovered about, attempting to steal their animals. Indian raiders got three of their cattle once, but the Kentuckians recaptured the beasts after a flurry of shots in which no one was hit. Another time an Indian slipped into their camp at night and made off with their best horse. The brave got away with his booty though

Castleman pursued him doggedly, tracking him a day and a night until he lost his quarry in the mountains.

The party also suffered a casualty from accident, a man named Tucker shooting himself as he slipped and floundered in an icy stream. The ball entered his groin and passed through his thigh. They consulted a new acquaintance, a Dr. Bradford, and were told that it was a doubtful case. The physician thought an artery was injured; if it were torn open, fatal bleeding would be the likely result.

They were in the mountains still, with snow coming on, and they couldn't wait. They rigged a litter for Tucker and jounced him along in a wagon, and despite all odds he began to mend.

They plugged on for three weeks, enduring hunger and hardship, but slowly putting the miles behind. And then, only three days from journey's end, the company was rent by a bitter quarrel. Perhaps it was something that had been brewing for a long time. Or perhaps the company leader, the man named Churchill, was the tyrant that Castleman made him out to be. In any case, as Castleman told it, he was ordered to go back for an abandoned wagon. He refused angrily, saying he was in no shape for it, and Churchill summarily banished him from the train.

At this point in his narrative Castleman revealed that he was suffering a new illness. He was, he said, "a little scurvied, which had drawn up one of my legs a little crooked, but could walk by limping."

He was also utterly without resources. When he was banished from the company a friend tried to help him, offering to share evenly all the money he had, but Castleman was too proud and touchy to accept. He did consent to borrow $5; with that he hobbled off defiantly.

Shortly he made a rich find. Not gold, but wild grapes. He gobbled them hungrily, pronouncing them "The best I ever tasted."

Then he went on to the diggings, where he learned that his $5 would not buy even the tools to work with. At Bidwell's Bar, however, he met a merchant who was willing to extend him credit. He ran up an $80 bill, good for a pick, a pan, a week's provisions. The groceries consisted of "a little Salt Pork and Flour that had become a little sower, but this was the best I could do."

Thus after 150 hard days on the road P. F. Castleman was ready at last to mine for gold.*

Many another gold rusher recounted similar ordeals. There was in even the average trek an epic quality that was summed up by newspaperman Bayard Taylor. Reporting from Sacramento, where he saw a migration come in, Taylor wrote, "The experience of any single man, which a few years ago would have made him a hero for life, becomes mere commonplace when it is but one of many thousands."

One quite commonplace experience was that of going on by foot after a wagon train disintegrated. Charles Moxley told what that could be like. In an eloquently ungrammatical letter, written to his sister Emily, Moxley compressed an entire saga into one long, loosely punctuated sentence:

"I arrived in the Sacramento valley on the 26th of Oct. '49, being near seven months on the way having endured privation and suffering from so long a journey on plains, mountains, deserts and lost on the Sierra Nevada desert everything I possessed except my arms for my protection and one blanket

---

* Castleman had no luck as a miner, turned to odd jobs instead, finally set himself up in a small hauling enterprise. He was in continual ill-health. After a severe siege of typhoid fever in 1850 he reported, "My physician salavated me, since which I have been labouring under the influence of mercury so much, that every cold, or even when I was exposed to the weather laid me up. I took the chills and feavers, and would doctor for them, which I would break, but in less than ten days would have another attack. This continued until April 20th, 1851, when I sold my intrust and sought a more healthy climate, as I supposed, which was the Oregon Territory." There we lose sight of him.

and a suit of indifferent clothes on my back, our company
taking the north or Oregon Trail which at best is a very difficult rout there being little or no grass for our mules for
300 miles and no water but boiling sulphur and salt water at
long intervals of 40 and 80 miles apart and in consequence
we lost 80 or 90 mules and horses and was compelled to leave
our wagons, goods and baggage on the plains and foot it as
best we could, the last three days of our trip previous to my
reaching the first settlement was truly trying."

Some of Moxley's correspondence fills in a few details of
his trek. His company left out of Iowa and had bad luck
right at the start, encountering a flood-swollen Missouri
River which Moxley described as an "avealanch of Waters."
When they attempted to cross the stream by ferry the boat
swamped. Moxley's terse summary of the affair: "The vessel
was an entire loss the ferry man drowned and several of our
men saved themselves on drift wood."

Moxley added that "a second attempt was successful though
attended with great labour so mutch that many sunk under
the fatigue. I myself was rather injudicious and drank too
mutch cold water when very warm from working the ferry
and the result was I nearly kicked the bucket."

When they took to the trail Moxley's party learned that
they were far back in the migration, a good five thousand
wagons behind. They pressed to catch up but without much
success; their animals got short shrift on grazing and grew
steadily weaker. By Nevada their position was critical and
they decided to gamble on that arduous "short cut" known
as Lassen's Route. And then the train started to come apart.
Animals died, wagons were abandoned, groups of men broke
off to scramble for survival. They were halfway down the final
stretch, and still 150 miles from trail's end, when the once
fine big train was reduced to a sorry remnant of two wagons
and a dozen mules.

At this point Moxley and four companions set out on foot,

carrying as sole provisions a pound of dry bread apiece. As Moxley said, "Well, some was hungery and et it all at once others made it last the first day and then we had nothing."

The next day they killed a crow. Moxley states only that "we five of us et it"; the reader is left to imagine the jealous care with which that tough and gamy bird was parceled out among five famished men.

After that it got worse. For three days, over a course estimated by Moxley at a hundred miles, their entire subsistence consisted of a few handfuls of acorns found at one spot on the way. Those were the last three days which Moxley described as "truly trying."

Like Castleman, Moxley finished the journey a physical wreck. A few weeks after reaching the gold fields he wrote, "I have been sick a good deal of the time and unable to work. My constitution which was a good one is very mutch shattered and I am not by any means what I formerly was." And later: "I am recovering from a spell of sickness of 4 weeks of the California fever and surely I thought that I should never recover."

For a tale of still more commonplace endurance one turns to the diary of forty-niner Bennett C. Clark. His experience is interesting precisely because it illustrates the trials imposed by the most routine, man-on-the-trail kind of gold-rush experience.

Clark was a Missourian, a clerk of the court in Cooper County, who joined a party of two dozen from his native state. It was a good company and lucky enough. They encountered disease, but not raging epidemic; they took no foolish chances; they sustained each other in time of distress. For them almost everything worked.

The Missourians got off to a fast start, ahead of the cholera, and at first it was a gay adventure. They rolled along in high spirits, exchanging good-humored raillery with friends and neighbors encountered on the trail; the trek itself was hard effort, but they were all young and strong and full of enthusiasm. A diary entry of May 26 conveyed the typical tone:

"Commenced our march at 6 o'clock. Our course continuing up the Platt River the road in many places being very heavy and trains dotting the road as far as the eye could reach, presenting a cheerful picture in this wild and barren country. I found on today's march several friends."

The next day's entry contained the first omen of danger: "On the roadside today I saw a human scull with several names written upon it with pencil."

Clark's outfit learned quickly what the dangers were and weren't. Thus on June 2 Clark wrote, "We passed today a hunting party of the Sioux some 30 in number which we were not at all afraid of as their wives and children were along."

And two days later: "On a review of our stock today we think they begin to fail considerably and in consequence there is considerable alarm manifested & long faces are very common. The 3 year old mules are considerably cut down."

In the Rocky Mountains they were stricken by disease. Clark reported it July 2, saying, "Here on account of the increased illness of Alfred Corum who had been sick a week or ten days we laid by a day."

And the following day: "Whilst lying by some 200 wagons passed us & Alfred continued to grow worse & as there was no prospect of his living it was deemed prudent for the wagons to start the next morning. Accordingly they left on the 4th leaving behind the Dearbourn (a light carriage) & a party of 6 men to render every service to our dying friend. As there was no wood nor water near us we concluded to move him about 1¼ miles where we found both. About 1 o'clock he died without a struggle and in full possession of all his faculties to the last."

Two weeks later they were crossing Nevada. Their struggles were just grueling at first and then tinged with desperation.

July 23: "Drove 6 or 8 miles this morning & camped for the day as it was important to rest and graze our stock. Every other train is reduced to the same necessity."

July 24: "No vegitation to be seen on the hills and mountains except the wild sage a growth which has become most sickening to us."

July 25: "A dusty barren bottom covered with the eternol dust from 6 to 8 inches deep. Passed another grave today."

July 26: "Nothing but sterile lands and dust immediately around us & naught in the distance to releave the eye, but bare rugged hills of basalt. Our feelings just now is that if we once get safely out of this great Basin we will not be cought here in a hurry."

July 27: "We are beginning to feel alarmed lest our stock will not take us through."

July 28: "A continuance of yesterday's hard work & poor fare for our stock. We were struck with the contrast between our appearance now & when we left home. Then we had gay outriders prancing along proudly on fiery steeds & our teams pressing forward with fierce resolution. Now what a scene—the teams crossing along slowly with their gaunt sides marked with many a whip cut & their rigging defaced with dust—a sorry show. And where are all those gay outriders? Look before the train & you see them strung along the road for a mile on foot their faces and clothes covered with dust and looking worn & livid. What a picture."

In the next entry Clark digressed from his travelogue to report some wild rumors that were passing up and down the trail. He had heard that the people in California were all starving, that guerrilla bands were attacking travelers in quest of food, that troops were being summoned to quell the disorder. Clark's reaction:

"We regret to hear these reports but if we knew them to be true & a return was practicable (which is not) we would still go on.

"Men who have risked their lives by sickness, casualties, hardships of every kind and the remote prospect of starvation continually present to their minds are not to be detered from endeavoring to obtain some reward by the uncertain reports that float along this great highway."

And then they were entering the last, worst stretch of the barren land. The Humboldt Sink lay just ahead of them, and beyond that the Forty-Mile Desert.

Aug. 1: "This is a more trying time than any we have yet encountered & as we have yet some 71 miles to go over the same kind of fare, we feel altogether uncertain about the result. We think, however, that at the worst we can walk the balance of the way."

Aug. 2: "Started early and drove 10 miles to the slough without water. The stock look very badly."

Aug. 4: "A general panic now seezed upon all & doubt & fear prevailed every where. There is yet a stretch of 45 miles ahead of us without grass or water except at the boiling spring 25 miles from this point.

"We left here at 4 oclk this evening . . . travelled all night & reached the Hot Spring at daylight.

"This is the most dreary desolate looking place we ever saw. It is on the top of a mountain & the water bubbles & boils up from the fissures in the rocks & forms into a small lake quite clear but so hot that it scalds. We dipped up the water & pourd it into some holes in the earth & cooled it & then watered our animals mixing flour with it. The mules were so hungry that they ate dust & gravel & chewed up whatever came in their way—gearing, wagon covers or anything they could reach."

Aug. 5: "We had 20 miles to accomplish & the heat of the day to make it. About 2 oclk we struck the heavy sand 10 miles from the Truckey river & had the utmost difficulty in getting our stock thro—stopping every few yards to rest. A little before night we reached the river. We all felt greatly releaved.

"All along the desert road from the very start even the way side was strewed with the dead bodies of oxen, mules & horses & the stench was horrible. All our traveling experience furnishes no parellel for all this. Many persons suffered greatly for water during the last 8 or 10 miles, and many instances of noble generosity were developed on these occasions. Some trains that got over before us sent water back in kegs & left them on the road marked for the benefit of the feeble. We slept here for the first time for four nights."

Clark's diary continued for nearly a week more, then ended abruptly as he passed through the Sierras. The last notation occurred on August 11 when he scribbled a dateline but made no entry. Clark had collapsed. Scurvy perhaps, or some chance fever, or just total exhaustion. Whatever the cause, he was a very sick man. His companions put him in a wagon, hauled him on to San Francisco, and there put him on a boat for home.

It was Clark's odd fate to make the long, hard, dangerous trek and never see the gold fields at all.*

Such were the ordinary hardships of the trek. There were also some extraordinary affairs. One of the most disastrous of all was the adventure chronicled by forty-niner William Manly.

As was so often the case, the trouble began with falling be-

* Josef and Dorothy Berger, editors of *Diary of America* (Simon & Schuster, 1957), point out some intriguing possibilities suggested by Clark's background. Thus Bennett C. Clark was a courthouse clerk in Missouri in the 1840s. In the 1930s Bennett Champ Clark was a United States senator from Missouri. The senator was the scion of a prominent political family which in 1912 produced James B. Clark, a Democratic candidate for President. If there was a family link to the old gold rusher, the Bergers were not able to establish it.

hind schedule. By mid-August, with the migration's advance
guard already in California, Manly and his friends were still
scrambling through the Rockies. In an effort to catch up
they resorted to some very rash expedients.

Their first and worst idea was to dispense with the whole
weary business of winding in and out among the mountains.
After all, they reasoned, they had reached the Great Divide,
and from there on all rivers ran west. Why not just raft down?

The notion struck them when they reached the Green
River and heard that its waters emptied into the Pacific. The
river did that, but first it cascaded wildly through rocky
gorges, and then it merged with the Colorado in a mighty
stream that became more treacherous still, and finally it
flowed into the Gulf of California at a wilderness site six
hundred miles removed from the gold fields. In short, of all
the suicidal schemes for going to California, this one was beyond compare.

They tried it anyway, but a few days on the Green was
enough to convince them of error. They got off the river,
trudged over to a Mormon outpost near Salt Lake City, and
found a big encampment of other strays like themselves.
Some were people who had started late; some were encumbered with children; still others had been delayed by illness
or accident along the way. The reasons didn't matter much;
the point was they were all in trouble, and they knew it, and
they were close to panic.

The assembled stragglers banded together and began casting about for an experienced leader who could see them
through. The man they chose was Jefferson Hunt, a captain
in a Mormon battalion, and a veteran mountaineer who had
been back and forth to California. He looked them over and
said he'd take the job on two conditions.

In the first place, Hunt told them, the gold-fields destination was out. It was too late in the season to risk the Sierra's

northern passes. He offered instead to take them down to Los Angeles by a long southerly detour across the desert.

In the second place, Hunt wanted it understood that he knew this business and they didn't. If he was to lead, they were to follow, with absolutely no nonsense about it.

As Manly recalled it: "Capt. Hunt said it was necessary to have some sort of system about the move, and that before they moved they must organize and adopt rules and laws which must be obeyed. He said they must move like an army, and that he was to be a dictator in all things, except that in case of necessity a majority of the train could rule otherwise."

There were no objections. Not then.

They formed up a huge outfit comprising 107 wagons and some 500 people, the total including many family groups. For purposes of easy management Hunt organized the train into seven divisions. As they moved out on the long desert march to Los Angeles they adopted the self-mocking name of Sand Walking Company.

Hunt made them work at staying alive, and for a few weeks things went well. Then the grumbling began. That was almost inevitable; they were a company of losers engaged in a hard trek to the wrong destination, and all the while they were confronted with the maddening knowledge that they had missed their real objective by only a few hundred miles. Soon they were pressing Hunt to try for a short cut. He wouldn't hear of it, not with this bunch on his hands. He reminded them that they had women and children to think of. But still the talk wouldn't die. Men gathered around the campfires at night and drew maps in the sand and spoke with heady optimism about a pass they thought they could find. The folly was encouraged by a garrulous old Utah trader who rode along in the train. Finally the more reckless spirits told Hunt that if he wouldn't help them explore they'd go it alone. And he informed them that that was exactly the way they'd have to do it.

So they split up, a big train trudging on with Hunt while a smaller but still sizable faction ventured hopefully into the great unknown. The dissidents numbered perhaps fifty people, including three women and seven children; the group represented a coalition of elements identified as the Manly party, the Jayhawkers, the Mississippi Boys, and the one-family outfit of the Rev. James Brier.

The new train was led by the Utah trader, but not for long; he ran out on them as soon as the going got rough. After that they just headed west, stumbling blindly across any terrain they found in their way, and expecting that somewhere they'd strike a pass. What they struck instead was Death Valley.

They wandered into the abysmal place, couldn't find their way out, and broke down completely. Meantime their loose-knit company was fast disintegrating. Various members had already deserted; now others who were able to pulled away to fend for themselves.

One group ditched their wagons and converted to pack train to make a run for their lives. After terrible suffering twelve of these men finally staggered into the southern mines in January of 1850. They had subsisted for weeks on a meager dole of mule meat, acorns, and a few fish, and they had survived at all only through the intercession of some friendly Indians who helped them along and showed them the way. When they reached the settlements they announced, hopefully, that they had left a family party that was about twenty days behind.

The family people were, in fact, still stuck in Death Valley. They squatted there in numb despair, so beaten and worn down that they could not rouse themselves for an attempt at escape.

They were able to hang on because Death Valley in winter offered a few grim comforts. The valley was rimmed all around with snow-capped mountains, and a little of the moisture seeped down. Near the base of the mountains some scraggly growth could be found. Otherwise it was stark and lifeless, described by Manly as a place of "dreadful sands and shadows . . . salt columns, bitter lakes, and wild, dreary, sunken desolation." And there was something like three thousand square miles of it.

Caught in this hideous trap were fifteen people who had divided into two camps. The larger group was that of Manly and his friends; they included Asabel and Sarah Bennett with their three children, J. B. Arcane with his wife and son, and a man named John Rogers.

In the other camp, quite apart, were the Rev. James Brier, his wife Juliette, and their three small sons. One gathers that the Reverend Brier was something of a loner; he was also a man imbued with a formidable determination to maintain appearances and standards in even the most desperate hours. Thus Manly visited the Brier camp one day and found the Reverend Brier coolly lecturing his sons on the importance of utilizing the idle time to improve their minds.

Said Manly in fine understatement: "It seemed very strange to me to hear a solemn discourse on the benefits of early education when starvation was staring us all in the face."

The reaction in Manly's own party was in a way quite as incongruous, though understandable in view of their shock and fatigue. For weeks they just sat there, slowly wasting away. One by one they slaughtered their oxen for food, while the beasts that remained became ever more gaunt and feeble for lack of water and grass. There was now no possibility that they could ever get the wagons moving again. Finally, however, they nerved themselves to a desperate last resort. It was decided that Manly and Rogers would walk out, find help wherever they could, and return to rescue the rest.

Everything they had they bet on this forlorn expedition. The others in the company dug into the secret recesses of their wagons and brought forth the money that had been intended for a new start in California. More important, they slaughtered one of the remaining oxen; the animal was so thin that only scraps of meat remained after two knapsacks were packed for the travelers.

Manly and Rogers set off through the valley, looking for a hole in the surrounding mountains. Manly was limping, perhaps from scurvy. Soon both men were almost felled by thirst; their mouths became so dry and puffy that they found it impossible to chew the tough, stringy beef they carried with them. It occurred to Manly that they might starve to death with food on their hands. But they pressed on and found water seeping from a mudhole, and that gave them strength enough to scramble over the rim of the Panamint Mountains. They kept on scrambling across the Mojave Desert and through the Soledad Canyon to a little settlement some 150 miles away.

At the settlement no help was available, and even supplies were hard to obtain. They were able to buy only a bare minimum of provisions, plus a small mule and three indifferent horses. The horses all died on the hard road back to Death Valley.

There was another ill omen on the return journey when they found in Death Valley the body of an erstwhile companion who had left them when the company dissolved. The man lay spread-eagled on the sand, face up and arms outflung; by his side was an empty canteen made of two powder flasks. It struck Manly that in that dry desert air the man might be mummified and preserved forever. So thinking, he went on, leaving the body as it lay.

Finally, after a round trip of twenty-six days, Manly and Rogers reached their camp. When they topped a rise and saw the camp they feared at first that this, too, might be a mummified scene. Nothing stirred around the pitiable little huddle of wagons. But then Manly fired his pistol and a tattered scarecrow of a man crawled out from under a wagon, crying hoarsely: "The boys have come! The boys have come!"

The Bennetts and Arcanes were all still alive, though more debilitated than ever. Moreover, when the rejoicing was done, the castaways had to face the fact that their relief expedition had brought back very little aid. There was, however, an enormous psychological boost in the mere fact that Manly and Rogers had managed to get out at all. Now they were all determined to try it.

To transport the youngest and sickest children they fashioned a crude carryall. It was done by sewing men's shirts together to form twin pockets which were slung in saddlebag style on a surviving ox. Little Charles Arcane was stuffed in one pocket and little Martha Bennett in another. Unfortunately that didn't work. The boy's back was covered with raw sores, and the rubbing movement of the bag lacerated him so that he cried continually. When they took him out it unbalanced the floundering ox, so the girl had to be taken out too. But she couldn't walk; she appears to have been badly swollen as a consequence of malnutrition.

In the end there was no other solution but to carry the two children. Charles Arcane was hoisted up on his father's back, and Martha Bennett was cradled, whimpering, in her mother's arms, and they went out like that. Astonishingly they all made it.

Some time later a recuperated Manly got a job in a lumbering camp and found himself working for a former minister—none other than the Rev. James Brier. He learned that the Briers had walked out in much the same way and in fact had used a similar technique. They had crossed the deserts with their two smallest sons bouncing along in the saddlebags of an ox, while Juliette Brier led her third son by the hand.

Thus in folly and ignorance, but with immense perseverance in trial, some wayward forty-niners added a chapter to the exploration of the West. It was for their adventures that Death Valley was named.

As for the other members of Sand Walking Company—

the prudent ones who stayed with Jefferson Hunt—they reached Los Angeles after routine hardship.

While Manly and his friends starved in Death Valley, J. Goldsborough Bruff was starving in the frozen Sierras. This was no case of mismanagement, but rather bad luck and desertion by comrades.

Bruff had pushed his company hard, forcing them to a high standard of discipline, and they were not grateful for it. At trek's end they abandoned him, leaving him alone in the mountains.

He was a man who had gone adventuring before, and the turn of events did not shake him much. When he was organizing his company he had stood some of his men before a justice of the peace, swearing them to a compact of mutual fidelity, and in wry aside he had confided to his journal that such oaths were about as binding as "singing psalms to a dead horse." Now he turned to his journal again, pouring out some measured invective against the perfidy of his comrades; with that off his chest he dismissed the question and gave his entire attention to survival. He was sure he could manage.

For a while he had plenty of company. The tail end of the migration was filtering in, and Bruff's proclivities were such that he became a kind of overseer for all the stragglers who passed his way. He bossed them around and helped them along as much as he could and recorded all that transpired in his voluminous journals.

There was a lot to see, and Bruff was just the man to put it down. He was a born reporter with a sense of history, and he had observed his fellow adventurers in trial and triumph across all the hundreds of miles. He caught the look of them now as the most hard-pressed survivors came staggering down the last cruel stretch.

On a single day Bruff witnessed a chance procession of such people as these: A sore-footed old man with a rusty saber who reminisced about other long marches he had made as a soldier with Napoleon—and a woman, widowed on the trail, who trudged through the snow with a boy and a girl, all of them encumbered with packs—and a physician clinging to a mule, the man nearly done in with scurvy, and the mule about gone, too—and a woman alone, swathed in a blanket, carrying a rifle, who stepped along looking "hearty and cheerful."

Another day he saw a widow with eight children; one of them was a ragged, feeble boy who could scarcely speak and was so sunk in torpor that he had to be led around. Bruff diagnosed it as a very bad case of scurvy.

He saw also an ex-army officer, a tall, strong man who carried only rifle and saber while his daughters, aged ten and twelve, floundered through the snow with heavy packs. The girls both suffered from bare, wet hands, and one of them wore a broken shoe through which the toes protruded. Bruff was incensed; he informed the father that "it was a pity to make pack-horses of them," and he suggested that at the very least the girls should be properly equipped. That matter Bruff took care of himself, rummaging around in an abandoned wagon to find socks and gloves, and contriving a rough fix for the broken shoe.

He intervened again when he discovered a four-year-old boy lying neglected in a damp shelter, half starved and nearly frozen. Bruff found the boy's father, a man named Lambkin, and gave him a strong lecture on attending to his responsibilities. There followed some further encounters between the two, Lambkin fleeing once when Bruff reached for a pistol with intent to "straighten" the scoundrel. And then, unexpectedly, Lambkin came around with the boy and asked if Bruff wouldn't look after him for a few days while the father went off in search of provisions.

That was the last seen of Lambkin. Bruff had a boy on his hands.

By now the parade of stragglers had all passed on, leaving only a handful of people who were stuck in the mountains for one reason or another. In Bruff's case it was rheumatism and general exhaustion, plus misplaced confidence. He had remained behind to guard some abandoned wagons, expecting that his comrades would return to help him, and when they didn't it became too late to risk the snow-clogged trails. But he found a dependable new friend in a fellow castaway, a man named William Poyle whom Bruff described as "a True Brother and an ingenious cook." Presently they were joined by Warren Clough, a roughhewn but gentle-hearted old hunter who presented his credentials thus: "I ain't a man of larning, but I am a tolerable good rough carpenter, and can turn my hand to most any thing." With these good companions, and the Lambkin boy and a stray dog named Nevada, Bruff settled down to tough out the long, bitter Sierra winter.

They lived variously in a tent, a cabin, a makeshift shelter rigged from abandoned wagons. The vast debris of the trek provided them with great quantities of lumber and cloth, plus pots and pans and coffee, salt, tobacco, and medicines. There was, however, very little food. They had fresh venison when they were lucky, and for a while they enjoyed a slim dole of flour, and after that it got grim.

They came down to foraging for dead oxen, poking through the piled-up snow with long poles to locate the carcasses. They had to compete with such other scavengers as eagles and buzzards, and bears and wolves, and sometimes they got only picked-over bones which they boiled into very thin soup.

If they found meat at all, they weren't too particular about the quality. Any fair state of preservation would do.

When they came upon a frozen but partly putrefied carcass they would chop away the spoiled part, making gingerly estimates as to just when to quit chopping, and then gamble on as much of it as they had to have. Pretty often that made them sick.

They got in the habit of dosing themselves with camphor after every meal, just in case.

They converted another medicine to nutritional purposes, imbibing quantities of tea brewed from a patent remedy called snakeroot. Bruff found that, by relative standards, it wasn't too bad. Another expedient was to spread out the ingredients at hand by thickening the broth with chunks of tallow and spermaceti candle.

And then there were those days when almost all expedients failed. At one meal Bruff, Poyle, and the Lambkin boy solemnly divided eighteen beans. The two men gave the boy a little the best of it and afterward felt guilty because they hadn't given him all.

The boy's condition became for Bruff a constant worry. The diary was studded with entries like these:

"The poor little child is failing, he is pale & weak, with sunken eyes, for want of bread and proper food. We shorten our rations in order to sustain him, as long as possible."

"We are much concerned about the boy; he is pale, complains of pains, very weak, and bled at the nose and ears last night."

"The child looks very haggard."

"The child cries regularly now, at least half the night; what for we cannot divine."

Bruff's solicitude seems to have been based not on affection so much as on pity and sense of obligation. There appeared also a note of something else, something more basic. It became an elemental struggle between life and death, with Bruff fiercely determined that the boy wouldn't die. At times Bruff would take the child in his big hands and propel him around and around inside the tent, exercising him, as though he could somehow force vitality into the frail and withered little body. It was, however, a hopeless cause. On New Year's Day there was a final entry:

"We done all we could for the poor little sufferer, but by

11 a.m. he was extricated from all the hardships of this life."

Bruff stripped the body, washed it carefully in snow, and wrapped it in a clean white cloth. The next day he scratched a grave from the frozen earth and buried the lad beneath a plank headboard inscribed with bitter epitaph:

WILLIAM,——
Infant Son of
LAMBKIN,———
an
Unnatural
Father,
Died Jan. 1
1850

The last rites for the boy cost Bruff a dreadful effort, for by this time he was failing very fast himself. For weeks he had suffered terribly from rheumatism, starvation, diarrhea, and all the effects of his ghastly diet. He noted a mélange of symptoms that came and went; it was fever and headache one day and stiff, aching legs another; his bowels became inflamed and he felt that even the blood was running hot in his veins. It required all his resources to flounder a few hundred yards through the snow, and once when he pushed himself too hard he fainted.

Bruff's companions were in better shape, but they too had reached the thin edge of endurance. Once Poyle and Clough were out seeking food when Poyle fell in the snow and just lay there, unable to rise. At the fallen man's request the other beat him with a ramrod until he got up and got moving again.

In a council of desperation it was decided finally that Poyle would try for the settlements and bring back food if he could. Bruff had no prospect of making it, so Clough volunteered to stay behind and take care of him until help arrived.

For nearly two months more Bruff and Clough stuck it out,

Bruff puttering around the camp, performing such small chores as his strength permitted, while Clough roamed the mountains in search of game. And then one day Clough didn't return. Bruff sat up late, keeping the campfire going and the coffee hot, trying to persuade himself that any moment he would hear the crunch of boots in the snow. The next day it was the same, and the next. Then Bruff faced the fact that Clough wasn't coming back.

The old hunter didn't desert; he wasn't the type. Bruff was certain of that. Probably the man met some lonely and violent end in the mountains, but his body was never found.

It was just Bruff now and the dog Nevada. The animal had survived in its own fashion, by gnawing bones and bits of hide, and once by making a meal of a bar of soap.

Every day Bruff looked at the dog and thought that he'd have to eat it and then put it off another day. He rationalized the choice, telling himself that it was a yappy little dog and so useful for standing guard against bears, wolves, or Indians that might come marauding at night. And besides, the dog was so gaunt and bony that he was good for only one meal at the most.

The days that followed were as terrible as any gold rusher ever endured. Once Bruff gleaned some old deer hides in search of any flakes of meat that might still be adhering to the skins. He had to scrape worms away first, and it was a close question as to whether the residue was meat or rotted hide, but he wound up with "about a gil of very *gamey* venison."

Another day it was a deer's head, similarly decomposed and worm-eaten, which he found lodged under a cabin. He salvaged part of the tongue.

Still another day and he was back at the hides, plucking the hairs out to make hair soup. Afterward he was violently ill.

He tried hunting, of course, but that was no good. He could scarcely move about, and when he saw game he was too weak to take steady aim. One day after jumping several deer and not getting any he returned to fill his diary with a long, raving passage; the substance of it was that he was doomed by providence, and the birds and beasts all knew it and were under orders from heaven to stay out of range and not contribute to his support.

He began to have hallucinations. Once while out hunting he leaned against a tree to rest and fell into something that was between a trance and a faint. He thought he heard a cock crow, a child laugh, a musician playing a sweet air on a lute. But he shook off the illusion, reminding himself sternly that he wasn't the sort of man to give in to that.

He was a little ashamed of the incident and frightened by it, too, so he half persuaded himself that it hadn't happened. He concluded that he'd heard some odd sounds in the forest as he was dozing off. But then it happened again. He was walking through the woods and he heard an eerie, haunting wolf call. Only it wasn't a wolf; it couldn't be. The cry lingered on one long, wavering, incessant note that followed him wherever he went, and when he stopped it stopped. This time he very much feared that he was going mad.

Wrote Bruff: "I asked myself if I was becoming superstitious? or crazy? I then recollected that prolonged hunger produced insanity, and I reasoned with my own mind on that subject. Can I not stave off these dreadful consequences of starvation & weakness? Can I not rally my mind to struggle against such disastrous results?"

He decided that he could, and would, and began immediately to cast about for some rational explanation of the continuing sound. He held his breath, thinking that perhaps it was some whine in his own windpipe. He probed his ears. He examined his hat and his ammunition pouch. While he was thus flailing about he kicked over his gun, and that gave him an inspiration. When he tested it, he was sure. The wolf call was the whistle of wind on his gun muzzle. Whether that really had anything to do with it or not, it was what Bruff wanted, "a reasonable and philosophical cause." He was immensely cheered, declaring: "It felt almost as serviceable as a good meal! I am not weak-minded! I am yet sane!—Thank God!"

About this time Bruff decided that he'd get out or die trying. It was April now, and thawing, so there was a chance for it. More chance at least than sitting there starving and going mad, while waiting for help that might never come.

It took him a day to pack up. He was a meticulous man, and now he very carefully gathered together a clean shirt, a pair of socks, a comb, towel, soap, a watch, and the pipe and tobacco he was too sick to smoke.

He had a hard choice when he came to his diaries and sketches. It added up to a big pile of notebooks weighing several pounds, for he had written daily no matter how desperate his situation. He couldn't bear to leave that behind, and weak as he was, he added his notes to the pack.

And then his coffeepot, and some coffee, and two candles representing the last of his provisions.

The preparations exhausted him, and he had to rest a day. The day after that he started down the mountains, heading for a ranch about thirty miles away. He was six days en route, foraging with just enough luck to keep him stumbling along.

On the fifth day he had a great temptation. He had just finished breakfast, drinking a pot of coffee and chewing the grounds, and as he took to the path he spied the fresh tracks of an Indian. "He was pigeon-toed," wrote Bruff, "and I judge small." As he pictured the man who had made the track he was moved to a wild excitement.

"Oh! if I can only over take him! then will I have one hearty meal! a good broil! I examined my caps, they were good. I felt relieved, it gave me additional strength to think I might soon get a broil off an indian's leg. I could not but laugh when I thought of it—the expressions I have heard, how people would starve to death rather than eat human flesh! Fools! how little could they form an idea of the cravings of hunger! Let them be placed in my circumstances, and see how soon they would discard such silly ideas! My mouth fairly watered, for a piece of an indian to broil!"

The very next day Bruff came upon an Indian, meeting him face to face on the trail. It was a short, dark, square-built man, and Bruff had every opportunity to appraise him thoroughly, for the brave was wearing only a fig leaf and a small mustache.

Bruff supplicated in sign language, pointing to mouth and stomach as he begged for food, and the Indian replied in sign language that he had nothing to offer and was himself hunting a dinner.

While they negotiated Bruff's dog Nevada went frisking off after a little black cur that accompanied the Indian. Bruff couldn't get his dog to return, but after some more sign language the Indian accomplished it for him, using his bow as a whip and chasing Nevada back to her master. Then the Indian was moving along and Bruff stood there, fingering his gun, looking at that broad, meaty back while he reconsidered the question of cannibalism.

"While he was going off, I turned round, thought of eating him; he was then about 30 or 40 paces; but I could not shoot the poor wretch in the back; besides, he had done me a favor. So I proceeded."

In truth, it would appear that neither the pigeon-toed Indian nor the square-built one was ever really in imminent danger. For there was Nevada still tagging at Bruff's heels as living proof that he put various considerations ahead of his stomach.

A few hours farther down the trail Bruff had an even more dramatic meeting. It was his old friend Poyle. The latter had been long delayed by trials of his own, but now he was returning to Bruff's aid with provisions of flour, meal, and pork.

The rescue was wildly ironic in that they met when Bruff was just 300 yards away from the ranch he'd been struggling to reach. Poyle thought they should stop by the trail and fix a hot meal at once, but Bruff decided that if he was that close he'd just stumble on in. And so he did, with Poyle helping him.

At the ranch he got a big meal, a stiff drink, and rest. His back ached so that he couldn't sit in a chair, but he stretched out on the floor. Someone brought him his pipe and tobacco, and after puffing contentedly he delivered himself of triumphant pronouncement:

"Well! I am not dead yet!" *

---

* There was a lot of life left in Bruff. When he had done with gold rushing he went back to Washington, D.C., and there lived on to become a white-bearded patriarch of eighty-five, surrounded by mementos of times when he had been variously a soldier, a sailor, a California miner. Otherwise he worked for more than sixty years as a government draftsman and was an active amateur participant in art and science. He died in 1889, having retired from his job only four months before the end of his long and vigorous span.

CHAPTER 12

——————————◆——————————

They look heaven-sent!

> —Sarah Royce, viewing some
> rather rough-hewn angels of
> deliverance.

The human cost of the trek was in part unavoidable, but much of it might have been alleviated by a bare minimum of good management and sensible planning.

The Mormons had demonstrated that it could be done. When they moved an entire people into the wilderness they made inquiries first and prepared thoughtful directives as to what was needed to sustain the march. As they took to the trail they sent scouts ahead to find the best routes, and they established supply depots for succeeding waves that came behind. In the words of Jefferson Hunt, that prudent, careful frontiersman who led Sand Walking Company, the Mormons moved like an army. It paid off in a trek which achieved its goal at the lowest possible price in suffering and death.*

The gold rushers were not like the Mormons, of course, and bore no resemblance to an army, either. If their seething movement was to know any order at all, it had to be imposed by an outside agency. Unfortunately, in the turmoil and excitement, only a few men glimpsed even the most obvious measures for averting disaster.

* The Mormons began their famous trek in 1847, after being driven out of Missouri and Illinois.

One who raised an early, unheeded warning was James Collier. He was a newly appointed San Francisco customs collector who joined the 1849 migration en route to his post. When he reached the Missouri frontier he sent back an ominous report to his superior, Secretary of the Treasury William Meredith.

Collier began by describing the "fearful havoc" caused by cholera. He offered no suggestions about the epidemic, merely reporting it as something that existed and had to be reckoned with. But in the midst of that crisis he was able to look ahead and see clearly the other, more preventable tragedy that was bound to ensue once the ill-organized travelers plunged into the wilderness.

"You must be prepared," he wrote, "for a gloomy account of them during the Season. I should think it to be the duty of the War Department to send out relief parties to furnish the famishing with food. If this is not done I should not be surprised if they were to make war upon each other."

Collier's letter might well have stimulated some thinking about other badly needed services which the army was equipped to provide. For, in fact, a few hundred properly directed soldiers could have changed the whole history of the trek.

The troops might have built bridges, manned ferries, provided trail-breaking assistance at such bottleneck places as torturous canyons and steep passes. They might have maintained a few water tanks across the worst desert stretches. Above all, they might have set up crossroads information centers, providing the best available intelligence as to distance, terrain, and general conditions along the alternate routes. In short, the army could have herded the migration along, cutting weeks off the travel time, and bringing many of the stragglers down the last lap just before rather than just after they began to collapse.

All that might have been done and wasn't. In the spirit of

the times the government held that a citizen had a perfect right to go to California, and it was the army's business to shoot any Indian who got in the way. But as to managing the trek itself, that was entirely the citizen's business. Thus it was that the government sent out some soldiers who merely clattered along, adding to the already perilous crowding, while providing at best only spotty protection against Indian raids that claimed a handful of lives.

Luckily the frontier community in California took a more practical view of affairs. In California there were people who had made the trek themselves, and they knew how hard the going could be even for seasoned pioneers. They had engraved on their memories the gruesome catastrophe that had overtaken the Donner party. They could imagine the kind of calamity that might engulf a mass movement if it ran into a dry summer or an early winter or almost any caprice of nature. When the frontiersmen who thought in these terms heard what was coming at them, and how it was coming, a kind of collective shudder ran through the territory.

California was really in no position to take on the problem. It was a new territory, only half organized; it was overrun with the thousands who were pouring off the boats; it lacked the means to sustain properly the burgeoning population it already had. But still, something had to be done about all those people out there in the wilderness. And so California did it.

The Westerners didn't know the dimensions of the problem until late in July 1849 when the first fast-moving parties came in off the trail and told what was behind. That left about two months to organize a rescue operation for those who were sure to be in trouble farther back. To California's military governor, General Persifor Smith, it meant also that there was no time even to consult with his superiors in Washington. The thing would be on him before all the communiqués could get back and forth. Fortunately General Smith was a type who regarded lack of communications as more asset than liability. He got off his dispatches and then got on with the job, knowing that he'd have it done before anyone could tell him to stop.

The governor's first act was to dip into his meager funds for a wholly unauthorized emergency appropriation of $100,000. He trusted, correctly, that Congress would have to approve it once it was spent. The appropriation was augmented by public fund drives, San Franciscans alone contributing $12,000. Then there was a great scrounging around to obtain supplies and equipment. It was late in August before the basic plans were set. By mid-September the relief trains were ready to roll.

Major D. H. Rucker was given field command of the relief forces, with a civilian named John Peoples as his chief assistant. They formed separate parties and fanned out along the major approach routes. They were instructed to meet the oncoming human streams, pass entirely through the migration, then swing around to shoo the stragglers in. They were told, too, that wherever possible they should withhold aid until they reached the end of the line. The available provisions had to be rationed tightly, and it was assumed that the last parties would be in the most desperate need.

It was a well-reasoned plan, except that nothing thereafter went quite as expected. It turned out that the travelers were not spread evenly over the various branch paths. Instead, the whole migration was shifting now this way and now that, with the bulk of the tailenders finally streaming in over that long northern detour called Lassen's Route. The relief trains lost precious time as they scrambled from one locale to another to meet the ever-changing emergency.

As for carefully controlled rationing, that went by the board early. In fact, they had to divert considerable aid to people who had already staggered in. Thus Major Rucker stopped by Peter Lassen's ranch, at the terminal point of

Lassen's Route, and found the place overrun with half-starved migrants who had finished the trek with nothing to spare.

"From the moment of my arrival," Rucker reported, "applications began to pour in for relief. Although my instructions did not include those who had reached the settlements, I could not refuse a biscuit and a slice of pork to the hungry."

Rucker passed out food as sparingly as he could and as generously as he had to; as his supply load dwindled he gave away his surplus pack mules on the same basis of most desperate need. One of the first to get a mule was a man named John Scroggins. He had lost his team and had left behind in the mountains a wife and two children who were unable to make it on foot. When his anguished importunities earned him the mule Scroggins headed back to rescue his family.

A week later, working up the trail, Rucker met Scroggins again. The man was walking with a child in his arms and leading the mule by the bridle. Perched on the animal's back was Mrs. Scroggins, wretched with scurvy. A small boy trudged along at the side.

"They seemed," wrote Rucker, "in a fair way to reach the settlement."

There were a lot of sights like that. More than half the travelers were on foot, and many were sick and hungry. Rucker estimated that "in 16 days not less than 150 families, and double that number of footmen, were relieved by me." *

For every one he aided there were several whom he had to refuse. Rucker gave priority to the sick, the starving, and those with families. Otherwise the general rule was that if a man looked like he could live without help, he didn't get much. It created some bitterness, but Rucker was a tough

* The frequent mention of family parties could convey a disproportionate impression as to the number of such people on the trail. The vast majority of the travelers were men but, for obvious reasons, the family trains appear often in the tales of distress and rescue.

customer; he had a job to do and he hadn't supposed it would make for popular decisions.

Oliver Goldsmith offered a migrant's view of the relief operation. Goldsmith was the man who had outlasted cholera in that tent on the plains. Now he was riding through the Sierra Nevada mountains with four companions, the remnants of his train. Toward the end they were just about making it from one meal to the next.

At one point on the way Goldsmith's party encountered an old man with a wagonload of provisions. They tried to buy food and were told that the price was $2 a pound. There was a furious argument, the famished wayfarers saying 25 cents a pound was fair and just, and the old man replying that from all he heard $2 was the going rate in California. They remonstrated with him, telling him that he'd never reach California with his heavy wagon, but they couldn't convince him. Finally they reminded the peddler that along with the law of supply and demand there was also a law called survival of the fittest.

As Goldsmith told it: "After a consultation we decided that we must make the most of this chance, so we marched up to him and said there were five of us to his one and that we intended to take what we needed at our own price, twenty-five cents a pound, which we did. The old fellow looked a bit dazed, but merely remarked, 'I guess you're all right.'"

Some days later, and a good deal hungrier, they came upon a bloated ox carcass stuck full of arrows. They hesitated, debating whether or not the Indians of the region used poisoned arrows. The idea of a mysterious Indian drug somehow terrified them, while the apparent condition of the meat fazed them not at all. Finally Goldsmith decided that regardless of risks he had to eat.

"I whipped out my knife," he wrote, "cut a strip of flesh

and carried it to where the men were. They were horrified at the danger. I made a fire, began to cook it, first baiting it on a stick, and asked them which was worse to die, by poisoning or starvation. The meat smelled very good while cooking, and tasted better. Unable to endure the pangs of hunger while another was feasting my companions secured and cooked some for themselves, which they ate with relish. We also took a supply for the next day."

Goldsmith and a man named John Root became violently ill after eating the spoiled meat. The stricken pair holed up to rest, urging the others to go on without them. About two days later Goldsmith and Root were up and moving again. As an act of kindness they joined forces with a woman whom they found wandering along with three children. The woman had lost her husband and oldest son in a trail accident and was reduced to such supplies as she and the remaining children could carry in crude packs improvised from old flannel shirts. In such condition the lot of them struggled on until they met a relief-train detachment.

The relief-train commander took charge of the destitute family but told Goldsmith and Root they'd have to forage for themselves. Discouraged and weary, they plodded on.

For the next several days they kept bumping into relief-train units. Each time Goldsmith heard of a rescue party in the area he'd go and beg food. Sometimes he was granted a few handfuls of bread and sometimes nothing.

Of one typical encounter Goldsmith said, "I begged a bite from one of the relief wagons one day; the man in charge told me that I looked strong and well and ought to be able to hunt. Unfortunately, I had washed my face at the creek, so I looked too clean to him to seem utterly wretched. I always thought of him as a man with a full stomach and a small heart."

Finally Goldsmith's friend John Root decided that he'd try his luck at begging. Goldsmith didn't have much faith in it, but on appraising his companion, he agreed that there just might be a chance. Root was tattered and dirty, appearing every bit as woebegone as he felt. And as it turned out he also had the advantage of a southern accent. When Root reached the relief camp he learned that it was a detachment commanded by John Peoples, of Lynchburg, Virginia. Root introduced himself as being from that city, too, and then he just stood around and stood around, talking up old Lynchburg days until there was really nothing Peoples could do but offer hospitality.

That night Goldsmith and Root sat very late around a campfire, feasting on thick, greasy soup made from three ox ribs, and chuckling hugely at the way Root had laid on that Lynchburg talk to connive a meal.

Some others were almost reluctant to be rescued. Peoples described one party in which obstinate stragglers clung to their property at the risk of their lives.

Involved was a group of some fifty migrants, about half of them women and children. They had made the long trek in reasonably good shape, and then almost at the end they had been undone by a single act of carelessness. They failed to post sentries one night, and the Indians ran off with almost all their oxen.

They were stuck in the mountains, with 150 miles still to go, and they had simply no idea of the danger they were in. When Peoples came along they were wrangling bitterly over which of their possessions they would abandon. It galled them particularly to leave behind the mining equipment they had dragged over all that weary distance.

Peoples broke that up in a hurry. Issuing pre-emptory orders, he rounded up all the women, children, and invalids in the stranded party and loaded them into his wagons whether they were willing or not. Then he swung his train around

and rattled off for the settlements, leaving the rest of the party
no recourse except to follow sheepishly behind.

Peoples worried constantly that other parties might be crippled by similar Indian raids. The danger mounted as the
stragglers grew weaker and more disorganized. Then, too, the
Indians were becoming more aggressive as the hungry time
of winter approached. By November there were clear signs
that the braves were gathering; they could be seen stalking
the high ridges by day, and their campfires winked ominously
from the heights at night.

It was not a question of war-whooping Indians swooping
down for a bloody massacre. The Indians might pounce on
a stray traveler for sport, but mainly they were in business
to make a living; what they wanted was not scalps but horses
to ride and oxen to eat. For the migrants, in turn, the loss of
such animals could represent the margin between life and
death. Faced with such a problem, Peoples staged a preven-
tive attack, killing six Indians and dispersing the others; then
he went back to his mission of mercy.

Relief operations were hampered also by outbreaks of
mountain fever which afflicted both the migrants and the
rescue parties. Peoples was among those stricken. For about
a week he laid up at Bruff's camp, at a time when Bruff was
able to render aid. And Peoples was no sooner back in action
than Major Rucker was felled by the same disease. Both men
forced themselves to go on with the rescue work though
greatly weakened by the effects of the fever. Peoples in particular was at times so ill and exhausted he could barely stay
in the saddle.

The worst hazard of all was the weather. Darkening skies
poured down rain, then snow, and then rain again. Each
time the rain returned it washed the snow away and granted
another small boon of time. But the rain was a menace also;
it turned the steep trail into a treacherous morass and swelled

to icy torrents the mountain streams that had to be forded.

In November, with time growing very short, Peoples sent a note to Rucker, saying: "Major, you can form no conception of the road, wagons are buried in the mud up to the bed, and cattle lying all around them. It is impossible to ride the strongest horse along it, and if they deviate one foot from the road they are irretrievably lost."

Through all such difficulties the relief teams slogged on, performing a prodigious labor. Peoples said of his men that "not one in the party had a dry blanket, or dry clothes, in half a month."

He added, "At every river and slough they stood ready to wade over, with the women and children in their arms; and even after reaching the settlements, many of them took money out of their purses, and gave to the destitute."

It went on like that for two months, and then finally the task was done. Rucker described the last contingent of stragglers from Lassen's Route as Peoples brought them into the settlements on November 26:

"A more pitiable sight I had never before beheld. There were cripples from scurvy, and other diseases; women, prostrated by weakness, and children, who could not move a limb. In advance of the wagons were men mounted on mules, who had to be lifted on or off their animals, so entirely disabled had they become from the effect of the scurvy."

There remained the scattered remnants still in the mountains. Peoples remembered Bruff and dispatched a messenger with some provisions to help him through the winter. This, however, was during the season when nothing was going right for Bruff. The messenger arrived with one small bottle of sour wine, plus a note describing the pork, flour, and whisky which he was supposed to deliver.

The other supplies were on a mule, the messenger informed Bruff, and the mule was ten miles back on the trail, stuck

pack and all in a quagmire of mud that was up to the animal's back. Bruff settled for the bottle of wine.

Rucker and Peoples concentrated on the Lassen Route
which caught most of the tail-end traffic. There were, however, some other scattered stragglers along the Carson and
Truckee rivers which led out of the Humboldt Desert. On
those paths, too, relief-train units performed dramatic rescues.

It was again a story of people wobbling in on their last
legs. There were the same familiar ills of starvation, scurvy,
and exhaustion, the same scenes of migrants plodding along
with pitiable little bundles containing all they had salvaged
from the ruin of some train.

One memorable incident involved two men who were
found wandering through the wilderness with chunks of
rancid, week-old mule meat strung around their necks. The
rescue teams were not inclined to be fastidious, but here they
drew a line; the wayfarers were required to discard the foul-
smelling provisions and wash thoroughly in a stream before
approaching the relief train for help.

By early October it appeared that the two river routes were
just about cleaned up. Then a relief unit rescued a storm-
whipped party at a mountain pass and learned from them
that there was at least one more outfit still out on the desert.

The one more was the family party described by Sarah
Royce. They were not quite the last in from the Humboldt
Desert, but they were among the last, and their troubles epit-
omized the grief shared by almost all who fell behind.

The Royces included Sarah, her husband, Josiah, and their
two-year-old daughter, Mary. In their trek they made most
of the classic mistakes. They started too late, traveled too
slow, and ran into a series of small misfortunes which added
up to near disaster.

Along the way their company dissolved. They had set out

with a good-sized train but were reduced in the Rocky Mountains to a bedraggled little one-wagon caravan consisting of themselves and three outriders.

They were slow to realize their precarious situation. Thus most outfits began to strip down for fast travel about the time they passed Fort Laramie. But a thousand miles beyond that point the Royce wagon was still laden with such luxury baggage as mattresses stuffed with straw.

Some other burdens were simply incumbent on their position at the rear of the line. In places they found the pathway so trampled out that they had to shuttle back and forth in an arduous, time-consuming search for grass. On one cruelly unrewarding day they went fifteen miles off the trail just to find fodder enough to sustain the next day's march.

They had a chance to get out of it when they passed through Salt Lake City and saw Sand Walking Company forming up for that long detour to Los Angeles. The Royces were invited to join, but Josiah was a stubborn man; he had come too far and endured too much to settle for anything less than his original objective. And so they pushed on, arriving very late and all alone at the edge of the Humboldt Desert. There they made a last mistake, one which nearly cost their lives.

They began the desert crossing well before sunrise, hoping to get a big jump on this hardest day. They knew they should stop on the way at a place where they could stock up on water and grass before venturing into the wasteland. In the darkness, however, they missed the side road which turned off to the meadow. They wound up marching straight into the desert with no reserve supplies to sustain their oxen.

They struggled all day through the barren land, advancing some fifteen miles into the desert before they realized that they had missed the oasis. By then their situation was desperate. They were down to two or three quarts of water and had

not a morsel of fodder for the animals. They debated whether
to go forward or back. Finally they swung around to retrace
the hard miles.

Now at last those mattresses proved to be worth their
weight. They ripped out the old dry straw and fed it a handful at a time to the famished beasts.

On the way back they met another belated party coming
across. They had a wild hope that the strangers might be
carrying enough hay and water to see both groups through.
When the trains met there was an anguished negotiation,
Josiah pleading for help on behalf of his family.

Reluctantly but firmly the strangers refused. They had
barely enough for their own needs. And in their train, too,
there was a family to consider.

Mrs. Royce couldn't quarrel with the decision. "It would
be," she wrote, "like throwing away their own lives without
any certainty of saving ours."

She added that even so the woman in the other party
seemed ready to offer aid at any cost. "As soon as she heard
what were the circumstances," Sarah wrote, "she hastened to
condole with me; and I think had the decision depended
alone upon her, she would have insisted upon our sharing
their feed and water to the last."

So the Royces were very much on their own. They trekked
back to the oasis, stocked up, and started over, determined
this time to "cross or die." Between the two attempts they
spent a total of four days wandering back and forth across
that forty-mile stretch of hell on earth.

For most of the way Sarah walked, in order to spare the
animals. Once, very weary, she lagged behind and lost sight
of the wagon. She felt no real fear, only a sense of numb wonder at being utterly alone in a weird and desolate world.

Another time, walking beside the wagon, she fell into a
delirium from heat, thirst, and fatigue. She thought of a
biblical story about Abraham's wife, Hagar, cast away in an-

other desert, and in her fevered musing her identity half
merged with the heroine of that ancient tale.

"My imagination acted intensely," she wrote. "I seemed
to see Hagar in the wilderness walking wearily away from
her fainting child in the dried up bushes, and seating herself
in the hot sand. I seemed to become Hagar myself." While
lost in that reverie Sarah heard her daughter whimpering
for water, and she found herself repeating over and over
Hagar's words, "Let me not see the death of the child."

They got through the desert, but it was a near thing; they
lost two oxen on the way. After that they trudged along the
Carson River, slogging through loose sand, and making only
a few miles a day with their weakened team. Ahead of them
they could see steep hills that appeared to offer even tougher
terrain.

"It did not look as though we could ascend them," Sarah
wrote, "but we could at least try to reach their foot."

In that grimly fatalistic mood they spied a dust cloud
weaving in and out among the hills. Horsemen, obviously,
and advancing toward them. They thought of hostile Indians,
but there wasn't much they could do about it if such were
the case, and so they moved on to meet whatever it was. Then
the dust cloud surmounted a rise and they saw two riders
coming on at a gallop, each of them leading a pack mule by
the reins.

To Sarah's ecstatic eyes they seemed angels of deliverance.
She described them as "clad in loose flying garments that
flapped like wings on each side of them. Their rapidity of
motion and the steepness of their descent gave a strong impression of coming down from above, and the thought flashed
through my mind, 'They look heaven-sent!' "

She was all the more convinced of a providential delivery
when the lead rider pulled up at the wagon and turned to
Josiah, saying, "Well, sir, you are the man we are after."

The rider proceeded to give an earthy account of the affair, telling them that he'd heard of their plight while working with a rescue team at a Sierra pass. "When we got there," he said, "we met a little company that had just got in. They'd been in a snowstorm at the summit—'most got froze to death themselves, lost some of their cattle, and just managed to get to where some of our men had fixed a relief camp. There was a woman and some children with them, and that woman set right to work at us fellows to go over the mountains after a family she said they'd met on the desert. She said there was only one wagon, and there was a woman and child in it; and she knew they could never get through them canyons and over them ridges without help. We told her we had no orders to go any farther. She said she didn't care for orders. She said she didn't believe anybody would blame us for doing what we were sent out to do, if we did have to go farther than ordered. And she kept at me so, I couldn't get rid of her. You see, I've got a wife and little girl of my own; so I felt just how it was; and I got this man to come with me, and here we are."

That was all very well as a soldier's explanation, but Sarah held fast to a "sweetly solemn conviction" that they were, in fact, heaven-sent. To her it was "that Providential hand which had taken hold of the conflicting moments, the provoking blunders, the contradictory plans, of our lives and those of a dozen other people who a few days before were utterly unknown to each other and many miles apart, and had from these rough, broken materials wrought out for us so unlooked for a deliverance." *

* The rescue on Carson River was an indirect but very valuable contribution to American letters. Six years later the Royces produced a son, Josiah, who was destined to become a major philosopher.

PART IV

CALIFORNIA

CHAPTER 13

———◆———

The buildings of this Sitty are generally rather poor . . .
                    —Leander V. Loomis surveys the promised land.

As the immigrant tide poured into California two whirlpools
of humanity began to take shape. The adventurers descended
on Sacramento by land, on San Francisco by sea; many thousands passed through those places and hurried on, but thousands more remained to form cities.

The term city is here loosely construed. What they formed
at first were boom-town encampments. At San Francisco
some 40,000 people milled through the first year, turning a
sleepy little village into one of the most untidy assemblies
that ever gathered on American soil.

The accommodations problem was alleviated, but not
solved, by several hundred abandoned ships which cluttered
the harbor. For a time arriving seamen almost all jumped ship
for the gold fields, and numerous deserted hulks were run
up on the beaches to serve as buildings.

Ashore there was a frenzy of new construction, but very
little of it went into housing. Lumber cost a dollar a foot
and bricks a dollar apiece; what went up at those prices were
saloons, bordellos, and gambling joints.

For sleeping purposes any rough sort of contrivance would
do. One entrepreneur took planks, laid them across saw-
horses, and rented them to gold rushers at $3 a night. In

some boardinghouse establishments the tables did double duty as extra beds.

Otherwise the adventurers lived variously in cellars and dugouts, in tents and canvas houses. One dank, unfurnished cellar twelve feet square rented for $250 a month. Canvas houses were a luxury, too, for such structures required tacks; the going price for tacks the first year was $160 to $190 a pound.

San Francisco was overrun also with tent dwellers, most of them congregating on an expanse of sand hills and flatlands which fringed the shore. At one point 1,200 such squatters clustered in an area half a mile in diameter. Low-lying portions of the campgrounds were periodically flooded and never wholly dry; there was no semblance of sanitary system, and the thick-swarming rats became so voracious that it was advisable to sleep well muffled up, the head covered with blankets. Gold rushers called that place Happy Valley.

Autumn of 1849 brought the additional discomfort of heavy rains, turning streets into such quagmires that wagon teams were sometimes stuck fast in the mud. To meet the problem San Franciscans dumped in brushwood, old packing crates, anything at all that would do for fill; on occasion barrels of spoiled food were used to firm up the roadways. The net result was described in a sign which someone tacked up at Clay and Kearney Streets, in the heart of town:

THIS STREET IS IMPASSABLE;
NOT EVEN JACKASSABLE

Street lights, of course, were out of the question. When a San Franciscan ventured abroad at night he held a lantern aloft, if he had a lantern.

A similar disarray pervaded almost every other aspect of life. Workmen commanded from $1 to $2 an hour, as much as they earned in a day back home, but they soon discovered an immense gap between wealth and well-being. A loaf of bread which cost four cents in New York went for 50 to 75 cents in San Francisco. Apples brought $1 to $5 apiece, eggs $10 to $50 a dozen. Laundry was so expensive, and so hard to obtain, that it was sometimes sent out to Honolulu or even China by clipper ships that provided an incidental delivery service as they shuttled back and forth.

In Sacramento the settlement began with squatters flocking around John Sutter's fort, and they ruined him just as he had feared. They overran his land, trampled his crops, even tore up his gardens in the hope of finding nuggets adhering to plant roots. Sutter in turn made the adventurers the bitter offer of a free graveyard, as big as they needed.

So insane was Sacramento's growth that men were paying anywhere from $600 to $20,000 for city lots of dubious title, at a time when the community's skyline presented a ragged row of about one hundred shacks. Forty-niner Leander V. Loomis described the scene:

"The buildings of this Sitty are generally rather poor . . . many of these are erected of small posts set in the ground for a sill, and a peace of inch board nailed across the top for a plate, then loose rafters thrown up, and two or three thin strips of narrow boards nailed across them for sheating which completes the fraim—the fraim was then covered with canvas or cotton cloth with a small hole left at one end for a dore, over which also swung a loose peace of canvas, which in order to enter might be easily pushed aside, the building was then considered complete, and ready for use of any Gentleman either to keep store or Tavern in, at the low rent of 150 or 200 Dollars pr month."

Of social services in Sacramento suffice it to say that the first attempt to form a local government was voted down by decisive margin. At a second attempt the city charter carried, though a resolute 40 per cent were still holding out for anarchy.

By October 1849 Sacramento's population had reached

2,000; the accommodations at that point consisted of forty-five wood buildings and some three hundred tents and shacks, but at least half the inhabitants were sleeping on marshy ground with only blankets for shelter. The following month pestilential fevers swept through the encampment, bringing deaths up to twenty a day. This was a rate sufficient to wipe out the community in three or four months except that new-comers arrived so fast that the population almost doubled in sixty days. In its second year of existence Sacramento bustled with 10,000 people, about two thirds of them permanent residents and the rest a stream of transients who continually floated through.

Throughout the early period both Sacramento and San Francisco changed so rapidly that the scenes and circumstances were hardly ever the same two months in a row. Dramatic transformations were wrought at times by mushrooming growth, at times by cataclysmic destruction. San Francisco was purged by half a dozen great fires; Sacramento was swept by both fire and flood. Each time a stricken community would rise again, lustier than before.

Actually the disasters served some constructive purpose in providing the opportunity for fresh starts. After several of those the cities began to look, roughly speaking, like cities.

Another measure of civic progress is provided by the casualty reports. Both the type and frequency of illness revealed a great deal about a community's state of development at any given moment.

During San Francisco's worst period the dead were often not even properly buried. Corpses were laid out on the beach at Miller's Point, there to be covered with sand or washed away at the next high tide. The beach became littered with skulls.

Epidemic conditions were much like those affecting field armies of the period, with dysentery the most prevalent complaint. Dr. J. D. B. Stillman reported that among those who passed through Happy Valley the first summer almost none escaped dysentery; he attributed it to the camp's reliance on hundreds of brackish little seep-hole wells two and three feet deep.

Other physician observers spoke of the great tribulations from diarrhea. That, however, was not a disease but a symptom. Most of it was probably from dysentery, though it could result also from numerous other ills, including typhoid fever.

Gold-field medical accounts must all be qualified by noting that the terminology was loose and statistical evidence was spotty and sometimes nonexistent. But as things settled down an approximate picture began to emerge. One of the first detailed reports appeared when San Francisco's State Marine Hospital issued a patient record covering the last eight months of 1850. The hospital account listed diarrhea as the leading cause of admission, with dysentery very close behind; the two conditions combined accounted for 464 of 1200 admissions, 58 of 149 deaths.[1]

It adds up to the fact that conditions associated with filth were responsible for more than a third of both sickness and death. This, moreover, was at a time when the community was beginning to take on some semblance of order. Earlier losses of that type were presumably a good deal higher.

The hospital report listed the other leading ills as rheumatism and intermittent fever (malaria). Less prevalent but highly malignant were scurvy and typhus fever. Among patients admitted for those ills scurvy killed about one out of three, typhus nearly one out of two.

Of course, not all these ills were endemic to San Francisco itself. In particular, the malaria and scurvy were picked up elsewhere, and the patients came to San Francisco for treatment. However, it was a town of transients, and the hospital case record probably mirrored pretty accurately the general state of San Francisco's health.

At Sacramento health problems were similar but worse. Social organization was even more primitive, and the circumstance of low-lying marshlands encouraged the spread of virulent fevers. The town's reputation was such that assorted contagions were often classified simply as "Sacramento fever."

Sacramento's birth pains were described by Dr. John F. Morse; he reported that the community became "a perfect lazâr house for disease, suffering, and death months before anything like an effective city government was organized."

Said Dr. Morse: "The early setting in of the rainy season aggravated to an indescribable degree the miseries of the sick and destitute. Fevers were now making their appearance, and in consequence of the general debility they assumed a low and perilous type; yet such was the lack of shelter that many cases of severe typhus fever were lying in such exposed situations that their bed clothing would be saturated with the piercing rain. And still they did sometimes recover."

Another witness to Sacramento's plight was Dr. Stillman, who settled there in November 1849. He found the town surrounded by a huge bivouac of people who had arrived too late to provide proper quarters or lay in provisions. His account of conditions:

"The principal food consisted of salt pork, hard bread, flour, fresh beef and venison; dried fruits and potatoes could be had at a high price, and grapes grew wild along the banks of the rivers in great numbers; but, from ignorance and mistaken economy, the greater part used no vegetables.

"The high price of building material put comfortable shelter beyond the reach of all, except a favored few. With no covering but their tents, or beds but their blankets, barely raised above the wet earth, clothing filthy and covered with vermin, their condition when sick was wretched in the extreme.

"The sick were often shamefully neglected. The ranks of the medical profession were crowded with pretenders, and a feeling of distrust was general when all were strangers, and caused many to reject all medical aid. A few were provided for by private charity, but the greater number were suffered to perish uncared for, when they could no longer render an equivalent for services. A provisional government was organized, but, without resources, it could do little more than furnish coffins. A debt of $12,000 was incurred for that one item alone."

More revealing even than such descriptions were some random incidents illustrating how men perished in gold-field communities. Thus in 1850 the *Alta California* published two brief news items which aptly combine as a tale of two cities.

One item appeared on April 8 and disclosed the coroner's verdict in the case of a corpse found in a San Francisco lodging. It was announced, with no particular surprise, that the cause of death was starvation.

The other story ran five days earlier and referred to an accident at Sacramento. The headline read "Burial Alive," but that was an exaggeration. What happened was that a man became bogged down in a morass of mud. He died, presumably of heart failure, while people were struggling to dig him out.

After 1850 health conditions improved immensely, not the least evidence of it being the fact that medical authorities were now able to maintain fairly detailed records of what was going on. The most comprehensive report was that compiled by Dr. Thomas M. Logan at Sacramento.*

Dr. Logan computed Sacramento's 1851 death rate at 1 in every 25.71 inhabitants. All things considered, that was really surprisingly good. According to Dr. Logan's figures, it compared with 1 out of 39 in Boston.

The next year Sacramento's losses doubled. Dr. Logan gave

---

* Dr. Logan's report was an unofficial estimate published by the *California State Medical Journal* in October, 1856.

the toll as 1 in 13.44. A cholera outbreak contributed heavily, and there was a general increase in epidemic diseases.

After that came steady improvement. In 1853 the casualty
rate was 1 in 27.05; in 1854 it was 1 in 33.83; in 1855 it was
1 in 36.92.

If the death rate was brought under control, however, the
causes of death still remained somewhat special to California.
In other, more settled communities a high percentage of
mortality could be traced to such factors as the conditions of
old age, the diseases of childhood, and the childbirth casualties among both mothers and infants. In gold-rush society
those were all very minor causes. Thus a spot check of one
Sacramento hospital covers 622 patients; of the lot seven were
female, twelve were children.[2] Similarly a spot check of death
reports indicates that only 7½ per cent were aged fifty or
older.[3]

In short, California's deaths were those of vigorous men
struck down in their prime. Dr. Logan again provides some
detailed information as to the causes.[4]

For the three-year period 1851–53, Dr. Logan listed Sacramento's deaths at 1,251. The leading cause was "fevers," a
loose category accounting for 262 fatalities. The combined
items of dysentery and diarrhea had dropped to second place,
but the two conditions were still responsible for 237 deaths,
or more than a fifth of the total. Cholera accounted for another 102, all in the outbreak of 1852.

Included also in the toll were 114 casualties classified as
"unknown." Those men simply died and were buried, and
no one bothered to inquire closely as to why.

The other big factor in Dr. Logan's list was a category
which he described as "arising from intemperance and exposure, murder, executions and sundry accidents." That accounted for 125 deaths, or almost exactly a tenth of the total.

To put it another way, Sacramento at the time was basically
a small town, and for three years it was running nearly a

CALIFORNIA 175

death a week of the type that are customarily described as sudden. The loosely assorted list included thirty-five from wounds and accidents and thirty from drowning. There were nine suicides, seven executions, four murders, and six men who burned to death.

In the larger community of San Francisco the deaths for the years 1851 to 1853 totaled about 4,000. Detailed breakdowns are not available, but it can be safely assumed that very few of them succumbed to old age.

CHAPTER 14

In this land of gold no law governs the art of healing.

—A French physician observes
the strange ways of Americans.

Like almost everything else in the new communities, the medical service was highly disorganized. It reflected the general tone also in that the physician participants were often inclined toward flamboyant style.

Medical adventurers flocked to the gold fields from almost every continent. Some of them were men of character and purpose, possessed of impeccable credentials. And some weren't. In the swashbuckling atmosphere it was difficult to tell the difference.

One of the more colorful figures was Dr. J. W. Palmer. He arrived broke in San Francisco, slept without tent or blanket on a flea-infested sand hill, then scraped up a stake of $50. He risked his slim capital in a monte game, won enough to open an office, and soon had a thriving practice which brought him $75 to $100 a day. In later years he liked to recall also that he once set up all night with a dying gambler, spooning beef tea into the patient while playing cards with him to determine a fee of double or nothing.

Aside from such flourishes, Dr. Palmer is remembered for a pioneer role in gold-rush medicine. He was San Francisco's first public-health officer.

Equally picturesque, though of opposite type, was Dr. W.

Grove Deal. He was a physician who doubled in duty as a Methodist minister, and for a few hours one morning he experimented unsuccessfully with mining. Thereon hangs another tale.

Dr. Deal arrived at the diggings on a Sunday and made his presence known by mounting a wagon and bawling through a long dinner horn to call the miners together. He led the assembly in a few rousing hymns, then announced to loud hurrahs that he was giving up his professional pretensions to become one of them, "an honest miner."

Early the next day Dr. Deal was up and at it with pick and shovel, but before noon he had acquired two badly blistered hands and a new resolve. Donning his black coat and top hat, he set off for Sacramento where he resumed the practice of medicine. It was well that he did so for he was a man of genuine humanitarian impulse. He became a hospital founder.

In Drs. Palmer and Deal the taste for theatrics was happily combined with substantial ability. Unfortunately there were other colorful types who must be put down as rogues or eccentrics, or both.

Seldom in history have conditions been more auspicious for charlatans. There was a clamorous demand for healing nostrums, there was quick money in it, and all the bars were down. The communities had no statutes regulating medical practice, the profession itself was divided and quarreling, and the protections usually afforded by reputation and public knowledge were all swept away in a society of strangers.

In such circumstances about all a quack required was a frock coat and a knowledgeable air. In fact, if a pretender didn't have the coat and couldn't manage the air, he could even make a virtue of that, by presenting himself as a homespun healer and man of the people.

The quackery was exacerbated by boom-and-bust economic conditions which made medicine almost as speculative as mining. Those who got in early often prospered beyond their wildest hopes; during the first two years practitioners regularly commanded $15 to $20 for an office visit and $50 to $100 for a house call at night. Such fees, of course, attracted hordes of charlatans. But brisk competition soon drove the fees down; within two years more California's "medical profession" was so overcrowded that consultations were being offered at $1 to $2.50. And that, in turn, forced out many good physicians. The total effect was that saloonkeepers and doctors could be found exchanging roles at both ends of the cycle.

The situation was described in clinical detail by Dr. Pierre Garnier, a Frenchman who joined the rush in 1851. Dr. Garnier viewed matters from a special perspective for his own country was then one of the world's most advanced in medical science. He was accustomed to the strict requirements of the Code Napoleon which specified that physicians must complete a four-year university course, passing rigorous examinations in anatomy, physiology, pathology, chemistry, dietetics, and hygiene. Under the French system even the druggist was obliged to undergo an eight-year apprentice training before he was licensed to compound his pills and powders. Coming from such background, and viewing what passed for medicine on California's wild frontier, Dr. Garnier was understandably astonished.

Writing of his adventures, in an account called *Voyage Médical en Californie,* Dr. Garnier returned repeatedly to the theme that among gold-rush practitioners absolutely anything went. With grave earnestness he assured his readers:

"In this land of gold no law governs the art of healing. . . . The Yankee with his characteristic industrious manner and belief in business considers medicine like any other trade. . . . The practical Americans avail themselves of their native humor to designate as *doctor* anyone who concerns himself with medicine."

He added that the doctor business was often merged in the

most curious fashion with other, quite unrelated occupations. On Commercial Wharf at San Francisco he noted one combination saloon and clinic which displayed "a painted billboard whose bright-colored bottles were a medley of alcoholic and pharmacologic wares. Within, the doctor dispensed medicines to patients over the same counter on which he poured drinks for his other clients."

Dr. Garnier met other healers whose side line, or main line, was that of speculator, trader, grocer, gambler, and boardinghouse keeper. And as he roamed the gold fields he kept adding to the list; he found a clockmaker, a wigmaker, a shoemaker, an architect, and an ex-soldier all dealing in medical advice.

"Amid this band of charlatans," he wrote, "there are a few true practitioners, but everywhere they are conspicuously rare." He estimated that among San Francisco's two hundred doctors not more than thirty were genuine. Of the city's hundred drugstores, he felt that only four or five met professional standards.

In his sheer amazement at such rampant malpractice Dr. Garnier probably underestimated the number of legitimate practitioners. His descriptions of the quacks, however, were not in the least overdrawn. He was right, too, in saying that reputable men often gave up in disgust rather than attempt to compete with a host of imposters.

Sacramento's Dr. Logan echoed Dr. Garnier's observations almost exactly. Writing to a medical colleague in New Orleans, Dr. Logan stated, "We physicians are at the most ruinous discount, and the ancient and time honored doctorate is in most cases held in so low repute that many a worthy physician studiously conceals his title. I have seen M.D.'s driving ox-teams through our highways—laboring in our streets like good fellows—serving at bar-rooms, monte tables, boardinghouses, etc., and digging and delving among the rocks to gather together their allotment of gold.

"Labor is honorable to man," he added, "and it is not because some are obliged to put their shoulder to the wheel that the profession is rated at so low a standard. It is because many, and among them those who assume without any moral or legal right to the title of Doctor, in their grasping cupidity have drained the poor miner of all his hard-earned dust, be it more or less, for a few professional visits. These incidents of medical rapacity have become so numerous and aggravated as to create a distrust on the part of the community toward the profession generally, and to bring odium on its practitioners. Hundreds who are able to pay a reasonable fee, would rather perish than lose all their means of support in satisfying the exorbitant fees of a physician. I do not suppose that in any part of the civilized world such enormous fees were ever charged and collected." [1]

Of course, there was another side to the complaint of larcenous fees. Most physicians provided the medicines they prescribed; they had to pay as much as $64 an ounce for quinine and up to $1 a drop for an opiate solution called laudanum. They paid exorbitant rents for their crude offices and clinics, and if they undertook nursing care of the invalids they ran up astronomical board bills. And then, too, they very often discovered that charging fees was one thing and collecting another.

Dr. Palmer presented that aspect of the matter. When he was named city health officer of San Francisco in August of 1849 he found himself presented with imposing, indeed impossible, obligations. He was held vaguely responsible for sanitation and quarantine systems which didn't exist, and he became in addition a kind of repository for all the indigent sick adrift in the city.

In his memoirs Dr. Palmer put the words into the mouth of another, unnamed physician, but he was undoubtedly speaking for himself as well. "Now here," he wrote, "is the beauty of being a doctor in good standing in this golden anomaly of a city. These men, being sick, destitute, friendless and completely wretched, apply to the Alcalde for relief. There is no public hospital, no hospital fund. The Alcalde cannot quarter them on the Town Council, for the simple reason that the Town Council is here to-day and gone to-morrow. He can hardly share his own couch with them. So he sends them to me, to be bedded and boarded, as though I were Abraham's bosom. I am to provide them with the necessary medicines, nursing and nourishment, till they die or get well, at my proper expense, for the pleasure and fame of my own beneficence. And I am to charge them to the City; that means that I am to present my humble bill a great many times to the Town Council, whose 'petitioner will ever pray'; by the time I have become quite desperate and have exhausted my resources of interest, bribes, and blasphemy they will refer it to a long succession of special committees, to be audited—each committee cordially voting me a bore, wishing me, and my accounts, and my benevolence and my grievances, all at the devil together; at last some verdant committee man, who has not been long in the business, will get my bill passed, by dividing the total by two; and finally the Comptroller will put the crowning glory on the whole, by ordering me to be paid in city script, at fifty cents on the dollar. I shall console myself with my first-rate grievance, and count on eloquent sympathy, and public meetings, and the thanks of public-spirited people, while my patients will vote me a rapacious villain, and seriously discuss the expediency of lynching me."

It was too much for Dr. Palmer. After six weeks he resigned the post.

Eventually some semblance of medical system emerged out of the general disorder. It was, however, slow going.

For the first two years neither San Francisco nor Sacramento possessed such rudimentary facility as a genuine public hospital. Various stopgap arrangements were made in the interim, but the main reliance was on private hospitals which sprang up in random fashion. Of necessity they were make-shift establishments, ill-equipped and understaffed; many of them were hardly more than collection points for the sick and dying.

At Sacramento the first hospital was set up under auspices so irregular that the institution is usually dismissed with scant mention in the official medical histories. However, it represented a hospital to those who used it, and in services rendered it did not differ too drastically from some others of more orthodox cast. The place in question was a drafty little canvas-walled clinic founded by Dr. Beeryman Bryant on June 28, 1849.

Dr. Bryant was a thirty-three-year-old South Carolinian who had come to medicine by way of preliminary careers as bricklayer, teamster, auctioneer, and horse trader. He had served a medical apprenticeship under an Alabama healer, and he had graduated from something called Botanica Med-ical College in Memphis. In sum he was a botanic, a follower only slightly removed from an offbeat medical cult founded by a Dr. Samuel Thomson about half a century earlier.*

If Dr. Bryant's medical theories were suspect, his judgment on some other matters was eminently sound. He arrived in California as part of a big company containing four other physicians; his professional brethren in the group had all come laden with pickaxes while Dr. Bryant had brought only his medicine chests.

"I had no idea of mining and have never worked a day in the mines," he observed later, "for when I left Alabama for

* Samuel Thomson was a self-appointed physician who based his healing system on steam baths and herbal preparations. His adherents later split into True Thomsonians, Physiomedicals, and Reformed Botanics; they would all be described as quacks today, but in their time they commanded a consider-able following.

California I had taken it for granted that people would get sick in this beautiful land, and I was not mistaken."

As to the founding of his hospital, Dr. Bryant gave this account:

"When I arrived in Sacramento there was not a place that I could find in which I could store away my medicines, so I went outside of the city limits and dug five holes and put my trunks in them and filled them up and put a stake at each end to represent graves and left them there until I was ready to use them. In a few days I bought some town lots and as it was impossible to buy lumber to build houses I resorted to willow poles to make studding and rafters. I then bought heavy sail duck for siding and roof, had the canvass well sewed up and then I put up bunks all around the house and had some bed ticks made and filled them with dry grass. I unearthed my trunks of medicine and opened my hospital (this being, to the best of my knowledge, the first private hospital opened in California) and put up a sign 'Home for the sick.' Very soon I had every bed or cot full of the sick. They would bring the poor fellows from the mines, frequently being four or five days on the road in the hot sun, and when they got them to the hospital, if they lived to get there, I would find them very sick."

Many of Dr. Bryant's patients were scorbutic, and he acknowledged that for them his hospital offered the most unsuitable fare:

"Our living was very simple as we had to do our own cooking, we could not get a variety, consequently we had for breakfast fried pork or bacon and flour stirred in water and fried in the grease of the pork or bacon and strong coffee; of course we did not think of milk. For dinner we would have boiled pork and beans. At night we would duplicate our breakfast—batter fried in grease and fried pork or bacon and strong coffee. We could not have anything else as it was almost impossible to get. So a great many cases of scurvy of the worst kind were the result."

Poor as the accommodations were, Dr. Bryant never lacked for patients. He maintained eighteen beds, always occupied, and he reported that he turned away at least one applicant for every one he admitted. At a per diem of $15 a bed, and with a brisk outside business at $10 a call, he was able to retire in five months.

"I made money very fast," he said, "and on the twenty-first of November I sold out my hospital and medicine to a doctor by the name of Hungerford, and on the first day of December started from San Francisco to the States having, as I thought, 'made my pile'." *

At least eight other private hospitals appeared during the early turbulent period at Sacramento. They were a varied lot, espousing precepts regular and irregular, and ranging in facilities from mere shacks to quite substantial establishments. Three are worthy of particular mention.

Dr. Charles Cragin set up the first orthodox hospital in August 1849. He installed himself at Sutter's Fort, using an adobe building hastily converted from a general store. The place was clean, cool, airy, and, above all, dry; the *Alta California* awarded it the accolade of "No. 1 as yet among such institutions in California." The rates were commensurate with such luxury, patients paying from $16 to $50 a day.

Another important figure was Dr. Deal, the preacher-physician who resumed practice after that half-a-day fling at the idealistic life of the honest miner. Dr. Deal opened a hospital at Sutter's Fort in the fall of 1849 and is chiefly remembered

* Dr. Bryant went home with his "pile," but California was in his blood; within a year he was back in the gold fields again. He lost heavily in a mining venture, recouped as an innkeeper, and became a successful rancher. The restless Bryant had thus crossed the continent three times and tried his hand at four trades by the time that Dr. Garnier came along to comment on the gold-rush physician's peculiar penchant for just such changes of professional pace.

for offering medical succor at the compassionate rate of $10 a day. A few months later he became co-manager of a small charity hospital sponsored by the Odd Fellows and Masons. It was the first of many such benevolent enterprises which sprang up in the gold fields under the aegis of fraternal, religious, and ethnic groups.[2]

A still more important hospital was operated jointly by Drs. J. D. B. Stillman and John F. Morse. They were a remarkable pair. Both were men of aspiration and intellect who combined large vision with an ability to make do in whatever fashion the circumstances required.

In the case of Dr. Morse, it will be recalled that when he came up from Panama he saved an infested ship by going into the steerage to "lead off in the noble function of cleaner and scraper."

Dr. Stillman knew how to take hold of things too. When he arrived in Sacramento he accommodated himself to the available materials and knocked a hut together out of empty dry-goods boxes which he scavenged from a river-front wharf. For months he sat in that ramshackle structure, receiving streams of patients and amassing bags of gold at the standard rate of an ounce a visit. The money he made was put to very good purpose when he joined with his partner in opening the finest medical institution the gold fields had yet seen.*

The Stillman-Morse hospital was a new building, a one-and-a-half-story structure made of Oregon pine. The facilities included an apothecary's shop, a dining room, eight small private wards lined with muslin, and a rough-finished garret which served as a general ward. In a letter home Dr. Stillman observed that the building would be considered a fair enough barn back East and could be duplicated there at a cost of about $2,000. In Sacramento it was the town's most imposing

---

* Drs. Stillman and Morse are remembered also as men who both made gold-rush history and wrote it. Stillman's *Seeking the Golden Fleece* and Morse's *First History of Sacramento City* are valuable sources.

structure, and the two physicians thought themselves lucky enough to rent it for $1,500 a month.

Such were the private hospitals. As for community program, the city farmed out the indigent sick to scattered private establishments. This provided for only a few of those stricken, and they were frequently consigned to shoddy institutions offering cut-rate services.

Dr. Morse called it the "infamous system of selling off the poor and friendless sick not to the *highest* but to the lowest bidder." He added that general conditions were such that 80 per cent of the ill could not obtain anything like adequate care.

Dr. Stillman echoed the complaint in more poetic vein, saying: "The fallen are trampled into the mud, and left to the tender mercies of the earth and sky."

Another voice for reform was that of the Sacramento *Placer-Times.* In the summer of 1849 the paper published a blistering editorial which charged, "Poor fellows are lying sick, and many dying, without a hand to minister to their sufferings."

The newspaper observed, "Several have objected to the establishment of a City Hospital, on the ground that there are enough here already. We grant that there are enough places for the sick, but the question is, can they get into them?"

If civic officials were slow to act, it must be acknowledged that they were faced with enormous difficulties. Sacramento was severely plagued with sickness of its own, and it became in addition a receiving point for many of those who became ill or injured in the surrounding mines. By December of 1849 the hospitalization and burial of paupers was costing the community $300 to $500 a day.

To all such problems was added a stroke of bad luck. Late in 1849 the city council decided to erect a public hospital, appropriating $14,000 for the purpose. The building was

only half finished, however, when a windstorm knocked it
down. The harried authorities were so discouraged that for
months more nothing was done.

In May 1850 a compromise solution was reached, the random method of farming out patients being replaced by a regular contract arrangement in which a single institution was
designated to act as the city hospital. In theory it reduced the
competitive scramble and gave the comunity some control
over facilities and services. In fact it was only as good or as
bad as the hospital selected. The program was only six months
old when a grand jury brought in a report charging city-
hospital administrators with criminal neglect.

At San Francisco the social evolution was similar in style
but far more contentious in spirit. Scandal, law suit, and endless acrimony all marked the birth pains of a community
health program.

Aside from palming off the indigent sick on the city health
officer, San Francisco's first impulse was to ignore the problem. Very soon, however, the question was forced on the attention of the city council. A public-spirited citizen accomplished that by rounding up a band of invalids, marching
them to town hall, and invading a council meeting to beg
for alms.

The city turned then to contract arrangement with a private hospital operated by a Dr. Melhado. He has passed into
gold-rush annals with his first name unrecorded and his last
name unhonored; he was another of those unconscionable
types who mined the miners. The city council, however, must
be charged as an accomplice to his acts. Despite the extrav-
agant inflation of the period Dr. Melhado was commissioned
to nurse the destitute at a miserly per diem rate of $5 a pa-
tient.

Dr. Melhado combined the public function with private
facilities for his own patients. In his private wards the ac-

commodations were primitive but tolerable. The rooms were small and dark but reasonably clean; the crowding was held to a maximum of twelve beds in a room; the inmates were washed regularly and made as comfortable as possible.

In the public wards the conditions were intolerable. A rude shed was divided by a partition into two sections; each section measured 15x20 feet and contained forty to fifty patients. Pallets were laid so close together that it was often physically impossible to step between them to tend the sufferers. Moreover, the question of nursing attendance was somewhat academic, since the staff for each ward consisted of a single ill-paid, untrained supervisor; about all the attendant could manage was to distribute the rations and see to the frequent necessity of carrying out the dead.

Considering that dysentery was a prevailing complaint, the look and smell of the wards was a circumstance that does not bear close description.

The state of hospital affairs was brought to public attention by a street preacher, the Rev. William Taylor. He was a man of curious parts. As minister he was possessed of such burning zeal that he might be termed almost a fanatic. But when he turned his attention to more temporal concerns he displayed a good deal more sense than some of the authorities in charge.

The Reverend Taylor became involved in the issue by chance. Passing along the street one day, he saw a big red-lettered sign proclaiming "City Hospital" and decided to drop in and console the sufferers. At the door his entrance was blocked by someone identified as the superintendent, probably Dr. Melhado himself. There ensued an angry argument, the minister being refused admission on the grounds that the patients were much too ill to be disturbed.

He got in anyway, shouldering his way past attendants after offering a reluctant promise that he would create no furor. Once inside, he found the promise impossible to keep. Moving through the wards, he preached, prayed, sang, distributed tracts, and exhorted the dying to last-minute repentance. So relentless were his persuasions that one unrepentant patient took refuge by pulling a blanket up over his face and huddling under it in stubborn protest.

In the weeks that followed the Reverend Taylor returned for repeated revival sessions. He found it a discouraging business; by his own estimate he was achieving a deathbed conversion rate of only one in five. In the midst of that passionate concern, however, he also saw clearly that the hospital was affording too many occasions for deathbed decisions of whatever sort. He first addressed himself to that problem by advising scorbutic patients to go out and find themselves something fit to eat.

"My friends," he declaimed, "what are you doing here? You are cooped up in this miserable place, without fresh air, without sunshine, without exercise, and without vegetable diet. You will die, the last man of you, if you don't get out of this place. You had better be turned out in San Jose Valley to graze, like old Nebuchadnezzar, than pine away and die in such a place as this."

The Reverend Taylor's specific and very useful suggestion was that they go out and graze on a species of wild lettuce which grew in the surrounding countryside. He described the plant to them and told them where it might be found. Some who were able took his advice, and they were presently praising him as a man who had saved them in a quite unexpected way.

The minister's other and still more valuable service was to conduct a one-man crusade against all the pesthole conditions which the hospital embodied. He roamed the streets, addressing crowds wherever he found them, pouring all his missionary enthusiasm into fierce denunciation of the system. He raised so much hell about it that the city council was forced to conduct an official inquiry. As a result, the hospital contract was plucked from Dr. Melhado's soiled hands and awarded to another physician, Dr. Peter Smith.

Dr. Melhado did not accept the decision. He announced that he would keep the patients, tend them at his own expense, and sue the city for the payments stipulated in his contract. However, his position was badly undermined when his patients learned of the council's ruling. All who could walk immediately decamped for Dr. Smith's hospital. Dr. Melhado was left with about thirty invalids who were too ill to escape.

In an attempt at cruel blackmail the physician announced next that he was suspending all care and treatment of the remaining patients until the financial dispute was settled to his satisfaction. With equally cruel indifference city officials shrugged off the threat. The city's absurdly legalistic position was that Dr. Melhado was shorn of official connection and so what transpired at his place was not a public concern.

The impasse lasted twenty-four hours, during which time the hostage patients received no food. The neglect inspired thirteen of the stricken to sufficient desperate energy that they hobbled away from their infamous keeper. But that still left seventeen who were too weak to move.

Into this breach stepped the Strangers' Friends Society, a benevolent organization in which the Reverend Taylor again appeared as the moving spirit. The society dispatched an emissary to reason with city hall and sent another to plead with Dr. Melhado. When both overtures were rejected the Strangers' Friends took matters into their own hands, marching on the hospital in a body. They just walked in, picked up the patients, and carried them off, commandeering Dr. Melhado's beds and pallets for use as emergency litters. The invalids were taken to a nearby empty building where they were scrubbed thoroughly and fed generously; then they were borne in triumph through the streets and deposited with Dr. Smith.

Under Dr. Smith's administration the hospital question subsided for a time. There were complaints, to be sure, but on the whole he appears to have managed things about as well as conditions permitted. And then suddenly his establishment was swept away by fire. Dr. Smith had just time enough to get his patients on the street before building, equipment, and all went up in flames.

The blaze occurred on October 31, 1850, and it brought in its wake another great hospital controversy. The issue this time was not medicine but money. For as the smoke cleared it became apparent that what lay in ruins was not just a hospital building but the whole structure of the city's shaky finances.

The trouble started with Dr. Smith's understandable desire to have some recompense for his loss. The fire had wiped out a $40,000 investment, and he was left with no assets at all save for a great bundle of city script acquired as payment for his services. In theory the script was redeemable for cash, but in practice script holders were party to a gentleman's agreement that they would hold the notes until city finances got straightened out. Under the circumstances Dr. Smith felt that he could no longer afford such courtesy. He presented his script, $64,000 worth of it, and demanded cash settlement.

City officials refused to pay, because they couldn't. Despite San Francisco's aura of booming growth and dazzling speculation, despite even the tons of real gold which circulated in daily commerce, the city till was empty. Officials tried to placate Dr. Smith by offering him municipal bonds, but that, of course, was merely a way of exchanging one promissory note for another. The physician was not so easily put off. He sued, winning court judgments which specified that public property must be sold at auction until sufficient funds were obtained to redeem his notes. And that in turn inspired a rash of similar suits by other script holders.

The city warned that it would contest the title to all property thus sold, a strategy which succeeded merely in making bidders cautious and driving prices down. There may also have been some skulduggery in which bidders connived with officials to loot the public domain. In any case, there was a scandalous auction in which 480 city lots brought a grand total of $50, or about 10½ cents apiece. Altogether, property totaling two thousand acres and valued at some two million dollars was auctioned off to pay the $64,000 bill. A subsidiary consequence was that property titles were tied up in court action for more than twenty years.*

The untidy financing brought a last blast from the Reverend Taylor. He pointed out that the two million dollars, more intelligently applied, would have gone a long way toward alleviating all the social ills to which the city was heir.

Meantime other men struggled on with the intractable problem of maintaining hospital service. After Dr. Smith's place burned down the city council purchased a building and set up an emergency medical center there under the direction of Dr. Edward B. Chapin. The difficulties he faced are recorded in a letter he addressed to the city council on December 17, 1850.

Dr. Chapin paid council members a presumably sardonic compliment on their "philanthropic intentions" and then went on to discuss the facilities they had entrusted to his care.

"The Building purchased," he wrote, "is perhaps the best that could be obtained for a temporary hospital, the most suitable in location, in construction, in size and condition. As it is susceptible of improvement only in the latter point, it is perhaps, at the present time the only one to which it is necessary to draw your attention.

"In its present condition it does not even afford a sufficient shelter to the unfortunate patients, and indeed adds much

* The legality of the sales was ultimately upheld. The property titles in question came to be known as "Peter Smith deeds."

to their suffering. The roof is leaky in many parts. The recent rains have swollen that of the main building so much as to lessen in some means this evil. The second story of the right wing is not weatherboarded and the roof is but half completed. During a rain the water pours in upon them thru the open roof literally flooding their apartments. The garden in the rear of the building is filled with garbage and refuse of every kind, and the hill rising abruptly the washings from it flow directly into the basement of the hospital. A sewer or breakwater should immediately be constructed to remedy this evil."

It wasn't attended to "immediately," but then Dr. Chapin could hardly have expected that. The great thing was to get anything done at all.

While city authorities threshed around with such exigencies a parallel health service was taking shape. The institution in question was San Francisco's State Marine Hospital, which opened in May 1850; as the name indicated, it was a state agency charged with care of the numerous invalid sailors.

State Marine had its share of problems. It, too, was wracked by scandals both medical and political, and it was moved frequently from one unsatisfactory location to another. But it was well financed, receiving a substantial endowment at the start, and benefiting thereafter from a hodgepodge of revenues which included a commutation tax on new arrivals. In 1851 San Francisco took advantage of the setup by merging the city hospital with State Marine. It became as a result California's first truly public hospital, the only one in the early period to be entirely owned and operated as a community enterprise.[2]

State Marine took over care of the city's indigents and was permitted to accept other patients under the loose stipulation that they pay a fee "from time to time." In addition the hospital pioneered in health insurance, a regulation providing

that those who were not already ill could assure themselves
of free care by paying a premium of $5 a year.

The insurance program appears to have been a wasted effort. There is no record that any of the improvident adventurers ever availed themselves of the offer.

CHAPTER 15

———◆———

. . . if we are swept away, we will all go together.

—Dr. Stillman, holding out with his patients
on the top floor of a flooded hospital.

In addition to the general and persistent problems, gold-rush society had to cope with a succession of random disasters. If entire communities can be said to be accident prone, then San Francisco and Sacramento were.

In Sacramento the calamities occurred chiefly from floods. The city sprawled over low-lying ground located at the confluence of the American and Sacramento rivers, and the two rivers together acted as a great funnel for a network of mountain streams which cascaded down from the Sierra slopes. When swollen by heavy rains or fast-melting snow the rivers could rise as much as twenty-five feet, turning the townsite into a vast lake.

The first deluge swept over Sacramento during the winter of 1849–50, at a time when the community was struggling with all the problems attendant to its sudden growth. The crisis began to build up in late November with a series of torrential rains. Within a month the low-lying portions of the city were inundated, ferries were plying back and forth across flooded streets, and the valleys all around were filling with water, cutting off the routes of escape.

Clearly it was time to pull out and seek refuge on higher ground. Such, however, was not the gold rusher's style. Each flimsy shack perched a foot or two above the menacing water represented thousands of dollars in investment and visions unlimited of wealth to come. And so they stayed, and hoped, and bet against rain. As Dr. Morse recalled it, "The reckless spirit of speculation had declared an inundation to be out of the question, if not physically impossible. Everyone was inclined to believe the ridiculous assurances of safety, which could scarcely be extinguished when the city was absolutely under water."

For a brief time it looked as though they might stick it out. During the last days of December the rain abated momentarily and the water actually receded a little. But then came a double blow. On January 8 a storm ripped through, tumbling the shacks about, and dumping fresh downpours on the beleaguered city. At the same time an unseasonable warm spell melted piled-up snow on the mountain slopes. After that the water came on with a terrible rush. By January 9 four-fifths of Sacramento was flooded, the threat was increasing ominously with every passing hour, and the populace was scrambling for survival.

When the water finally leveled off it stood almost chest-high on the average, and in some areas it was literally deep enough to float a steamboat. One such craft was seen plying the impromptu channel of a street. On another street men came and went in rowboats from a second-story hotel window.

Dr. Morse described the resulting toll: "When the deluging waters began to overwhelm the city there was no adequate means of escape for life and property, and consequently many were drowned, some in their beds, some in their feeble efforts at escape, and many died in consequence of the terrible exposures to which they were necessarily subjected. The few boats which belonged to the shipping moored by the levee were brought into immediate requisition in gathering up the women, children, and invalids that were scattered over the city in tents and canvas houses. Some of the women who were living in tents in remote low places were found standing upon beds and boxes in water which was still rising with perilous rapidity. Sick men, totally helpless, were found floating about upon cots that seemed miraculously buoyant, and in enfeebled tones crying for help."

Among the disaster victims were a dozen or more abandoned inmates of a canvas hospital. The physician in charge was absent when the flood swirled through the place, and the attendants all panicked and fled. The stranded patients were discovered by sheer accident; they were in such wretched condition that all but two of them soon after succumbed.

Most of the invalids were gathered at first in a combination store and lumberyard, the site offering a reasonably secure building perched on high ground. There was a grim advantage, too, in the presence of the lumberyard facility, for as the death rate mounted among the stricken refugees the necessary coffins were easily procured.

At frequent intervals a disposal crew loaded the coffins into boats and rowed out from the store in search of burial grounds. That arrangement led to still another casualty. The ironic circumstances were recounted by Dr. Morse:

"They used to send a Dutchman and another individual out with the corpses to bury them. The Dutchman was very suspicious of everybody so far as his money was concerned and consequently carried it about his person, in gold dust. This he had accumulated to the amount of two thousand dollars when, unfortunately, he made a mistake upon one of his burying commissions and placed the coffin with the corpse across their smallest boat. The two got in and succeeded in getting some distance into deep water when the boat commenced careening and finally sank. The Dutchman, who was a powerful swimmer, cried to his companion, who was holding on to the coffin, 'Holt on, I'll swim ashore and get a boat.' He had not swum but a short distance when the weight of the gold dust drew him under water. By a tremendous strug-

gle he came up again and struck out anew, but only to repeat
the sinking and rising several times and finally to sink forever into a death which he preferred to detaching and losing
the gold dust upon his person. The other was saved by the
buoyancy of the coffin, which had been made very tight."

Another place of refuge was the Stillman-Morse hospital.
The decision to remain in the hospital was a calculated risk
as the building was badly flooded, the ground floor being entirely drowned out. However, it was a sturdy structure which
seemed to offer about as much hope as any of withstanding
the threat. More important, it was a post manned by resolute
spirits. As the water level rose Drs. Stillman and Morse re-
treated with their patients into the garret; together with some
other physicians who joined them they held out there for
more than two weeks.

The hospital soon became a receiving point for critical
cases from other centers. Often such refugees arrived in pitiable condition. Patients were brought in and died and were
replaced by others as the facilities were converted into an
always busy and crowded emergency ward. At the peak period
nearly fifty people were huddled in the attic, sharing a space
which measured 35 by 55 feet.

Dr. Stillman kept a journal throughout, and his jottings
recapture the scene in vivid detail. Hope and fear mingled in
his account with a note of incredulous surprise at the circumstances into which he was thrust.

On the morning of January 11, in the third day of the
crisis, he was still clinging to a determinedly optimistic mood.
It was reflected in a rhetorical flourish or two as he penned
this portrait of the group bracing itself for another day of
siege:

"We are all, about forty of us in the upper story of our
hospital! Dr. Morse and myself writing, Higgins (a physician)
reading Demartine's 'Raphael', the cook preparing something

for breakfast, two or three others, quartered with us, talking in an undertone, some asleep, and a few patients muttering in delirium. A lone woman, sick and destitute, is curtained off in one corner of the room.

"Some are lying on the floor; others, dead, are sewed up in blankets and sunk in the water, in a room on the first floor. Dr. Morse pours some brandy in his ink, to give spirit to his letter; I pour from another bottle standing on the table, containing laudanum, to quiet the apprehensions that mine may awaken; then we all laugh and go on as before."

The next day's entry struck a somber note: "The water is still rising—at the rate of six inches an hour. Tents, houses, boxes, barrels, horses, mules and cattle are sweeping by with the swollen torrent. To-day there is no first floor in the city uncovered. I have some misgivings about our fate, but sure I am that we will not desert the sick, and if we are swept away, we will all go together."

On the following day Dr. Stillman concluded that there was no hope for early relief, so he attended to the burial of three bodies deposited in the water below. He rented a whaleboat for the purpose, paying $40 for it, and used a hook and line to fish up the corpses. With the assistance of four others he rowed out about a mile to a high ridge where he buried the victims beneath an oak.

Another entry told of additional deaths and compressed a new element of terror and tragedy into a few terse words: "To-day two more emaciated remains have been deposited below. One patient went suddenly insane. All, doctors and others, took their watch."

Still another entry reported, "Six more emaciated victims of chronic diarrhea were brought to us. They were found accidentally in a canvas house, when the inundation had reached their beds, and for two weeks have been lying on the ground, without fire; two days, they tell us, they were without food."

The diarrhea patients had apparently come by way of the lumberyard. Dr. Morse added some details, saying that one of the cases was an old man reduced almost to a living skeleton by his illness, and wretched from cold because he had lain long neglected in sodden garments. They stripped off his clothing and hung it up to dry, and when a physician came around to tend him a few hours later it was seen that the coat and pants had changed color from black to gray. The garments were swarming with lice.

Another, more gruesome case involved a young man who was stuck fast to his blanket by his own festering sores. Dr. Morse reported, "An attempt was made to unroll the blanket, but it was found to be so adherent to many parts of his body as to make it difficult of removal—so difficult that the effort was delayed, after the face was relieved, for the victim to revive if possible, or if not that death might free him from a sense of his situation. Fortunately for him, death was the speedy alternative."

When they prepared the man for burial they discovered the real horror. Pulling the blanket away, they saw that he had been eaten alive by maggots.

Many another grim scene was played out in the crowded attic. Through it all the two physicians performed a truly heroic labor, exhausting their energies and emptying their purses in the struggle to sustain their institution. And then, finally, it was over. The water drained away into surrounding sloughs and valleys, and Sacramento began to dig itself out from the mud.

City authorities refused to reimburse the physicians for their expenses in providing food and medicine to stricken refugees. Dr. Stillman accepted the loss philosophically, saying, "Of those who are destitute, and who get well, we take their notes; if they die we take a check on Heaven."

The city meantime was taking a check on heaven of another sort. Having just survived a disastrous flood, men now went about assuring themselves that it couldn't happen again. Dr. Morse described the prevailing mood:

"The sky became again clear and beautiful, day and night. Under the influence of this agreeable change the water began rapidly to abate, so that in a few days some of the stores and hotels on Front and J streets were enabled to enter into a brisk and profitable business again; and during the month of February a communication with the mines was reopened, and the city presented an appearance so cheerful and busy as to induce a general forgetfulness of past losses.

"Such was the infatuated determination to believe the cool reiterations of the speculators in respect to the liability of the city to be inundated, that a few weeks only were required to induce a confidence of future security almost as great as that which had been manifested prior to the flood. A few people allowed themselves to cherish a little skepticism on the subject, and, engaging in building soon after, they elevated their foundations above high water mark; but their position being not only an eccentric one but exceedingly inconvenient, some of them were really induced to lower their buildings just in time to be a second time submerged by the spring inundation."

A small minority carried skepticism so far as to suggest that the community stave off future floods by building a levee. But, as Dr. Morse said, "nothing could exceed the unpopularity of this project." So long as fair skies persisted the general opinion held that a levee wasn't needed and wouldn't work anyway, and besides, no one had time.

Then came March, with heavy spring rains and melting snow, and the water came rolling out of the hills to engulf them once more. It would have been the same story all over again except that this time a leader appeared to take charge of the common defense. Dr. Morse resumes the tale:

"The rivers rose with great rapidity, the sloughs filled up to the overflowing, and the city must have been nearly as severely flooded as in January but for the masterly and herculean efforts of Hardin Bigelow. This man had declared from the first in favor of the practicability of defending the city by a levee. Having thus committed himself to the proposition, he was determined to demonstrate his theory in this second flood.

"With a moiety of means and a handful of men he commenced damming up the intruding waters at every low point and finally extending his temporary levee almost to its present limits. Night and day he was in the saddle, going from one point to another and stimulating his men to an almost superhuman action. For a few days this man met tide and torrent, mud and darkness, and croaking discouragements that few men in the world could have endured, and to the utter astonishment of all he saved the city from a severe inundation. As a natural consequence everybody praised him, and on the first Monday of April succeeding he was elected with a most cordial vote as the chief magistrate of this city."

For the resourceful Bigelow the office thus gained proved a dangerous eminence. Four months later he was shot and critically wounded while ousting rioting squatters from property which the city claimed. He went to San Francisco to recuperate, and there he was fatally stricken when a cholera epidemic swept through.

As his legacy to the community Bigelow bequeathed the beginnings of a great levee. Once the idea became firmly established enormous energies were poured into the project; by the end of 1850 it was extended and improved to embrace a system of dikes nine miles long, the embankments in places measuring seventy feet wide at the base and twenty feet high. It was California's first major public works, and it drew exclamations of praise and wonder from even so acerbic a social critic as Dr. Morse.

"Long may it stand," he declaimed, "as the monument to our enterprise! No other city of its population has ever completed so grand a work within the first two years of its existence as Sacramento."

The levee served the city well, but it was not a perfect defense. In March of 1852 Sacramento was swamped again by floodwaters which poured over the embankments. That was a bad year generally, the community being ravaged also by a fire which destroyed ten million dollars' worth of property.*

In San Francisco there was a veritable epidemic of fires. Six times in eighteen months great sections of the city were reduced to smoldering ashes.

The cycle of fires ran from December 1849 to May 1851. The mildest of the holocausts consumed about fifty buildings, while the worst destroyed 1,500 buildings in a single night. The loss of life was comparatively small, for San Franciscans soon became agile veterans at the art of survival amid the flames.

Several factors contributed to the recurrent disasters. The shanty construction provided a perfect tinder. Gusty winds often whipped the flames along, and the hill-and-dale topography created channels through which fires roared in blazing fronts a block or more long.

In addition to such ordinary causes conflagrations became something of a San Francisco tradition. Initially the holocausts occurred by accident and were accompanied by incidental looting. Later the criminal element took to setting fires as a prelude to sacking the city. The arson was carried to its final extreme in an anniversary fire, a disaster apparently staged in malicious commemoration of the fact that the city had been gutted on the same date a year before.

In response to the repeated burnings San Franciscans

---

* For Dr. Morse the great fire at Sacramento was an indirect factor in personal tragedy. His property was destroyed in the blaze, and his wife, who was in late pregnancy, was sent to San Francisco for sake of convenience. She took a riverboat, gave birth en route, and died within a few minutes after reaching her destination. The child, a son, died at age four.

evolved a volunteer fire department. When the first great blaze broke out the only defense consisted of men who came running with buckets of water and wet blankets to hold against the flames. Soon after, however, the volunteer companies began to appear. They did prodigious work, notwithstanding the fact that their approach to fire fighting was somewhere between a public service and a rowdy sport.

When a general alarm sounded the companies engaged in a wild race to be first at the scene, the hand-drawn engines being hauled through the streets by hundreds of shouting men. Custom decreed that the first outfit to arrive had the honor of hosing down the blaze while the others lined up behind to serve as relay stations, each engine crew pumping from its own water box to the reservoir of the engine ahead. The sporting element arose when a company undertook to "wash" a rival by pumping so fast as to overflow the other's tank. It made for a grand excitement, the crowd hooting and cheering, the men at the hand pumps sweating mightily, and the rival fire chiefs striding up and down crying hoarse exhortations through tin trumpets.

Hook-and-ladder companies pursued their calling in similar boisterous fashion. The standard practice was to scale a building, chop a hole, and sink a huge hook attached to a long pole or rope; then many hands would grab hold and with a great tug a wall would come crashing down. It was in its way quite an effective technique, conflagrations being stopped sometimes by leveling whole rows of buildings to serve as firebreaks.

Amid such scenes and circumstances San Francisco played out again and again a drama in which fiery destruction was followed always by lusty rebirth. The city arose so often from its ashes that it took the phoenix as its symbol.

Gold-rush observer Albert Bernard de Russailh commented later on the astonishing resilience with which the disasters were met. "Even while his house is burning," he said, "an

American will think only of how to rebuild it. He lets his friends save the furniture, jumps on his horse, and gallops like mad to the next town, so that he can arrive before news of the fire and buy building material before prices have gone up."

Others reported that ruined areas were restored so fast that one could walk through a burned-out block a month later and never suspect what had taken place. Of course, the rebuilding was expedited greatly by the fact that the gold rushers merely flung up new shacks to replace the old.

Eventually they saw that there was no future in rebuilding hovels every few months, and the shacks began to give way to solid, fireproof construction. In that sense the fires were a real contribution to civic progress. From the standpoint of casualties, too, it seems likely that the lives lost were more than balanced by the purging of malodorous conditions which menaced the existence of all.

A medical witness, Dr. Joseph Middleton, went so far as to speak of "the blessed conflagrations." In his first reaction to San Francisco Dr. Middleton described it as "a nasty, dirty, slushy, raviney, sand-hilley place. Not a good house in town. The best houses, and few of them, like beggarly cow stables." But only a year later, after cleansing disasters, he observed proudly, "We have now a fine extensive town with many buildings as staunch and good as any of the best in the U. S."

"I was pleased to see them," he said of the fires, "as I was confident of the result, but did not expect it so soon."

As Dr. Middleton acknowledged, much inconvenience was attendant to that kind of progress. He had a personal experience with such difficulty as one of his first introductions to San Francisco life.

When Dr. Middleton arrived in the city he was in bad shape, broke and exhausted from the vicissitudes of the long trek. He had been forced to leave all his books and medicines behind in the mountains. In desperation he applied for a clerk's position at the customs office. It was his bad luck that the job interview was conducted at a moment when black clouds of smoke were billowing forth from one of the general disasters.

The customs official dismissed him harshly, saying, "Do you ask me for office when the town is burning?"

Dr. Middleton's reaction: "He does not reflect that other people must eat whether the town is on fire or not."

It was a problem common to a great many people in those turbulent days.

CHAPTER 16

―――◆―――

Our cemeteries look like newly ploughed fields.

—The *Transcript*, describing what
cholera did to Sacramento.

The adventurers had scarcely recovered from the blows of
fire and flood when they were stricken again by the old enemy
of cholera. An epidemic swept through in the fall of 1850,
taking heavy toll in the two principal cities, and fanning out
from there to infect both miners and Indians in the surrounding countryside. Lesser but still serious onslaughts followed in 1852 and 1854.

It was characteristic of the gold rushers that cholera's first
onslaught in California caught them not only unprepared
but astounded. They thought they had left that particular
danger forever behind.

The false optimism was encouraged by some incidental
good luck. In 1849 cholera had spread in a matter of weeks
from New York and New Orleans to Panama. There would
seem to be no particular reason why it should not have
jumped just as quickly from Panama to California. For
nearly two years, however, it didn't, and men began to assume that it wouldn't. Those who warned otherwise did not
thereby become popular prophets.

The notion of California's immunity was buttressed by the
theory that disease arose from earth emanations. The concept
was widely held by both physicians and laymen, and naturally

enough it was embraced all the more eagerly on those few occasions when it seemed to offer some advantage. Thus when cholera did not appear at once the adventurers concluded that their gold-bearing earth was somehow incompatible with the devastating malady.*

A few suggested that for safety's sake the communities should institute such measures as sanitation and quarantine. There was, however, very little impetus behind such reform. In both San Francisco and Sacramento filth and garbage were strewn everywhere; there was almost no public effort at street cleansing and not even a semblance of system for maintaining the purity of communal water supplies.

The situation was a little better in regard to quarantine, but the advances there were mostly on paper. In April of 1850 California's territorial government enacted quarantine regulations for infected ships arriving at San Francisco; the measure was patterned after a New York law which in turn was based on a code evolved by the ancient gateway city of Venice. In theory, then, they had maritime quarantine. In practice, they didn't believe in it, and only token enforcement was achieved.

The public opposition to quarantine was reflected in the pages of the *Alta California*. On March 3, 1850, at a time when the question was still under debate, an *Alta* editorial denounced the measure in unequivocal terms:

"We see that there is a bill before the Legislature providing for the establishment of quarantine regulations in San Francisco harbor. We do hope that this odious system will never be engrafted upon our statute books. The doctrine of contagion is almost entirely exploded, and there is not more than one disease we believe that is now presumed among the best informed physicians to be contagious—that is, small pox.

* The emanations theory worked both ways, of course. The prevalence of malaria in Sacramento was frequently blamed on the fact that miners had released that affliction by breaking the sod and stirring the earth.

None of the other diseases for which quarantine regulations are mainly established are ever likely to come to our shores and could certainly never be brought here in ships. The hardship which always arises from quarantine laws are excessive, and of no earthly use. It is merely an excuse for bestowing a few fat offices upon political partisans."

The *Alta* went a bit far in ascribing medical authority to its view, but it was true enough that a good many physicians joined in the opposition. Thus a day after the editorial appeared the newspaper published an open letter from Dr. S. Russell Gerry, the city health officer of San Francisco. Dr. Gerry was the man charged with enforcement of the proposed measure, but he emphatically disclaimed all onus as a quarantine supporter. The city was being saddled, said Dr. Gerry, with provisions that were "unnecessary, vexatious, and highly oppressive to the great mass of immigrants and to the commercial community."

Dr. Gerry was replaced soon afterward—the job regularly changed hands every few months—but health-office attitudes remained essentially unchanged. The "vexatious" features of quarantine were always greatly modified by an official inclination to look the other way.

Just when and how the contagion first slipped through this loose guard is a matter of some speculation, but apparently it happened on October 7, 1850, when the ship *Carolina* arrived in San Francisco from Panama. The voyage had been marked by a severe cholera outbreak, twenty-two passengers being stricken and fourteen dying. However, the last death had occurred several days before arrival, and port authorities decided that the danger, if any, was safely past. The *Carolina* survivors were allowed to disembark at once and disperse in the city. Shortly afterward a dark rumor began to run through the community; the public concern became such that on October 10 the *Alta* attempted to allay fears with an editorial as follows:

THE CHOLERA

There has been some little apprehension excited for a few days past, from the fact that steamers having arrived which had had cases of cholera on board and come from regions where the disease was known to have prevailed. We consider these apprehensions utterly groundless, however, although we should be the last to lull the public into false security, if danger of an epidemic disorder absolutely threatened. But we can see no pretext for indulging in such an expectation. That cholera can exist here we have not the slightest doubt; but that it can be brought here by ships, we do doubt, for we are and always have been non-contagionists and have always opposed the oppressive quarantine laws. The fact that there has been a good deal of dysentery and diarrhea prevalent within the last few weeks, has been calculated to alarm people; but when it is well known that this fall there has been great quantities of fruit brought into the market, mostly but partially ripe, we do not consider this fact at all surprising or alarming. We have heard that there have been one or two cases very closely resembling cholera in the city, but the symptoms were similar to those exhibited in other diseases; and we do not believe there has been a single case which has come under the knowledge of any respectable physician here, unless it might have been some passenger who was sick on board the "Carolina", which could positively be pronounced Asiatic Cholera. Still it is a subtle foe, and one to be guarded against, and it behooves people, while it is hovering over the continent with its poisonous, deadly breath, to be careful of their diet, and abstemious in their habits generally, for there is no knowing where it may appear, or when.

Despite the chin-up pose the *Alta*'s editors were plainly worried, and with cause. One of the *Carolina*'s passengers had died in the city the day before, and two physicians had pronounced it "Asiatic cholera of the most malignant type."

In less than two weeks the disease appeared in Sacramento. Again the initial reaction was to evade the awful truth. The record is thus slightly obscured, but in all probability the first case was that of a man found dead on the levee on the morning of October 18. The condition of the corpse excited sufficient suspicion that City Physician Volney Spaulding was summoned immediately and an inquest was held. After some hesitation the coroner's jury arrived at the optimistic verdict that it was not cholera but cholera morbus; the latter condition was similar in symptoms but presented far less danger as a general scourge.

Public alarm in Sacramento was momentarily diverted by a grand occasion. On October 19 the news came that California was admitted to the union. At 2:15 A.M. a horseman galloped through town, shouting the tidings, and men poured out on the streets to gather around bonfires in wild celebration. The jubilee continued all through the day; at one market place an auctioneer interspersed his chant by passing out buckets of free champagne to a cheering crowd. There was, however, at least one man who didn't enjoy the party. That was Dr. Thomas M. Logan. He was the pioneer epidemiologist who had assigned himself the task of collecting the town's medical statistics. He had a passion for discovering the exact truth about the incidence and death rates of the various diseases, and with that, of course, went an insistence on correct diagnosis. Dr. Logan's specialty placed a lonely burden on him now, for as he watched his hurrahing fellow townsmen he knew with cold certainty what they were in for. He had checked around after that affair on the levee, and he had already found an unmistakable case of cholera.

By the time the town sobered up everyone knew, though the newspapers were still attempting to play it down. On October 24 the Sacramento *Placer-Times* had this to say: "We are informed by a gentleman whose practice has called him to various cholera patients in this city, that he has neither seen nor heard of a single case here, where the patient had not been suffering from the diarrhoea for several days previous to the attack. We feel there is really very little danger where this suggestion is attended to promptly, and due regard had to proper diet."

In San Francisco the *Alta* was calling for calm, too, though its own tone was tinged with hysteria. In decrying panic the paper announced, "Thousands and tens of thousands have died with the fear of cholera, whom the disease never attacked at all."

That about marked the end of efforts to wish it away. After a slow start the epidemic caught on with cruel force, and men braced themselves to withstand still another time of trial.

Of the two cities affected San Francisco received much the lighter blow. Even so, that community endured two months of siege and a toll which the *Alta* estimated at some five hundred dead.*

The *Alta* itself was accused of deliberately withholding the full extent of the disaster, a charge which the paper furiously denied. On November 4, at the peak of the outbreak, an editorial stated, "We should be glad to furnish our readers with an accurate statement of the cholera existing in our city at the present time, but all attempts to do so have been comparatively abortive. It is utterly impossible to ascertain either the number of cases or deaths."

A little later the paper illustrated its point by citing the inquest on one John Mundos, a seaman who died after a twelve-hour illness. The coroner's jury brought in a verdict of "Death by the visitation of God." The *Alta*'s comment: "We have supposed that all deaths are attributable to just such a cause; but if one disease is any more 'the visitation of

---

* The estimate of five hundred cholera casualties corresponds roughly with another figure. For the year ending July 31, 1851, the burials from all causes were 1,475, a 50 per cent increase over the previous twelve-month period. The deaths can be reckoned against a San Francisco population of about 30,000.

God', than another, we should like for the intelligent Jury who sat upon poor John Mundos' body, to throw a little enlightenment on the subject."

Beyond such outrageously whimsical cases there was the usual jumble of reports ascribing casualties to diarrhea, convulsions, fever, and "unknown causes." Then, too, some deaths were not recorded at all by either press or public officials. The exact toll must therefore remain a matter of speculation. It was in any case a tragedy sufficient to shock the city into drastic action.

The *Alta,* to its credit, had always campaigned for a cleaner city; now it thundered against open sewers, demanded that contagion sites be disinfected with chloride of lime, and urged every citizen to appoint himself a "one-man Board of Health" in charge of cleaning up his own premises.

The question of quarantine was viewed in a new and more pragmatic light. When an infected steamer arrived from Sacramento, bringing a new infusion of the contagion, the *Alta* assured its readers, "The city authorities, the health officer, etc., have acted promptly in the matter, putting the vessel under quarantine and not suffering the bodies of the deceased to pass through the city. If the disease be contagious —which we do not believe—these measures must effectually prevent its spread."

The municipal government took action on many fronts. A grand jury was appointed to look into malodorous conditions which had gone unheeded for nearly two years. A law was passed establishing stiff fines for the pollution of streets. A Board of Health was set up to maintain continuing surveillance over sanitation and other problems.

The city also established a special hospital for the care of cholera patients. That action would have been called for in any case, but it was no doubt hastened along by a confluence of disastrous events. It happened that the epidemic erupted in full fury at the time when fire leveled that city contract hospital operated by Dr. Peter Smith.*

San Francisco physicians for their part worked around the clock and often took time out to serve on all the special committees which were suddenly galvanized into action. A strong appeal by a medical-society committee was instrumental in pushing through the Board of Health measure. Some physicians also sat up far into the night, writing by lamp or candle, counseling the public on the question of health. The papers just then were full of quack nostrums for cholera—sulphur pills were a particular favorite—and thoughtful doctors took the trouble to answer in print. The bulk of such correspondence urged people to keep clean, stay sober, eat with due caution, sleep warm, dry, and regularly, and summon professional help early rather than late when symptoms appeared.

Public officials, physicians, and press all joined in a continual stream of pronouncements exhorting the public not to panic. But that advice was hard to follow. The atmosphere was reflected in a news item published in the *Alta*. The stubbornly noncontagionist editors insisted on interpreting it as sheer callousness, but one can smell also the fear. The story:

"In no city are the inhabitants so thoroughly selfish as in San Francisco. Yesterday the police was called to a corpse lying on Pacific Street. Investigation proved that the man had died of cholera, in a neighboring house, and had been thrust into the street, wrapped in a blanket, in order that the inmates of the house might be spared the trouble and expense of burial. On the previous night a man was found sick, lying upon the sidewalk, and unable to help himself in any particular. Application was made at several houses to admit the

---

* An incident connected with the hospital fire illustrates the speed with which the contagion sometimes struck. A man who helped fight the blaze was seemingly in full health and vigor, but four hours later he was dead of cholera.

sick man, if only for the night. But a distinct refusal, in every instance, was the result."

In Sacramento the epidemic struck a calamitous blow. The precise losses are again uncertain—new graves appeared in numbers far exceeding the reported deaths—but some have estimated the toll at 10 per cent or more. There was also a mass exodus of people fleeing the city; in a matter of weeks the population was reduced by half.

Among the casualty estimates were those published by newspapers. The Sacramento *Transcript* and the *Settlers and Miners Tribune* both made daily tabulations of the dead; the two reports often varied widely on a given day, but by some process of rough average they wound up about the same. The *Transcript* figured deaths for the epidemic period at 466, of which 367 were ascribed to cholera. The *Tribune* arrived at 468 deaths, 325 from cholera.

The always careful and conservative Dr. Logan made another count, based on a check of undertakers and coffinmakers. He placed the provable toll at 364, a rate of one for every seventeen inhabitants. He added that his was "a most moderate calculation" which took no account of victims who were shoveled hastily into unrecorded graves.

Others attempted to assess the tragedy from the evidence of the cemeteries. It was a loose method which lumped together deaths from all causes, but the estimates thus arrived at were probably closer than any others. When the epidemic subsided Dr. G. W. Woolley found 826 new graves in the principal cemetery, plus 51 more in a smaller plot; his count did not include a third small cemetery at Sutter's Fort.

A similar report came from that assiduous observer, J. Goldsborough Bruff. Visiting the town soon after, he noted "the long parallel lines of graves, of cholera victims." Bruff calculated that the burial grounds held some 1,700 bodies;

of that number about 800 represented the accrued casualties of fifteen months while the other 900 had all fallen during the brief, terrible spasm of cholera.

To all such grim statistics the *Transcript* added simply, "Our cemeteries look like newly ploughed fields."

Sacramento's ordeal was compressed into a period of a little more than three weeks. Official notice of the danger was first taken on the night of October 21 when the city physician announced to a tense meeting of the common council that cholera had stricken seven victims, five of them dying. The council responded with an emergency measure, decreeing that the city be cleansed within twenty-four hours, and establishing fines up to $500 for property owners found guilty of maintaining filthy premises.

The urgency of the moment allowed no time for hauling away the city's vast litter and refuse, and so it was thrown into the streets where it was collected in great piles and burned. By the next night the process was well under way. The *Transcript* described it thus:

"J street, from Third to Eight, was lit up by innumerable bon-fires. An immense quantity of rubbish was thus consumed. The city presented, at a distance, every appearance of a general conflagration. To one standing on the levee and looking up J street, the sight was most splendid. The long line of houses on each side was lit up by the red glare, and volumes of thick smoke rolled off towards the south, while the figures moving among the fires, collecting together material, seemed like anything but earthly beings."

The scene was enacted just four days after those same men had gathered around other bonfires to celebrate the birth of a state.

The cleansing was followed up by a series of other actions. A special cholera hospital was established under Dr. Gregory Phelan. A grand jury was appointed with Dr. Morse as foreman to investigate general sanitary conditions, and a reward was offered for the apprehension of anyone who defiled the streets or alleys.

The *Transcript* was soon reporting with satisfaction, "We are glad to find that the law on nuisances is now being rigidly enforced. A firm was fined $25 on Monday for throwing slops and offal from their kitchen. The health of the city must not be endangered by such nuisances, and other establishments had better take timely warning."

The flurry of activity engendered a brief feeling of security. On October 24 the city physician, Dr. Spaulding, expressed guarded hope in advising the common council that the danger appeared to be under control. In fact, however, the attempt at cleanup had come too late, and the epidemic was just beginning to gather momentum.

In the week that followed it picked up speed. It was six cases in a day, then twelve, then nineteen. On October 31 the outbreak surged to full peak, the toll that day being 150 cases and 50 deaths.

The onslaught produced a clamor for still more intensive cleanup. A physicians' society, the Medico-Chirurgical Academy, issued a proclamation calling on the citizens to fall out in a body and devote a day to scrubbing down the infested city. Said the Academy statement:

"One half of the lives now daily sacrificed may be saved by this means. . . . We do feel that we are but asking people to save their own lives; for no man knows who is to be the next victim."

The common council agreed on the need for increased cleanup effort, but the city had no funds to finance such a program, and so in another emergency session the treasurer was authorized to borrow $300, at an interest rate of 5 per cent a month. The sanitary appropriation was in savage contrast to another medical expense incurred a little later. The city's contract undertaker would shortly submit a bill of $4,250 for the burial of paupers, at $25 apiece.

Meantime masses of people were fleeing in panic. The *Transcript* observed later: "Crowds flocked by every road from the city. The steamboats left the levee crowded with passengers. From one point alone, the Horse Market on K street, men left for upwards of a week at the rate of 100 a day."

Among those who remained the epidemic raged on, though with diminishing force. The *Transcript*'s record showed the reported cholera deaths dropping from thirty-five on November 5 to fifteen on November 8 to four on November 12. On November 16 the paper announced that twenty-four hours had passed without a single new admission to the cholera hospital; as symbol that the siege was broken the daily casualty list was suspended in favor of weekly reports.

The last days of the epidemic coincided with another, wholly incidental calamity which must have seemed by contrast a quite manageable affair. On November 9 a fire broke out, possibly as consequence of some belated cleansing, and a block-long swath of saloons and hotels was burned to the ground.

The mortality charts and public proclamations yield one measure of the epidemic. Another dimension can be seen in the personal accounts which convey what it was like to be in Sacramento when cholera passed through.

George W. B. Evans sketched in a paragraph the human circumstances which surrounded one death out of many. It happened that Evans himself was seriously ill, though not from cholera; he had caught some other infection while working in the mines and had come to Sacramento to recuperate. He lay in a boardinghouse, wrestling with a fever that would destroy him a few weeks later, and while his strength ebbed away he observed how a fellow lodger met the end. The diary entry was dated October 23:

"Mr. Coman died last night. Yesterday he was actively engaged in writing home to his wife, and told her with his own hand that the cholera was on him and he must die, and left this sad letter to be closed by his partners."

A far more lonely and cruel death was that of Lawrence Wolf. When he was stricken he crawled into an abandoned wagon which he found parked at a street corner. For three days he lay moaning in the wagon, unable to help himself and receiving no assistance from those who passed by. When his body was found a coroner's jury labeled it "Death from diarrhea."

And then there was the fate of the Pratt family. They were seafarers from Maine who arrived in their own ship, the bark *Abby Baker.* The head of the family, Capt. Timothy Pratt, died of an unspecified illness just before they reached San Francisco. His son, Augustus, took charge of the vessel and sailed it up the river to Sacramento, arriving at the height of the epidemic. In quick succession cholera claimed Augustus, his brothers, Ebis and William, and the mother, Jane. The family's only survivor was the youngest son, a nine-year-old lad; he was "taken charge of," according to the newpaperman who reported the story. The stout ship which had borne the Pratts across 15,000 miles was left abandoned at a wharf.

Other fearful experiences occurred among the refugees who streamed out of the city, for often they carried the infection with them as they fled. The danger was particularly acute on the crowded vessels which plied the river. The brig *Christiana,* the schooner *Montague,* and the clipper *Splendid* all endured cholera-ridden passages while en route from Sacramento to San Francisco.

In the case of the *Splendid* there was a macabre complication. A big ship, rigged for swift passage on the open seas, she could not negotiate the river channel. The passage was to have been accomplished with the aid of a towboat, but that arrangement fell through when the towboat engineer became a cholera victim. In a decision born of desperation the *Splen-*

did's captain turned his vessel loose to float downstream. For eight or nine days the clipper drifted placidly along, her great sails furled, her prow lodging frequently on sand bars, while all the time an epidemic raged aboard. The toll was about 120 persons stricken, 17 dying. Dr. W. W. Taylor was present as ship's physician and described the affair:

"Late on the evening of the 28th (October), we weighed anchor and dropped down with the current, on our way to San Francisco; but we had scarcely gotten our anchor clear when I was summoned in haste to the forecastle to see the cook. On reaching him, I found him laboring under a severe attack of cholera. Wishing to avoid the ill effects of a panic, after giving him a heavy dose of anodyne and carminative medicine, I immediately went to the mate, and had him conveyed to the shore, and sent to the hospital, without letting the passengers know the nature of the malady. At the same time I ordered the chloride of lime to be freely used in the hold of the vessel."

The disinfectant attempt and the precautions against panic were both in vain; within thirty-six hours there was another case, this one fatal. After that the passengers began falling ill at the rate of ten to fifteen a day. It may not all have been cholera, but they thought it was, and they were scared stiff. "It was with the greatest difficulty," said Dr. Taylor, "that I could induce the well to nurse the sick, or give them any attention." Of his own efforts he added that the incessant emergency demands permitted him less than an hour of sleep a day for the entire passage.*

Dr. Taylor appears to have acquitted himself well, though it must be added that he was pressed into service against his own inclination. He had signed on the *Splendid* in an attempt to flee from stricken Sacramento.

---

* Whatever his medical merits, Dr. Taylor was a bad writer. In describing grisly scenes aboard the *Splendid* he reported that "the ear was pierced every moment with the screams and groans of the dead and dying."

Most of the physicians did not permit themselves the luxury of flight. Whatever their other defects, they were not cowards; when their community was stricken they considered it their duty to stay and fight, and they paid a price for it. Sixteen Sacramento doctors gave their lives during the epidemic. The death rate among the community's medical men was at least twice that of the general population.*

There were others who performed heroically. One of them was a young Catholic priest, Father Augustin P. Anderson. He was the first representative of his church in Sacramento, and three months after he took over his parish the epidemic struck. Father Anderson made the cholera hospital his virtual headquarters; when not there he was performing his rites at the cemeteries or hurrying in and out of infested rooming houses to seek out the sick and dying. At epidemic's end he, too, was dead.

Another, more fortunate example was a man named John Bigler. He assigned himself to arduous volunteer tasks of first aid and litter bearing. He is remembered also for the fact that he carried with him a fist-sized lump of camphor which he pressed to his nose every few minutes in situations of peril. As we know now, the camphor was quite useless from a medical point of view, but no doubt it had its value in helping a brave man to sustain his nerve. Bigler survived to become a governor of California.

Still another kind of courage was exemplified by a merchant named Isaac Perkins. He lived by trade and believed in the importance of doing business, and perhaps he had other, personal reasons for the course he chose. The letters which Perkins wrote to his brother depict a man who in the midst of catastrophe went downtown every morning and opened his store, thereby maintaining some thin thread of

---

* Some accounts give Sacramento's medical casualties at seventeen. The discrepancy apparently stems from the fact that in the confusion one victim was recorded twice, as Dr. Noble and Dr. Knoble.

continuity in the ordinary and necessary affairs of daily life.

On October 27 Perkins wrote to say, "Our city is visited with the Cholera there has been a good menny deaths within the last few days & some of them have been very sudden some have been taken who were to all apperance in Good Health & have died in a few hours some are leving the city it has all redy affected the Trade. It is quite difficult to git the real State of the sickness here thare are so menny different reports but from all that I can gather I dont think it is on the increase, as regard my self I have no fears. I beleve the only way is to persue a strateforward corse living temperantly in all things I dont beleve in running a way from such things. I hope You will not giv Your self any trublle about me but rest assured I shall not do any thing that will put me in Danger."

So he stuck it out, and he had the luck to survive. On November 14, with the main thrust of the epidemic behind, he wrote his brother again:

"Your favor of the 25th Sept came duly to hand I was glad to here You ware all well I see Grandmother is dead. I wrote You by the last mail in which I stated the cholera was raging in our city it has continued to rage up to the last few days. You will see by the list in the paper which I send You that it has cut them down to a fearfull extent & I thank God I have been spard through his kind providunce wilst so menny have fallin my health has been quite good ever since I have been in the countery. I have had a sore hand for the last week which has trubbled me some nights but it has cum to a head & begins to discharge so that I am in hopes it will soon get well."

A week later in a third letter he advised that "the cholera has interely desipeard from amonst us. Trade once more begins to assume its usal apperance the Humbrees begin to return to the city."

In more laconic style, but in much the same spirit, the

Settlers and Miners Tribune offered its own short history of the epidemic. On November 14, in a story headlined "General Summary," the paper compressed into two sentences the drama of a city's sudden death and swift resurrection:

"The only professional and business men which have been actively engaged here for the last 2–3 weeks were the physicians, the clergy, the undertakers, coffin makers, and grave diggers."

And then: "In a few days a stranger coming into the city, could not tell save by hearsay that the cholera had been among us."

The epidemic struck most brutally at the two major communities, but the effect was felt also in smaller settlements and mining camps. Coloma, Jamestown, Marysville, Placerville, San Jose, Stockton, and Weberville all were caught up in the outbreak. Infected, too, were Indian encampments along the American and Feather rivers.

The scope of the tragedy affords a view of two quite different societies confronting the same problem. For both the gold rushers and the Indians cholera represented something they could not really cope with and yet, being human, they had to try to do something about it. When the crisis came, each group turned to its own methods.

The gold rushers had a host of remedies and used them all. They relied in particular on opium and brandy and chloroform, and calomel and Dover's powder, and sulphur pills and camphor balls, and poultices of red pepper and mustard applied to the chief areas of distress, the belly and buttocks.*

The Indians had simpler ways, and quite naturally the adventurers looked on them as benighted savages who didn't

---

* In 1850 more than 150 different cholera remedies were being used in the United States and Europe. Extreme examples included such measures as administration of petroleum and huge enemas of hot water infused with tobacco or pepper.

understand the marvels of science. A hint of that attitude is displayed in a story carried by the *Transcript* on October 30:

"The Indians have a singular mode of treatment for this disease. When the subject is taken, several of them carry him down to the river and immerse him, leaving him there until he can bear it no longer, when they take him out and place him in the sun. The operation is repeated until the person dies or recovers. We learn that several Indians have died at the village below Sutterville."

When the epidemic passed through San Jose, Dr. John Townsend was on hand. He was the erstwhile mayor of San Francisco and the man who had helped to hoist those first covered wagons over a Sierra pass.

Fortune had never rewarded his pioneering efforts. In his first attempt at mining, when he led that initial rush out of San Francisco, he had contracted a fever which nearly killed him. After that he returned briefly to San Francisco; he was elected mayor again and dabbled in real estate, but he misguessed the direction in which the town would grow.

He had drifted on to San Jose, doing some ranching there, and some digging, and probably some doctoring too. And he had fathered a child. Then cholera invaded the camp.

Dr. Townsend must have risen to the emergency, for he was a first-rate physician, and he never lacked courage. There are, however, no details of his epidemic service. All that is known is that one day at the height of the siege a neighbor passed Dr. Townsend's cabin and was moved by some dark intuition to open the door. He found Dr. Townsend and his wife stretched out dead in their bunks while, all unheeding, their infant played happily on the cabin floor.

There were others for whom the epidemic meant not danger but fear. They were the people who waited and worried in homes far removed from the scene of events.

It resembled a war situation in that reports of heavy losses arrived much sooner than word of individual fate. And it was like that, too, in that those who bore the burden of waiting were the parents, wives, and sweethearts. That aspect is glimpsed in two letters which must have crossed in the mails somewhere on the long shipping route which ran through Panama. The correspondents were Anthony Lewis Tasheira and his wife, Eliza.

Tasheira was working at the Mormon camp in Tuolumne County, California. On November 9 he got off a casual letter addressed not to his wife but to a family friend. The missive rambled along with general comments and then made passing reference to a possible danger:

"Our weather at present is very pleasant but changeable; ice frequently forms at night, and at noon the thermometer stands 80 to 90 deg. in the shade. I have just been informed a man died from cholera at Jamestown, a place about 3 miles from here. This is the first case I have heard of in the Southern mines."

A continent away, in New York City, Eliza Tasheira heard of the epidemic but received no news of her man. Each time a mail ship arrived she would sweat it out, hoping for a letter, and fearing one too. When such vigil proved fruitless she would hurry up and down the streets, calling on friends who had people in California, asking the same questions over and over. Finally, when fear spilled over, she dispatched a desperate plea in which she asked her husband to choose between California and her.

Eliza's letter was dated December 10. The epidemic was over by then, and it had never assumed any major proportions in Tasheira's camp, but she had no way of knowing that. Her anguished mood was reflected both in the way she couched her appeal and in the sharp little strokes she used to underline her words:

"I am most unhappy . . . three mails have arrived without

bringing me a letter from you. [She recited a list of letters received by others, including one message saying, "I have not *yet* heard from Mr. Tasheira."] . . . This and the news that the Cholera is in California has made me *miserable*. Lewis you *must* come directly home *if you love me*. . . . I *cannot* endure this suspense . . . 58 have died in one week in Sacramento of Cholera, it will spread *everywhere*, what *shall* I do? I have the most dreadful forebodings, that the next letter I receive, will be from Mr. Tuttle saying you are dead."

In the next paragraph she modulated it a little with some cheery news of a returning friend, a carpenter named Murphy, who "gives California a good name, he has been gone 9 months, had his health all the while, and has brought home $1400." Then she returned to her appeal:

"Father and Mother send their love to you, and many messages but *all* saying in a hundred different ways *come home.*"

Tasheira did come home, but he couldn't stay in New York, not after seeing California. By 1853 he was back on the gold coast. In 1860 he died in San Francisco. A biographer attributed it to "the seeds of consumption, sown probably through the exposures incident to his life in the mines."

CHAPTER 17

———————

I like this wild and barbarous life.

—Dame Shirley, at Indian Bar.

Out in the hills, scrabbling in the earth with pick and shovel, or sifting the streams, were the men who really supported the wild new society. They produced the gold.

Mostly they did it the hard way. Thick, rich veins of the mother lode were not to be found in California, and there were only occasional pockets where the stuff could be collected in any quantity at all. The geologic history of the region accounted for that. Immense upheavals had thrust the ore up into the thin top stratum of the earth, and after that the streams had come tumbling out of the mountains, dispersing the metal through the land.

Mining such ore demanded prodigious labor. Often a prospector sifted through a ton of sand and gravel to find an ounce of gold. In cash value the average day's take varied between $10 and $20, depending on prospecting luck and the fluctuating price of the product.

The mining developed in two basic patterns. There were the dry diggings of the ravines, hillsides, and mesas, and the wet diggings of the rivers and creeks. Each operation offered its own distinctive hardships and hazards to health.

In the wet diggings the crudest, most elementary method was panning. A man filled a shallow pan with sand and gravel and sloshed it gently back and forth in a stream, washing the waste material away and leaving, hopefully, a few grains of the heavier gold. To "wash" one pan the miner had to submerge his hands for ten or twelve minutes in water that was usually ice-cold. There was a further choice of discomforts in that the prospector might work from the bank, bending down to wash from an awkward, back-straining angle, or else he might squat in the stream submerged up to his thighs in the chill waters.

Another river-mining method involved the team operation of a cradle or long tom. The typical cradle was an open-end box mounted on rockers. Sand was shoveled in by way of a hopper and water poured through while the cradle was rocked violently; as the sand washed away the gold lodged against cleats along the bottom. The long tom was similar in principle, consisting of two coffin-shaped sluice boxes mounted one on top of the other with a perforated piece of iron serving as sieve between the two. The system was more efficient than panning, but also more arduous. Continual shoveling and pouring were what got results.

A still more elaborate technique was to expose the stream bed in order to get at the ore. Sometimes it was done by diverting the water into a side channel or wooden aqueduct. More often the miners built a "wing dam," the barrier extending halfway across the stream; through further walling off of the water they then laid bare an area below the dam. It was rough and dangerous work, the men wading waist-deep or more in the mountain streams, wrestling with the huge timbers and boulders they used for construction; there was always the risk that a rush of water would come down from the slopes to sweep their dam away and perhaps themselves as well.

In the dry diggings the basic method was coyoting, a term borrowed from the burrowing habits of that animal. The prospector would select a likely area—often it was the bed of a long-extinct stream—and tunnel down to bedrock in the hope of hitting a pocket. A typical shaft went down twenty-five to forty feet, with side tunnels extending out in all directions at the bottom. The tunnels were dank and muddy from seeping water; the air below was so fetid that miners sometimes lapsed into unconsciousness, and there was an omnipresent risk of cave-in. The combined rigors were such that one coyoter ruefully described his occupation as "really unworthy of a rational being."

Another prospector summed up the whole business with "all the gold a man gets here, he gets by hard licks."

The demands of mining left little time or energy for the ordinary necessities of life. Camp conditions were capsuled by George Cornell who wrote his wife after six months in the gold fields: "I have not had my pants off to sleep since I bin here. I have not laid on a bed nether." And as to food: "We had fresh pork for dinner today and had it Christmas and that is all I have had or expect to get till I come home."

The usual camp fare was a diet of salt meat, saleratus bread, and dried beans. Fresh fruit and vegetables were luxuries to be exulted over and paid for dearly.

So avid was the fruit hunger that a farmer at Coloma devised an unusual kind of future commodity market for pears. Miners offered $1 apiece for unripened pears that were still on the tree; the purchaser would select his fruit, tag it with his name, and wait hopefully for it to mature.

The miners in Indian Valley engaged in a similar scramble for vegetables. A prospector recalled, "As soon as the men saw the dust of the pack-train coming down the trail they would make a grand stampede for it and fight for onions." The price again was $1 apiece.

The produce market was keenest, of course, in scorbutic camps. When their legs swelled and their skins turned black the miners would pay almost any price for fruit and vegetables. What they wouldn't do was hoe gardens when gold lay waiting to be gouged from the earth.

As to living accommodations, the adventurers sometimes camped out in the open, spreading their blankets on pine boughs, and trusting to luck that it wouldn't rain. If they remained long in one place, however, they usually contrived some sort of rough shelter. The typical site presented a hodge-podge of shacks, tents, lean-tos, and "bush cabins"; the last-named was often a mere strip of canvas or calico suspended as awning from the spreading branches of a bush or tree.

An entertaining account of camp construction was pro-vided by Adolphus Windeler, a German sailor who skipped ship to roam the gold fields with his partner, Carl Christen-dorf. They were equipped with a tent, but when they settled down on the Yuba River for a spell they decided that a house would add a dimension of grace and comfort to their lives. With the help of a third party, a man called "Theodor," they put the structure together in half a day. Windeler told it thus:

"Built a bush house, had it all finished, Theodor on the top putting on the thatching when just when he was putting on the last branches, down came the whole building, Theodor singing out: 'Hurrah, here we go.' There laid our house as flat as a pancake. So we had to put it up again."

They rebuilt the house, moved in their provisions, and were sitting around feeling quite pleased with themselves when a downpour occurred. Their roof leaked so copiously that they had to rush around in the rain transferring their provisions back to the tent.

After that they worked out an ingenious solution which combined the most attractive features of both abodes. They pitched their tent inside the house.

A more substantial abode was described by Mrs. Louise Clappe, a physician's wife who wrote from Feather River camps under the nom de plume of Dame Shirley. She in-spected "the best built cabin on the river" and reported cheerfully, "Of course, it has no floor, but it boasts a perfect marvel of a fireplace." Moreover, it had a glass window. To accomplish that the builders had removed a three-foot section of log from the wall; they lined the aperture with liquor bottles of various shapes and sizes, then chinked in with clay around the uneven edges.

Like liquor itself, the window afforded a view that was distorted but rosy.

Mrs. Clappe added that empty bottles were profusely available for such other household purposes as candlesticks. Drinking was the miners' one real luxury, she said, and they indulged it freely. Though her camp was almost inaccessible in winter, and suffering always from chronic supply shortages, she had only to look out from her own cabin to see "a perfect Pelion upon Osa-like pile of beautiful glass jars, porter, ale, champagne and claret."

She went on to describe a staggering brawl thrown at Indian Bar in commemoration of Christmas Eve. The adventurers were sunk in ennui, foul weather preventing work in the mines, and when the boys gathered for festive observance at the camp's Humboldt Hotel they were in a mood to tie one on. Mrs. Clappe's account:

"At nine o'clock in the evening, they had an oyster and champagne supper in the Humboldt, which was very gay with toasts, songs, speeches, etc. I believe that the company danced all night; at any rate they were dancing when I went to sleep, and they were dancing when I woke the next morning. The revel was kept up in this mad way for three days, growing wilder every hour. Some never slept at all during that time. On the fourth day, they got past dancing, and, lying in drunken heaps about the bar-room, commenced a most unearthly howling;—some barked like dogs, some roared like bulls, and others hissed like serpents. Many were too far gone to imitate anything but their own animalized selves."

For lesser celebrations they just got drunk, usually on Sunday, though if the opportunity presented, any day would do.

Oliver Goldsmith told of an impromptu drinking bout which occurred one cold, rainy winter morning when he and his friends found a peddler with a wagonload of whisky mired down in the mud. The peddler made them a bargain price of $5 a bottle; they couldn't afford that, but Goldsmith's companion, Hugh Phillips, offered to stand a round of drinks at another special price of 50 cents a swig.

"We had nothing to drink from but a pint cup," said Goldsmith. "The man brought out his whiskey and we helped ourselves; there were five of us and Hugh paid two dollars and a half for the treat, and it took two entire bottles."

He added, "It was not a very good bargain for any of us. The seller remarked that in the future he should sell by the bottle. Hugh was a little too liberal in helping himself, and we all felt the effect of taking such vile stuff on our empty stomachs. We survived, however."

Such, then, was the prospector's life. He performed grueling labor under spartan conditions, enjoying occasional wealth but never comfort, and when he sought relief from his labors he often suffered from his own extremes. But the roistering aspect is easily exaggerated; it was mostly work, and there were many who kept at it earnestly for months at a time.

Melvin Paden was one of those who resisted the sprees. He was the man referred to early in this chronicle as carrying so much gold in his pockets that it "puld the Coat to peaces." Paden clung to that gold and sent it home, for it represented to him a chance to change the whole pattern of his life. To his wife, Jane, he wrote of his hopes and dreams:

"Jane i left you and them boys for no other reason than this to come here to procure a littl property by the swet of my brow so that we could have a place of our own that i mite not be a dog for other people any longer. . . . i think that this is a far better country to lay up money than it is at home, if a man will tend to his business and keep out of licker shops and gambling houses. that is the way the money goes with many of them in this country. thare are murders committed about every day on account of licker and gambling but i have not bought a glass of licker since i left home. . . . i never knew what it was to leave home till i left a wife and children. . . . i know you feel lonsom when night apears but let us think that it is for the best and do the best we can for two years or so and i hope Jane that we shall be reworded for so doing and meet in the family sircal once more. that is my prayer."

Paden well earned his reward, but he never got it. He died in the gold fields.

The ills of the miners were manifold. From an epidemic standpoint they were better off than those in the crowded cities, but still they had their share of contagion; dysentery was a particular hazard, and in given locales they were also much subject to malaria, typhoid, and mountain fever.

Some other afflictions were directly associated with their way of life. Coyoting and river mining were an invitation to pneumonia and rheumatism, and the working conditions led to disastrous accidents.

There was further hardship in that often the stricken miner had to sweat it out without aid. Physicians could be found in the camps, and some tent hospitals were set up in the field, but with the adventurers strung out across wild country it was a matter of sheer luck as to whether medical help was available when and where it was needed.

Some camps attracted a surplus of doctors. Thus Rich Bar at one time had twenty-nine physicians for a thousand residents. As a result, most of the doctors were out digging for a living.

Other locations had no doctors at all, or at least none worth the name. At one such site an acknowledged quack set up a practice but became alarmed when one of his patients con-

tracted a difficult fever. The quack walked ten miles to another camp to seek advice from a real physician and was both
surprised and indignant when the consultant solemnly agreed
with his diagnosis and treatment.

"That settled it with me," he wrote. "I knew then he was
an imposter."

On still other occasions men were stricken while working
in some lonely gulch and were forced to make do with self-
help. That situation was starkly etched in one miner's complaint: "Am poisoned again, down sick, no medicine, no bed
but the ground."

Under such haphazard circumstances neglected conditions
sometimes built up until small things assumed large proportions. In a typical instance Oliver Goldsmith told of a boil
which he allowed to fester too long:

"We all suffered more or less from disorders of the blood.
I had countless boils that caused me great misery. The middle
finger of my right hand puffed up and became so painful that
I could hardly work, and sleep was out of the question. I
went three miles up the river to see a doctor, who told me it
was a felon and must be lanced. I told him I had no money
to pay him. He said he was there to help those who had no
money as well as those who had, and put the knife into the
bone. I danced around a stump saying some very big words
and holding onto my wounded hand—the relief was won-
derful!"

Goldsmith couldn't manage the mining chores while his
hand healed, so his companions found what they thought was
a nice job for him. They made him the camp cook.

Windeler's friend Theodor had a rougher time with another infection. As Windeler told it, "Theodor has been
laid up 6 days with a swelling in his jawbone, today he got
mad and hit himself a lick on the place, which broke the
abcess and now he can talk again. Hard case here for a man to
be sick, didn't know what to do."

Other decidedly casual medical arrangements were reported by Richard Ness. He doctored himself through a bad case of dysentery, using morphine and charcoal, and then was called on to perform rough repairs on a wounded companion. A note from his diary:

"I am only able to work part of a day occasionally I have a relapse of the dissentary every 2 or 3 days which keeps me very weak. My next neighbors had a quarrel last week and one cut the others head open. about 1½ inches long. I sewed up the wound and it has done well since."

For Edwin Morse dysentery and self-imposed neglect very nearly proved fatal. Morse was a youngster, only seventeen, and his affliction wore him down to a skeleton-like 101 pounds. In some perverse refusal to burden his friends he made the ordeal even worse by crawling off into a bush to suffer alone. His story:

"Owing to the nature of this disease, I decided not to remain in the tent with my former companions, but took my blankets and sought the shelter of a manzanita bush up on the hill and away from the trail. Every day toward evening, I would crawl down the trail to the spring and fill a jar with water and buy a few soda crackers at the store. This was my only fare."

Fortunately for Morse his friends found him one day and carried him back to the camp. They constructed an arbor for him to lie in and summoned a physician. Morse resumes the tale:

"I was in terrible distress from cramps, so they went for a doctor from Cedar Bar. On his arrival, he found me in great agony with my knees drawn up to my chin and unable to straighten out. He immediately demanded mustard, but as none could be obtained in the entire camp, he directed my friends to fry flapjacks very large and thick and apply them to my abdomen. This they did, bringing them right from the frying pan and so hot they almost blistered the skin. A singular use for flapjacks certainly, but they proved a very efficacious remedy for in a short time I was quite relieved of my pain."

And then there was scurvy. A great many of them suffered from that.

Windeler had "a touch" of it, saying, "My arm swelled twice as big as before and I had to knock off picking and washed only. Went to Dr. Vaughan who told me it was scurvy, he gave me some tartaric acid to clean the blood and raw potatoes, onions and vinegar to eat."

Goldsmith was stricken too. He paid almost no attention to his condition until all at once his body failed him; when that happened he knew immediately that he had to correct his diet.

"I began to notice," he wrote, "that when I undertook to climb a hill I was soon out of breath, and if I sat down to rest it was hard to get up again. One day I was at the river bank to wash a pan of dirt, and stooped down, with my knees bent, to wash it. I tried to rise when it was done, but was unable to do so. After rolling over and pushing my legs out straight I managed to stand up. In testing my legs I found that if I pressed with my thumb or finger below the knees a dent appeared in the flesh which remained a long time. . . . We commenced at once to make tea from the branches of spruce trees, and to eat every green thing we could find."

Edward Gould Buffum survived a still more wretched experience with scurvy. "I noticed its first attack upon myself," he wrote, "by swelling and bleeding of the gums, which was followed by a swelling of both legs below the knee, which rendered me unable to walk; and for 3 weeks I was laid up in my tent, obliged to feed upon the very articles that had caused the disease, and growing daily weaker, without any reasonable prospect of relief. There were, at that time, about 800 persons at work on the river, and hoping to get some medicine, I despatched one of my companions one morning, with instructions to procure me, if possible, a dose of salts, and to pay for it any price asked. He returned at night with the consoling news that he had failed, having found only 2 persons who had brought the article with them, and they refused to sell it at any price.

"I was almost in despair: with only a blanket between myself and the damp, cold earth, and a thin canvass to protect me from the burning sun by day, and the heavy dews by night, I lay day after day enduring the most intense suffering from pain in my limbs, which were now becoming more swollen, and were turning completely black. Above me rose those formidable hills which I must ascend ere I should obtain relief. I believe I should have died, had not accident discovered the best remedy that could have been produced. In the second week of my illness, one of our party, in descending the hill on which he had been deerhunting, found near its base, and strewn along the foot-track, a quantity of beans which sprouted from the ground, and were in leaf.

"My companion gathered a quantity and brought them into camp. I had them boiled, and lived entirely on them for several days, at the same time using a decoction of the bark of the spruce tree. These seemed to operate magically, and in a week I found myself able to walk; and as soon as my strength was restored, I ascended the hill, and with two companions walked into Coloma, and by living principally upon a vegetable diet, which I procured by paying 3 dollars per pound for potatoes, in a very short time I recovered."

Buffum added that the beans which saved him were found through a most fortuitous chance. The plants had sprouted at a place where some wayfarer had dropped and broken a sack of provisions.

Another hard bout with scurvy was that of Charles Ferguson. His was a bemusing tale in that he was a cocky young man who sometimes posed as a physician; he pulled teeth, sold "searching and raking pills," and confessed without qualm that when his supply of medicine was low he stretched it out by mixing it with flour. Naturally when he was stricken he wanted help from someone more reliable than himself. What he got was a physician who mixed sense and nonsense in the treatment, but Ferguson didn't know the difference.

"For a long time I had been feeling that something was wrong with me," Ferguson wrote. "I had never felt so before—sluggish, tired, lazy—the latter I had never been guilty of before. Finally my gums got sore and began to bleed, and I became subject to excruciating pains. The boys sent for Dr. Gardner, who pronounced it scurvy, contracted in crossing the plains, induced by exposure, anxiety of mind and starvation. He prescribed spruce boughs boiled to a strong tea, which I was to drink, and nothing else. A wash of the same with vinegar and tinctured with cayenne pepper, including a steam bath of the same, at a pretty high pressure, were the doctor's directions to the boys for my daily treatment. It was pretty tough treatment, harder to bear than any I had ever inflicted during my professional career among my patients. I was put through the steam kettle process by the boys for ten days; was helpless as an infant, having to be carried to and from my bed. The painful part of my affliction seemed to be in my feet and legs. The only way for a long time I could get at ease was in lying on my back on the floor and putting my feet on the table, a luxury I dearly paid for afterwards, for when I came to put them on a level with my body, the pain was still more unbearable. I would pity the meanest dog in the world that had the scurvy. But thanks to Dr. Gardner, the boys, the steam kettle and raw potatoes sliced in vinegar, after some two weeks my pains left me."

Ferguson didn't say how the high-pressure steam baths were devised, but probably they just hosed him down with the hissing kettle. In any case, the steaming did no appreciable harm, and the spruce tea and potatoes saved his life.

Some others turned to really weird remedies for scurvy. Dr. Stillman reported a particular oddity in which men buried themselves up to their necks in the earth, hoping thereby to soak up healing powers from the soil. A company thus immobilized usually appointed one or two men to walk about as guards against predators, animal or human.

The miners were subject also to innumerable injuries, accidents arising both from the nature of the work and from the often reckless way they went about it.

One source of peril was the proliferation of open-faced mining shafts. No one ever bothered to fence off a coyote hole, or fill it in afterward, and so a stroll through the diggings at night presented the possibility of plunging suddenly into a dark pit. Broken arms and legs and sometimes deaths occurred.

Other human havoc resulted from careless felling of trees and from landslides set off by men digging on the slopes. Mrs. Clappe reported one instance in which a careening boulder crushed the leg of a young miner identified only as "W." A physician treated the injury, but the wound would not heal, and for six months the victim languished in a miserable cabin; while in that weakened condition he survived a bout of typhoid and then was attacked by erysipelas which settled into the shattered leg. At that point Mrs. Clappe's physician husband, Dr. Fayette Clappe, stepped in to recommend a drastic amputation. Other camp doctors condemned the idea; they had written off the case as hopeless and considered the operation a cruelly useless experiment. Dr. Clappe insisted that where life was at stake the slimmest chance was better than none. He sawed off the festering leg—whether with or without benefit of anesthesia is not recorded—and achieved a small miracle of surgery. The man lived.

Described also by Mrs. Clappe were the rough ceremonies attendant to camp funerals. In one case the deceased was a

young woman who died of peritonitis, leaving as survivors a
miner husband and two small children. The adventurers attended to the necessities in their most solemn mood:

"The bereaved husband held in his arms a sickly babe ten
months old, which was moaning piteously for its mother. The
other child, a handsome, bold-looking little girl six years of
age, was running gaily around the room, perfectly unconscious of her great bereavement. . . . Poor little thing! It was
evident that her baby-toilet had been made by men; she had
on a new calico dress, which, having no tucks in it, trailed
to the floor, and gave her a most singular and dwarf-womanly
appearance.

"About twenty men, with the three women of the place,
had assembled at the funeral. An *extempore* prayer was made,
filled with all the peculiarities usual to that style of petition.

"As the procession started for the hill-side grave-yard a
dark cloth cover, borrowed from a neighboring monte-table,
was flung over the coffin. Do not think that I mention any
of these circumstances in a spirit of mockery; far from it.
Every observance, usual on such occasions, that was *procur-
able,* surrounded this funeral. All the gold on Rich Bar could
do no more; and should I die tomorrow, I should be mar-
shaled to my mountain grave beneath the same monte-table
pall, which shrouded the coffin of poor Mrs. B." *

It should not be assumed that life in the diggings was an
endless round of cruel ordeals. There was enough of that, and
the existence was always uncertain and hard, but there were
compensations for those who were suited.

It offered wild freedom, and simple, primitive pleasures,
and the sense or triumph which comes from contesting with

* "Mrs. B." was twenty-six-year-old Nancy Ann Bailey, and her tiny grave-
stone is one of the few surviving markers in the old cemetery above Rich
Bar. The funeral as described by Mrs. Clappe was rewoven into Bret Harte's
tale, *The Luck of Roaring Camp.*

the elements. Thus it was that some men like Windeler went on prospecting for years after changing conditions had rendered it an unprofitable occupation. A diary entry gives us a glimpse of what he saw in it:

"Went to work again made 5$ forenoon, 12$ afternoon, water falling, but hard at work we have to be, the sweat runs down as in streams, and now as sundown draws nigh we go home for supper, consisting of flapjacks, mint tea, and some bread which we baked Sunday and it is as hard and solid as it can be. We feel as happy and content as if we had been in New York in the best boarding house, for our meals taste as good and we sleep soft and sound."

Mrs. Clappe was drawn to it too. As a "petticoated astonishment" she was catered to, and her husband's position gave her other advantages, but even so she saw rough times. And then it came time for the adventure to end, and as she and Dr. Clappe packed up to go she realized suddenly how much she was going to miss it. To her sister, Molly, she wrote:

"My heart is heavy at the thought of departing forever from this place. I *like* this wild and barbarous life; I leave it with regret. Yes, Molly, smile if you will at my folly, but I go from the mountains with a deep heart sorrow. Here, at least, I have been content."

In this last letter from the diggings she said also:

"Really, everybody ought to go to the mines, just to see how little it takes to make people comfortable in the world."

CHAPTER 18

He was jerked up and down several times to break his neck.

> —Adolphus Windeler
> assists at a hanging.

Added to all the other hazards was a huge toll from violence. That was inevitable. In a land swarming with adventurers, almost all of them armed, there was bound to be shooting. And their solution for that was hanging.

Curiously enough, the violence was muted during the early and most anarchic stages of the adventure. The trek, for example, had presented the spectacle of men struggling for survival under often desperate conditions. Observer James Collier had predicted that when the travelers reached the point of starvation they might make war upon each other. And yet they didn't. On the last leg of a fearful hunger march a man like Goldsmith had used the threat of force not to steal food but merely to buy it at what he considered a reasonable price. And Bruff, after all, didn't eat that Indian he thought he fancied.

The trek did produce an occasional killing, but such incidents were rare. In one case a quiet, inoffensive man named Williams was bullied savagely by another member of his train. Finally, so harried and threatened that he feared for his life, Williams crept up on his persecutor by night and shot him dead. Afterward Williams went from one company to another to give himself up and ask for trial; invariably his fellow migrants heard out his tale and then turned him loose with the advice that he forget it and go on about his business. In the court of public opinion the verdict on that one was justifiable homicide.

Both during the journey and in the mining camps the gold rushers attempted to establish some sort of rough justice by common consent. When a new camp was formed the question of government was often settled in an hour, by drawing up a covenant based on the town-meeting principle in its simplest form. The law of property was reduced sometimes to the proposition that a man signified his claim by leaving his pick in the ground. The law of life was based on the ultimate right of self-defense.

Initially it worked well enough, but within two years robbery and murder had become commonplace. The corrosive change could be blamed in part on the lusts which gold inspired and in part on a steady erosion of civilized values over a long period of raw, rough life. But also much of the trouble originated with men who had dark and bloody records before they ever set foot in California. Some of them would be regarded today as psychotic types.

In discussing the insanity problem one gold-field physician observed with advanced insight that the adventure itself contained nothing to unhinge a man. Rather, he said, the situation attracted an abnormal number of those who were already highly unstable. And it took only a small percentage of that sort to transform a peaceful camp into a very volatile and dangerous community.

A witness to the resulting deterioration was Mrs. Clappe. She went to the diggings in September of 1851 and spent three months in the camps before reporting a death by violence. By August of the next year, however, she was writing, "In the short space of 24 days we have had murders, fearful accidents, bloody deaths, a mob, whippings, a hanging, an attempt at suicide, and a fatal duel."

Also in 1852 miner Jesse Shuart wrote home from the Feather River to say, "Seventeen dead bodies were found on one road alone within the last four months and no clue to the perpetrators of this wholesale slaughter has as yet been discovered."

Shuart added, "California is yet sadly wanting in an effective judicial and constabulary organization and will remain so probably so long as the majority of the inhabitants look upon it as a temporary residence to be abandoned at the first favorable opportunity."

Innumerable others attested to a similar state of affairs throughout the gold fields. One common estimate is that in the first five years the new society produced 4,200 murders and 1,400 suicides. More than $6,000,000 was invested in pistols and bowie knives over the same period.

The violence soon gave rise to stern repressions by "peoples' courts" and vigilantes. In fair assessment, that represented a response to an urgent problem that had to be dealt with under the most primitive conditions. The result nonetheless was to meet crime with terror.

The terroristic overtones derived in part from the crude arrangements for camp justice. In the camp proceeding the judge, the arresting officers, the prosecutor, and defense spokesman were unpaid volunteers drawn at random from the community. The traditional jury of twelve was sometimes appointed, while at other times the entire camp elected to sit in judgment. Invariably they were in a hurry to get on with it, for they were miners by trade, and the court officials might be in camp one week and gone the next. And looming over the whole process was a simple fact of life which ruled out one kind of solution. In most cases they had no jails.

The miners evolved a system of four basic punishments. In the simpler cases, usually a first offense at theft, the culprit was banished from the camp. A more severe sentence was flogging, generally accompanied by banishment. A third penalty was ear cropping, justified presumably as a warning to others to beware of the marked man; the mutilation was sometimes performed by a physician appointed for the purpose. And then, finally, there was hanging.

Whatever the verdict, it was usually arrived at, and consummated, in a matter of hours.

There were those who approved that style of justice. In a pretty typical comment Dr. Horace R. Pond reported with apparent satisfaction, "Lynch law prevails in the mines. Mostly Americans there. They do not countenance any crimes whatever have them strung up at once. If each man minds his own business he has no trouble at all."

The English adventurer J. D. Borthwick was another who recommended the system. After witnessing a typical miners' trial he wrote, "I never saw a court of justice with so little humbug about it."

There were others who saw such justice as containing something much worse than humbug. For in fact there was always a thin, uncertain line between democratic verdict and mob vengeance.

The miners could indulge in such rough sentiment as flogging a man and then collecting money and clothes to get him off to a fresh start. Or then again they could whip themselves into wild hysteria. When that happened, a man's fate might depend on the color of his skin, or his popularity with his fellows, or the state of public resentment against other, unrelated crimes, or the amount of alcoholic libations which accompanied the general excitement.

Too often the circumstances conspired to abolish all human restraint. Sadistic judgments were meted out on such occasions, and hanging became an entertainment.

The atmosphere of a camp execution is glimpsed in an

affair at Rich Bar which was chronicled from two points of view. The reporters were Windeler, who considered it justified, and Mrs. Clappe, who viewed it as mixed outrage and tragedy.

The victim was an inept and drunken thief, a man of so little consequence that those who passed judgment on him never quite got his name straight. To Windeler, who helped to hang him, he was David Brown, while Mrs. Clappe called him William Brown. There is no doubt, however, that they described the same case.

The affair began when Brown and another man robbed camp residents of dust worth about $1,800. Suspicions were such that the two culprits were arrested and tried, but in the lack of firm evidence they were acquitted, and shortly afterward they left the Bar. Soon Brown returned alone. He spent several days loafing around, drinking heavily. The men he had robbed suspected that he had come back for cached loot, and they had a shrewd notion as to where he might have hidden it. Accordingly they piled up stones and brushwood around the area in such a way that they would know immediately if the place were disturbed.

When Brown nerved himself to retrieve the stolen dust he was easily caught. He confessed readily and returned what he had left; it amounted to $600 which he had moved to a new hiding place in his bunk. Windeler participated in the arrest and described what followed:

"Then the miners assembled, a court formed, a jury empannelled & Brown given in custody of the sheriff Davis & Constable James Thompson appointed for the occasion, & David Brown (this was A. M. 8 ocl') condemned to be hung at 4 ocl P. M. Then I, Br., and H. had to go up on the burial hill & dig a grave, a little distance from the graveyard, an oak tree close by, chosen for a gibbet. James brought up a rope, noose fixed & greased. I hove the rope over a limb of the tree. At 4 ocl the prisoner led up to execution. He was asked by the sheriff if he had anything to say. No, he said. So the noose was fixed round his neck, a white cloth drawn over his face, & at the word given by the sheriff we hoisted him up & I belayed the rope end round a stump, then he was jerked up and down several times to break his neck. Before he was hung he paid 2$ to a man whom he owed it."

To Windeler that was all there was to it. A troublesome but necessary business, cleaned up in a day.

Mrs. Clappe was not present at the hanging, but she heard all about it. Her secondhand account varied a little in detail and a lot in outlook.

She noted that Brown was reportedly persuaded to confess and return the money by a promise of immunity. Of that she said, "Whether the men, who had just regained a portion of their property, made any objections to the proceedings which followed, I know not; if they had done so, however, it would have made no difference, as the *people* had taken the matter entirely out of their hands."

Her version of the swift execution was that Brown was sentenced to be hanged in an hour, but "By the persuasions of some men more mildly disposed, they granted him a respite of *three hours,* to prepare for his sudden entrance into eternity. He employed the time in writing in his native language (he is a Swede) to some friends in Stockholm; God help them when that fatal post shall arrive."

In her account of Brown's last moments she wrote, "He had exhibited during the trial, the utmost recklessness and *nonchalance,* had drank many times in the course of the day, and when the rope was placed about his neck, was evidently much intoxicated. All at once, however, he seemed startled into a consciousness of the awful reality of his position, and requested a few moments for prayer.

"It is said that the crowd generally, seemed to feel the solemnity of the occasion; but many of the drunkards, who form a large part of the community on these Bars, laughed and shouted, as if it were a spectacle got up for their particular amusement. A disgusting specimen of intoxicated humanity, struck with one of those luminous ideas peculiar to his class, staggered up to the victim, who was praying at the moment, and crowding a dirty rag into his almost unconscious hand, in a voice broken by a drunken hiccough, tearfully emplored him to take his 'hankercher', and if he were *innocent* (the man had not denied his guilt since first accused) to drop it as soon as he was drawn up into the air, but if *guilty*, not to let it fall on any account.

"The execution was conducted by the jury, and was performed by throwing the cord, one end of which was attached to the neck of the prisoner, across the limb of a tree standing outside the Rich Bar grave-yard; when all, who felt disposed to engage in so revolting a task, lifted the poor wretch from the ground, in the most awkward manner possible. The whole affair, indeed, was a piece of cruel butchery, though *that* was not intentional, but arose from the ignorance of those who made the preparations. In truth, life was only crushed out of him, by hauling the writhing body up and down several times in succession, by the rope which was wound round a large bough of his green-leafed gallows."

Mrs. Clappe added charitably: "I have heard no one approve of this affair. It seems to have been carried on entirely by the more reckless part of the community. There is no doubt, however, that they seriously *thought* they were doing right, for many of them are kind and sensible men. They firmly believed that such an example was absolutely necessary for the protection of the community."

Mrs. Clappe described also the twenty-four-day orgy of violence which convulsed the neighboring camps of Rich Bar and Indian Bar in the summer of 1852. An explosive string of events began with armed riot and ran on through murder, hanging, and random slaughter; the various killings had no particular relationship one to another except that the miners that month were in a bloody mood.

The first flicker of trouble appeared at Indian Bar when a Fourth of July celebration wound up as an ugly brawl. Inflamed by "whiskey and patriotism," some Americans attacked a contingent of Spanish miners, inflicting serious injuries on two or three victims.

The following Sunday seven Spaniards banded together to avenge national honor and even the score. They had drawn up a list of the most offensive Americans and planned that each of them would challenge an opposite number to a duel. However, the killing was not destined to proceed in so orderly a fashion. The Spaniards stopped at a bar, fortified themselves with champagne and claret, and put a fine edge on their temper through an incidental fist fight with a quarrelsome Englishman; then they moved on to a chance encounter with one Tom Somers, an American described as "a dangerous person when in liquor." Somers knocked down one of the Spaniards, a man named Domingo, and he replied in hot rage with a knife to the heart.

The stabbing took place next door to the Clappe cabin. She was arranging flowers and chatting with a friend when they heard angry shouts; then the cabin door burst open and a man rushed in, yelling for Dr. Clappe. The physician appeared almost simultaneously from another direction, but the affair was beyond his ministrations. Within minutes Somers lay stretched out in death, with a Spanish woman wailing in wild sorrow over his blood-spattered corpse.

Domingo, meantime, was parading up and down the camp's dusty street, waving his gory knife, threatening destruction to all Americans. A Mexican woman clung to his free arm, bestowing admiring glances on her hero.

At Domingo's first triumphant swagger through the streets Americans scattered from his path, but soon they were back with guns, and it was his turn to run. He made it to the river, swam across, untouched by a volley of bullets, and vanished into the forest. In the camp, meantime, American and Spanish contingents were gathering in mixed fear and fury against each other. "The Spaniards," said Mrs. Clappe, "thought that the Americans had risen against them; and our own countrymen fancied the same of the foreigners."

The rest of it Mrs. Clappe observed from a spot high on a hillside, her husband having sent her there for safety's sake. With two other women she sat on a log and gazed down on a mob scene of miners waving guns and clubs. There was a great milling around, a shot was fired, and as the crowd parted she saw one man helped into a cabin and another man carried in.

This time it was wholly an accident. The miners had sealed off the street with a row of armed guards, and the character identified only as the quarrelsome Englishman had attempted to force his way through the line. It is useless to inquire of his motives; probably he just wanted in on the action. Someone waved him back with a gun; he grappled for the weapon, and it went off. In the close quarters the shot felled two men, both badly wounded.

After that unfortunate interruption a Committee of Vigilance was formed to march on the Spaniards. They met no resistance except for a Mexican spitfire who blazed away at them with a brace of pistols. Domingo's sweetheart, one presumes. Fortunately she was a bad shot. They disarmed her somehow and banished her from the camp.

Five Spaniards were arrested. Three of them were convicted of inciting to riot, with punishment set as banishment and confiscation of their claims. The other two received an additional penalty of flogging.

If the results fell short of impartial justice the vigilantes must be credited with resisting mob outcries for a general hanging. One Spaniard, however, didn't see it that way. To him it was again an affair of honor, and he begged to be executed rather than whipped.

Mrs. Clappe wrote with entire seriousness, "He appealed to his judges in the most eloquent manner—as gentlemen, as men of honor; representing to them that to be deprived of life, was nothing in comparison with the never-to-be-effaced stain of the vilest convict's punishment. Finding all his entreaties disregarded, he swore a most solemn oath, that he would murder every American that he should chance to meet alone, and as he is a man of the most dauntless courage, and rendered desperate by a burning sense of disgrace, he will doubtless keep his word."

She added of the flogging that she didn't see it but couldn't help hearing it. When the sound of lash against flesh reached her cabin, the gentle lady buried her head in her shawl.

That wound up the riot, but there was more to come. In the hills nearby a man named Bacon was found with his throat cut and his money gone. Gone also was Bacon's servant, a Negro known as "Josh." It happened that Josh had cooked for Mrs. Clappe for several months, and she thought him "the last one anybody would have suspected capable of such an act." The newly formed vigilantes thought otherwise. They tracked Josh to Sacramento, found him well supplied with gold which they assumed to be Bacon's, and brought him back in chains to be hanged.

At what passed for the trial Josh met the accusation with stubborn silence, refusing to plead either guilty or innocent. "He said, very truly, that whether innocent or guilty, they would hang him; and so he 'died and made no sign'."

The next affair occurred when one Henry Cook was found on a hillside, his throat cut from ear to ear, but still breathing. On regaining consciousness he accused "Paganini Ned," a mulatto who was the camp's chief fiddler and most talented chef. Ned had friends, which was fortunate for him; a mob of several hundred gathered to hang him, but they were talked out of it. Meanwhile Dr. Clappe was patching Cook up, and as the injured man babbled on it became clear that it was really a case of attempted suicide committed in a fit of delirium tremens.

Mrs. Clappe wrote, "Their majesties the mob, with that beautiful consistency which usually distinguishes those august individuals, insisted on shooting poor Harry—for said they, and the reasoning is remarkably conclusive and clear, 'a man so hardened as to raise his hand against his *own* life, will never hesitate to murder another!' They almost mobbed F. [Dr. Clappe] for binding up the wounds of the unfortunate wretch, and for saying that it was possible he might live. At last, however, they compromised the matter, by determining, that if Henry should recover, he should leave the Bar immediately. Neither contingency will probably take place, as it will be almost a miracle if he survives."

The final excitement was a duel. One of the principals was the unnamed Englishman who had pushed through a crowd to set off that accidental gunshot during the big riot. The other chap, also English, was known as Billy Leggett. The two had been boon companions, but some dispute arose between them, and they agreed to shoot it out. A big crowd gathered to see it done.

The initial exchange of shots went wild, whereupon the first Englishman offered to call off the quarrel. Leggett, however, insisted on shooting until one of them was dead and suggested that the distance be shortened for efficiency's sake. It was done that way, and they buried Billy Leggett.

As still one more casualty, there was a delayed fatality from the riot. The victim was Señor Pizarro, an aristocrat from South America, and by Mrs. Clappe's account a man who stood out for qualities of good sense and quiet courage. He was moving through the riot crowd, very probably acting in a peacemaker's role, when the accidental gunshot went off and shattered his thigh. He failed to survive an amputation.

Such were the crowded events at Rich and Indian Bars in the month of July 1852. The toll: five dead, two others badly wounded. As leftover business there was a man loose in the mountains, his back scarred by a lash, who may or may not have kept his promise to wash out dishonor in blood.

Another and more lurid drama was enacted at Downieville in 1851. The occasion of violence arose again through a Fourth of July celebration, though this time patriotism was not involved. Just liquor and sex.

It began as minor encounter between a Scot named Cannon and a Mexican woman, Juanita. On the night of the Fourth a drunken Cannon went careening through the camp, singing, shouting, banging on doors. Presently a sagging doorway gave way under his assault and he lurched into a shack which Juanita shared with her lover, a gambler. The intrusion was greeted with a stream of Spanish invective and Cannon backed out, mumbling thick-tongued excuses. That was all there was to it for the moment. Cannon went on his way, still making the night clamorous with what was to be his last hurrah.

The next morning he groped through a fog of recollections and remembered Juanita. Some glimpse of her, or some tone in her voice, had left its mark on a man who had been without women too long. And so he staggered back to the shack—to apologize, he said. This time she met him at the doorway, blocking his entrance, and dismissing his clumsy overtures with contempt. In angry response he spat at her the word *puta,* or whore. Moments later he was on the ground, gasping out his life, with Juanita's knife in him up to the hilt.

The news spread quickly through a camp that was just rousing itself from alcoholic stupor. Within hours the miners had gathered in mob spirit; they found Juanita hiding in a saloon and dragged her into the public square for immediate trial. The proceedings were held on a bunting-draped speak-

er's stand which had been the scene of rude pomp and ceremony the day before.

In another mood, or with a woman of different complex-
ion, the miners might have saluted her for defending her
honor. But not on this day or with this woman. They clam-
ored for her life, and when she responded with defiance it
served only to whip up the temper of what one witness called
"the hungriest, craziest, wildest mob." Several times they
rushed against restraining ropes, wanting to seize and hang
her at once, but they were put off with pleas to let the trial
take its course.

The defense attorney was a bespectacled young lawyer
named Thayer. He stood up bravely, employing whatever
eloquence he had, but they didn't want to hear him. When
he mounted a barrel to make a final plea someone knocked
the improvised rostrum out from under his feet. He was
picked up, passed bodily through the crowd, pummeled savagely, and thrown into the street. That ended the statement
for the defense. The jury retired for a brief ritual of delibera-
tion and came back with a hanging verdict.

Juanita's last defender appeared then in the person of Dr.
Cyrus D. Aiken. He announced that they couldn't hang her,
because she carried within her another life. The crowd
howled the finding down. Three other physicians were em-
paneled—they are identified as Drs. Kibbe, Chase, and Carr—
and they provided a more popular diagnosis which declared
her not pregnant.

Dr. Aiken was given twenty-four hours to leave the camp.
Juanita was granted one hour to prepare for death.

The miners rigged a gallows by suspending a plank from
a bridge. Juanita walked to it with her head up, smiling,
maintaining her defiant spirit to the end. Unaided, she
climbed the four short steps which led to the plank. She took
off a jaunty little straw hat and tossed it to a man in the
crowd, crying, "*Adios, amigo!*" Then she adjusted the noose

around her own neck, sweeping her heavy braids aside to set the rope in place.

She was asked for the customary last remarks, and she replied that if so insulted she would do it again.

They bound her hands behind her, and someone with an eye to the decencies came forward to tie her skirt around her legs. When all was in readiness a white handkerchief was placed over her face. Through the veil she called out in a loud, clear voice, *"Adios, señores!"* A shot was fired as signal, the plank was released, and she plunged to her death. Thus Downieville became the only miners' camp to hang a woman.

As a strange denouement Juanita's medical witness, Dr. Aiken, returned later and was appointed as one of two physicians to serve the indigent sick of the area. He shared the post with Dr. Kibbe, who had refuted the diagnosis of pregnancy.

One of these two men had surely lied, whether from humanitarian motive or out of fear of the mob. Between them there could be no real pretense as to the part which each had played. One is left to wonder what they said to each other about the case.

Camp physicians were drawn into innumerable other dramas of gold-field violence. The doctors, in fact, played a triple role. Officially they presided at the autopsies; professionally they treated the wounded survivors; and personally they sometimes took part as combatants.

Of the various roles the official one was usually the least important. Autopsies were conducted in the most casual fashion, though it did not necessarily follow that the results were invalid. In most cases elaborate inquiry was not required to ascertain that the deceased had succumbed to knife or gun.

The French physician, Dr. Garnier, described the atmosphere at a typical inquest. When summoned to perform an autopsy he found the coroner's jury assembled in the same room where the cadaver was laid out. The presiding judge proffered a Bible, swore Dr. Garnier in, then motioned to the corpse and told him to get on with it; the examination of the body was conducted while witnesses paraded through to give their version of events. Dr. Garnier added dryly, "Everything is very fast for the Americans."

A much more important function was that of patching up the victims of violence. Occasionally, in the more formal duels, the doctors stood by with bandages and instruments. More often they were called in haste when someone was wounded. In either case their services were badly needed, and they attained a special status. The physician who attended strictly to his own business could often move with impunity among armed and dangerous men.

Dr. William B. Eichelroth was one who enjoyed such privileged position. He was a German refugee, an aristocrat of liberal principles, who had fled with a price on his head after the revolution of 1848. In California he became a noted frontier character and was summoned often to treat men who lay up in the hills with bullet holes in their bodies. He made it a particular point to limit his questions to the medical aspects of the matter, and he boasted that he could travel anywhere in the bandit-infested countryside without fear of the consequences.

When he encountered a holdup man, Dr. Eichelroth said, the typical dialogue went about like this:

Bandit: "Hands up and hold 'em high!"

Doctor: "What the hell do you want of me?"

Bandit: "Oh, it's you, Doc. Go ahead."

Of course, if a physician wanted to fight, that was another matter. Dr. Eichelroth had his experience with that too. He once dueled with an insulting editor, nicking his opponent in the shin; it was an affair of honor which originated in an argument over a dog.

Another, wholly whimsical duel involved two feuding doc-

tors who shot it out in a Nevada City saloon. The incident
was reported by the quack healer, Charles Ferguson, and from
his account of it the medical gun slingers were men of about
the same standing as himself.

"The affair," wrote Ferguson, "was between two doctors,
rivals for notoriety if not for practice also, whose names I
have forgotten. As they met, one pulled out a pistol and told
the other to draw. He threw up his hands and said he was
not armed. Whereupon, the first pulled out another pistol
and handed it to him, and in less than half a minute the house
was clear of people—all that could get out. I was one of the
unfortunates that could not get out, and took refuge behind
a counter and a fifty gallon beer barrel. It was a close range
struggle—pop, pop, and then a suspension for a few seconds,
when I would stick my head up from behind the barrel to
see if it was all over; then it would be pop, pop, and down
would go my head again behind the friendly beer cask. At
last each had discharged his five shots and what seemed very
remarkable, neither was hurt. After it was all over they
shook hands and drank together at a bar. The whole affair
was simply a farce."

There was a farcical air also to a duel at Stockton, though
this time the cast of characters included men of desperate
repute. The central figure was a "Dr. Roberts," real name unknown, who was hiding out under a medical alias; he had
earlier achieved some small fame as Captain Yeomans, the
leader of a bandit gang in Mexico.

Roberts was a personable rogue, and for a time he carried
off a double impersonation as lawyer and doctor. However,
his command of medicine was so sketchy as to create doubt,
even by California standards, and presently he was denounced
as a fraud by Stockton's Judge G. C. Belt.

Close inquiry into his identity was about the last thing
Roberts wanted, and he might well have chosen to ignore the
challenge, but another party stepped in to take up the quar-

rel. The belligerent interloper was David S. Terry. He was a state supreme court justice whose eminent position did not in the least inhibit him from a long string of violent escapades. Acting as a friend of Roberts, Terry thrust himself into the matter and insisted on fighting a duel to avenge the slur.

The affair might have ended bloodily, except that the men appointed as seconds put their heads together and decided that a charge of quack healing was hardly a thing to get worked up about. Accordingly they loaded the pistols with blanks. Judge Terry and Judge Belt blazed away at each other with harmless enthusiasm, and Dr. Roberts quietly left town before his criminal identity could be exposed. As Captain Yeomans, he returned to his old trade and was last heard of in Panama where he led an unsuccessful attempt to rob the Wells Fargo Express.

The most famous of all duels involving doctors occurred at Placerville. The instigator was the camp's first physician, a Dr. Hullings, who went to deadly lengths to defend what he considered his medical "claim."

Dr. Hullings was a picaresque figure, a tall, heavy-bodied man who swaggered about in a costume of black coat, Mexican sash, and velvet *calzoneras* of bright green. He was said to be competent enough when sober, but his usual condition was drunk. He was also a vicious brawler; he had left New Orleans in a hurry after killing a man in a café, and he had driven off several physicians who attempted to practice in the camp he considered his private province.

Presently there appeared a competitor who couldn't be driven off. He was Dr. Edward Willis, a quiet-spoken Englishman, and he baffled Dr. Hullings at first because he would neither fight nor run. Ignoring threats and insults, he proceeded to set up his establishment, a tent divided by sailcloth into compartments of office and dwelling.

Dr. Hullings had impressed the miners as being one of

them, but Dr. Willis offered the rival attraction of a man apart. He was a graduate of Edinburgh University, the finest medical school in Europe, and his tent reflected that aura. On rough pine shelves he laid out all the paraphernalia of his profession; there was a microscope, a stethoscope, a glittering array of surgical instruments, a mortar and pestle, some chemical retorts and alembics, an assortment of medications and splints, and a great jar of leeches. He displayed also several jars containing anatomical specimens preserved in alcohol; to a friend he confided that the specimens were just for show, because the miners expected it. As final flourish he tacked up a neat blue sign with gold letters inscribed "Surgery"; below it he affixed a red-lettered banner which read, "Dr. Edward Willis, M.R.C.S., Surgery and Physic in all branches. Sets bones. Draws teeth painlessly. Bleeds. Advice gratis."

It was too much for Dr. Hullings. He strode into the tent, spat a stream of tobacco juice at the pills Dr. Willis was rolling, and told him to "make tracks." Dr. Willis wiped the tobacco juice away and announced with infuriating calm that he did not make tracks at any man's bidding.

Dr. Hullings spent several days working himself up for the next encounter. When he was ready he assembled a pack of rowdies and barged into the tent where Dr. Willis sat chatting with a friend, a young Virginian named Paul Clam. Dr. Hullings demanded to see his rival's credentials; when the diplomas were produced he grabbed them, tore them in two, and spat in the other's face. Before Dr. Willis could react Clam had felled the intruder with a blow. Dr. Hullings came up bellowing, a bowie knife in his hand, but someone got hold of him to prevent an immediate slaughter.

There was no out for it now but a duel. Before that could be arranged, however, they had to settle a preliminary dispute as to who was going to shoot who. Clam said he'd be happy to handle the matter; Dr. Willis said that he preferred to do his own fighting, and Dr. Hullings said no, he'd kill both of them, but Clam first. It was set up that way, as Clam vs. Hullings, with Dr. Willis standing by for a second round if necessary.

The duel was held in an abandoned pit. That offered a double convenience; the spectators could gather above without much risk of being hit, and the excavation provided a ready-made grave for the loser. In the interests of making everything as proper as possible, the camp sheriff was appointed as referee.

The pit selected was about twenty-five feet long, a deadly range, and so deep that the combatants stood in semidarkness. Before descending Clam whispered to Dr. Willis that he had a bit the best of it; he knew the hole well and had maneuvered his opponent into the broad end where his figure would be silhouetted against what light there was. The two men took their positions; the spectators leaned over the top with avid curiosity, and the sheriff called down solicitously, "Are you ready below?" The duelists assured him that they were. He called "Ready" again, clapped his hands as a signal, and the pit erupted with the roar of shots.

After the shots came a groan and then silence; no answer came back when the sheriff called, "Is it over?" A delegation descended and found Dr. Hullings dead, shot through the heart. Clam was unconscious, three bullets in him, but Dr. Willis was able to nurse him back to health.

In a possibly apocryphal fillip, some assert that Dr. Willis' first official act at Placerville was to sign a death certificate for Dr. Hullings.

CHAPTER 19

———

Hang the Sheriff!

> —A crusader demands
> a cleansing.

It remained for San Francisco to provide the wildest episode in all the annals of gold-field violence. The tale was one of passion and politics in which dramatic events were set in motion by two small objects—a bullet and a sponge.

The backdrop was a city infested with crime. A Committee of Vigilance had effected a rough cleansing in 1851, but after a brief flurry of reform the community returned to its wild ways. Vice flourished, law officers allied openly with criminals, and murder and robbery became daily occurrence.

By 1856 some 1,200 San Franciscans had died of violence. The vast majority of murderers were never brought to account, and not one case in a hundred stirred more than a ripple of public response. Beneath the surface, however, there was a slow-building mood of fear and anger. It was crystallized by two killings.

The first was an affair of love. A hot-blooded young gambler named Charles Cora was enamored of a bordello madam, Arabella Ryan; she called herself Belle. On a November night in 1855 Cora escorted his mistress to a theater and there encountered United States Marshal W. H. Richardson and his wife. Prodded perhaps by Mrs. Richardson, the marshal made a scene, insisting that Belle be ejected on moral grounds.

When the theater management refused the Richardsons departed the premises in haughty indignation. Three days later, in the Blue Wing Saloon, Cora avenged the insult by gunning Marshal Richardson down.

Immediately after the shooting Cora surrendered to his good friend, the sheriff. The move signified not repentance but prudence, for that night a fire bell was heard tolling in a particular rhythm which San Franciscans knew well. The Committee of Vigilance, long disbanded, was gathering again.

Some vigilantes were for storming the jail and hanging Cora at once, but for the moment calmer councils prevailed. It was agreed instead that they would prepare themselves while waiting to see what course, if any, the law would take.

Meanwhile a not so calm voice was raised by a young newspaper publisher, James King of William. An unusual man this, as evidenced by the unusual name. He had been born plain James King and had added the sobriquet "of William" in reference to his father; it served the desired purpose in effectively distinguishing him from all other James Kings of the world.

King was a crusader, impulsive and fearless, as hotheaded in pursuit of justice as Cora had been in defense of honor. He was also the possessor of a powerful voice; his newly founded *Daily Evening Bulletin* was the town's most aggressive newspaper, and he put the full force of it behind a strident campaign demanding that the culprit pay with his life. Soon King was warning of plots to thwart justice; he asserted that a slush fund was being raised to bribe the jury, and he speculated openly on the possibility that Sheriff David Scannell and his henchmen might conspire to help Cora escape.

"Look well to the jury!" cried the *Bulletin*. "If the jury which tries Cora is packed, either HANG THE SHERIFF or drive him out of town."

And again: "If Mr. Sheriff Scannell does not remove Billy Mulligan from his present post as keeper of the county jail and Mulligan lets Cora escape, hang Billy Mulligan; and if necessary to get rid of the Sheriff, hang him—hang the Sheriff!"

Such appeals notwithstanding, the public excitement fizzled out; when Cora was brought to trial all that was hung was the jury. That slush-fund story had very probably been true. The prisoner returned to the jail, languishing there in not too much discomfort, and consoling himself with the reasonable expectation that if he just sat tight for a while the fuss would blow over.

King meantime was firing away at other targets; he had taken on by now the entire political machine which battened on the city's crime and corruption. Thus it was that on May 14, 1856, he published an incidental attack declaring that Supervisor James P. Casey deserved "to have his neck stretched" for the ballot-stuffing fraud which procured his election. And while he was on the subject King reminded his readers that this particular civic father was a former inmate of Sing Sing.

The story brought Casey storming into the newspaper office, demanding apology. He didn't object so much to the charge of election fraud, that being a common practice, but the Sing Sing allusion he regarded as personal. "I don't wish my past acts raked up," he warned King. "On that point I am sensitive!" King threw him out, and Casey departed, muttering ugly threats.

When King left his office that evening he tucked a small pistol into his breast pocket. It was more gesture than precaution, for he put on a tight-buttoned cloak which prevented easy access to the weapon. King was accustomed to fighting with words, not guns. He went home by his accustomed path— he had long since defied his enemies by advertising the route— and so came to the fog-shrouded street where Casey crouched waiting behind an empty express wagon.

As King approached Casey stepped out, threw back a cloak

which covered one arm, and flourished a revolver. "Are you armed?" cried Casey. "Defend yourself! Come on! Defend yourself!" He spat out the words in a breathless rush, and before he had finished speaking, he shot. King reeled into a nearby building, the Pacific Express office, and Casey fled through the dusk to seek refuge in jail.

The first physician to reach King's side was Dr. J. K. Nuttall. He was a skilled practitioner, licentiate of the Royal College of Surgeons of Ireland. Dr. Nuttall found King sprawled in a chair, bleeding profusely, half-conscious, and almost incoherent from shock.

The physician ripped away the blood-spattered clothing and found that the bullet had entered the left chest just over the first rib. King by now was completely prostrate; he had no discernible pulse in the left wrist and only a feeble one in the right; his extremities were cold and he was obviously hemorrhaging. Dr. Nuttall poked a cautious finger into the wound and explored it gently; the bullet had followed a passage that led inward, upward, and backward, emerging under the armpit.

The critical question was whether or not the subclavian artery was severed. If so, there was acute danger of massive internal bleeding which would lead quickly to death. The indicated passage of the bullet made such damage seem likely. Closer examination might have established the question, but that in itself posed another danger. The physician concluded that he was dealing with a torn artery which was clotted for the moment, and he feared that the least movement might rip it open.

While Dr. Nuttall pondered the problem Dr. R. Beverly Cole arrived. He too was a physician of the first rank, though his contentious spirit made him disliked by his colleagues. With characteristic decisiveness Dr. Cole began to take matters in hand, applying mustard plasters to the patient's hands and feet to restore the faltering circulation. King rallied a little under the treatment and reached out to grasp Dr. Cole's hand, saying, "Oh, Cole, in the name of God, stay by me!"

A third physician, Dr. H. M. Gray, now appeared on the scene, and the three of them put their heads together over that question of the severed artery. Dr. Nuttall wanted to insert a sponge as plug. Dr. Cole objected. The hemorrhaging had stopped, and he thought it best to leave well enough alone. He doubted that the artery was involved at all.

The other two overruled him. Dr. Nuttall took a piece of white sponge the size of a goose egg, moistened it thoroughly, and shoved it forcibly into the wound. Wet compresses and bandages were then applied.

The fine points of the medical dispute aside, the sponge had some merit as a temporary expedient. If a plug was needed, that did it. Now they had time to think. Unfortunately they were caught up in an atmosphere which made rational consideration all but impossible. Outside the building a hysterical mob was gathering, while inside confusion steadily increased as a continuing stream of doctors and others came rushing to offer help and advice.

The chaos was described later by Dr. Hugh H. Toland, an eminent surgeon who was called in as consultant. He arrived at 8 P.M., about three hours after the shooting, and found the place a madhouse. A groaning, half-conscious King was laid out on a counter with his wife beside him, weeping. Some twenty doctors were milling around in a room thickly clouded with tobacco smoke. The patient's personal physician, Dr. Hammond, was in theoretical charge, but he lacked sufficient sense of command to clear the place out. As a result an endless succession of physicians pawed over the wounded man, repeating each other's examinations, countermanding each other's instructions, arguing endlessly about what to do. Under the circumstances Dr. Toland did not attempt to make his own examination; he settled for polling his colleagues in an effort to arrive at some reasonable estimate of the situation.

An hour or two later some measure of order was achieved and the room cleared. It was agreed that King's condition was too precarious to risk moving him, so they made him as comfortable as possible and left him on the counter for the night. A medical vigil was maintained at his side, Dr. Hammond taking the first shift until 1 A.M., and Dr. Cole keeping the watch until dawn.

At 7 A.M. Dr. Hammond returned to hold another consultation. With him were Drs. Toland, Gray, and Bertody. Present also, though apparently not by invitation, were the men who had first treated the patient, Drs. Nuttall and Cole.

Dr. Cole informed the others in his usual brisk and authoritative fashion that the artery question had to be settled now. If the vessel was severed, he said, then the thing to do was to take it up and close it with sutures. There was risk in that to be sure, but it had to be taken. And as to the sponge, that had to come out; it wouldn't do as a permanent solution, and it could lead to putrefaction.

Dr. Nuttall agreed. He had insisted on inserting the sponge in the first place, but he had intended it only as an emergency measure. He too now felt that it was time for decision.

Dr. Hammond bristled angrily at the advice. Like most physicians he was sensitive of his professional prerogatives, and he may have resented the intrusion of his more famous colleagues. Or perhaps, more charitably, he was reacting to all the physical and emotional strain of a hectic affair. In any case, he cut off the sponge discussion abruptly, saying, "Well, I guess I have some crude notions on the subject myself." Withdrawing to a corner of the room, he motioned to Drs. Toland, Gray, and Bertody to join him in a whispered consultation from which Drs. Nuttall and Cole were pointedly excluded.

Dr. Nuttall swallowed his pride and overlooked the snub. But Dr. Cole stomped out of the room, declaring furiously that he could assume no further responsibility for the case.

Thus began a drama within a drama, for the medical dispute developed into a bitter feud.

The city meantime was in the grip of a tremendous excitement. All that first night, while King lay on the blood-spattered counter, a mob milled around the jail where Casey had sought refuge. King's brother was there, haranguing the crowd to storm the jail; once or twice they made a move to do it, but the sheriff and his men stood in the doorway with cocked guns and backed them off.

The next day the Committee of Vigilance began to reorganize. This was no mere mob, but rather something closer in spirit to a revolutionary council. The key members had been stirring restlessly since that shooting by Cora, and now they were able to form in a hurry.

Openly and defiantly they met in a public hall to choose their officers, announce their aims, and recruit a following. Men stood in long lines to join up; as each new vigilante was mustered in he took an oath of fidelity and signed his name to a membership roll. Within forty-eight hours there were 3,500 of them, with thousands more still to come.

Almost as quickly as they formed they armed and organized, dividing into military companies of one hundred men each. They were equipped with several thousand muskets and bayonets, obtained partly by purchase and partly by raiding armories. The latter was accomplished easily, without bloodshed, by marching massed men up to the door and demanding the key. Soon they had also obtained twenty cannon, purchased or borrowed from ships in the harbor.

They turned their meeting hall into a stronghold by piling up rows of sandbags ten feet high and eight feet thick. Fort Gunnybags, they called it. Supplies were laid in sufficient to withstand a siege, and a medical corps set up in case of casualties. Dr. Cole was named surgeon-general, heading a staff of some eighty physician members.

All of it was done in hot haste; in just three days they were ready to march. Meantime the opposition was arming, too, under the name of the Law and Order Party. That group was a curiously mixed assortment which included the controlling political machine and its hoodlum allies along with some eminently respectable citizens who feared the vigilante spirit even more than they despised corrupt government.

Caught in the middle was a vacillating politician, Governor J. Neely Johnson. He rushed to the scene, issuing orders which everyone ignored, and offering placating assurances which no one believed.

When Governor Johnson met with vigilante leader William Coleman it was Coleman who laid down the ultimatum. He said the vigilantes would hold off briefly if the governor could guarantee "an instant trial, and immediate execution."

The governor emerged from that conference with a soothing statement that the vigilantes were willing to leave everything in the hands of the court.

What chance there was for accommodation rested chiefly on the possibility that James King of William might show some sign of recovery. But the news from that quarter was bad. King's physicians had moved him to a specially prepared sickroom where he lay in critical condition. On the evening of May 15, at the end of the first twenty-four hours, a bulletin announced that the left arm was entirely paralyzed, cold, blue and swollen, while the exit wound under the armpit was draining fluid. The doctors were still assuming that the artery was injured, but they considered the patient's condition too precarious to operate.

In the next three days King sank, rallied a bit, then sank again; his left breast had become badly swollen. Drs. Toland and Gray feared congestion induced by the sponge and began pressing for the operation originally suggested by Dr. Cole. The others, however, were not willing to risk it, and still an-

other consultant was summoned in the person of Dr. John
S. Griffin, an army surgeon from Los Angeles.

Dr. Griffin vetoed operation, left the sponge in, and attempted to relieve the congestion by an incision under the
armpit. Great quantities of pus drained out, but the patient
remained sunk in a now desperate condition.

That same day, on May 18, the vigilantes made their move.
Twenty-five hundred of them marched forth from Gunnybags, tramping through the streets in solemn silence to as-
semble in massed ranks before the jail. It was done smartly,
with military precision; they converged on the jail by a
variety of routes, but they had planned it so perfectly that
every company arrived at the destination within sixty seconds
of the allotted time.

The sight of a city square filling so suddenly with armed
men was chilling enough, but that was not quite all. As a
final convincer the massed ranks parted abruptly to admit a
last company of sixty men, dragging a cannon. They aimed
it at the jail door while a gunner stood by at the ready, waving a smoldering fuse.

A huge crowd had gathered on surrounding hills to watch
the fireworks, but there were none. Sheriff Scannell was
caught short with a defensive force of only 150 men, and he
was not the type for lost causes. The prisoners Casey and
Cora were surrendered without resistance.

The two were taken to Fort Gunnybags and placed on
trial before a vigilante court. The defendants had counsel,
and the proceedings were deliberate enough, but the out-
come was hardly in doubt. If the prisoners had any hope at
all, they lost it in mid-trial when a courier arrived to announce that James King of William was dead.

For both men the verdict was guilty, the sentence death,
with execution set to coincide with the hour of King's burial.
Casey broke down when he heard the judgment, but Cora

maintained a stoic courage. He asked to see Belle and a priest, and both were hastily summoned.

About an hour before he went to the gallows Cora enacted a pathetic ritual to tidy up what was left of his life. With Belle's trembling hand in his, he stood before the priest and heard the vows of matrimony pronounced. She had asked him to do it.

By the end of May, King, Casey, and Cora were all in their graves, the vigilantes were preparing new actions, and the governor was making futile efforts to muster forces against them. Meantime the doctors who had treated King were guarding an uneasy secret. They had learned through autopsy that the artery was not injured after all. The wound involved only a lesion of the vein, along with damage to the surrounding tissues. Under other treatment King might very well have recovered, and in that event things might have taken a somewhat different course.

But all that was conjecture and hindsight. The spark had been ignited, the vigilantes had taken to the streets, and they were in a mood now to see it through.

On June 3 Governor Johnson issued a proclamation declaring the County of San Francisco to be "in a state of insurrection" and calling on the people to quell the rebellion. The manifesto had all the force and effect of a paper wad hurled against Fort Gunnybags. For the vigilantes were now riding high; they had the troops, the guns, and, indeed, the public support.

As counterforce the governor attempted to muster the state militia under the leadership of William Tecumseh Sherman. That famous soldier was at the moment retired from the army, working as a banker in San Francisco, and he accepted a militia commission as major general. He did so reluctantly, however, for his sympathies were torn. Sherman had friends among the vigilantes and approved many of their aims; he thought also that the governor was handling the situation all wrong. But he was a soldier, with an absolute respect for vested authority, and when orders came he obeyed.

On assuming command Sherman found that questions of conscience were somewhat incidental to the simple facts of the situation. Many of the militia had deserted to the vigilantes, and those that remained were of questionable loyalty. Sherman's forces were outnumbered fifty to one, and vigilante control was so tight that he could not even procure sufficient arms for his men. Gratefully, perhaps, he concluded that he could do nothing and resigned his militia commission.

Another who stood aside was Captain David G. Farragut, a naval officer who would later win fame in the Civil War. He commanded a navy yard in the harbor and politely declined a request that he shell the city to "exterminate the insurrectionists."

The federal army commander in California also refused to intervene until he got orders from Washington, and when the answer did come it was negative. President Pierce cited states' rights in tossing the problem back to Governor Johnson.

That left the vigilantes without effective opposition. So complete was their control, in fact, that they were able to exercise it with a good deal of restraint. They hanged two more culprits, both murderers, and sentenced twenty-six men to banishment. Otherwise they engaged mostly in conspicuous assembly and a great deal of marching up and down. And that had its salutary effects. In the six months before the vigilantes took over San Francisco recorded about a hundred murders. In the six months afterward the total was two.

The vigilante reign accounted for one other fatality, a suicide. The man in question was James "Yankee" Sullivan, an ex-prize fighter and barroom brawler who acted as strong-arm

man for the political machine; he had acquired the name
Yankee from the fact that he was accustomed to gird his loins
with the American flag while engaged in the prize ring.

When Sullivan was jailed at Fort Gunnybags he quickly
shed his air of bravado, assuming instead a morbid repentance. He confessed everything he knew, and probably some
things he didn't know, and then in a fit of black despondency
he got hold of a knife and sawed his wrists with lethal results.

Surgeon-General Cole was charged with seeing to the health
of prisoners, and the suicide troubled him. It seemed out of
all proportion to the situation, as the worst penalty the man
faced was banishment. After reflecting on it, however, Dr.
Cole came up with a likely answer. Yankee Sullivan had
been accustomed to a quart of whisky a day, and he had been
without that comfort for several weeks of incarceration. In
all probability, then, the man had come unhinged while drying out. Thereafter Dr. Cole provided alcoholic prisoners
with sufficient liquor to keep them propped up until their
fate was decided.

Dr. Cole's other great service was in saving the life of a
wounded vigilante. He thereby spared his fellow insurgents
all the embarrassments which would have accrued from hanging a supreme court judge.

The incident began when a Law and Order man named
Rube Maloney made death threats against vigilante leaders.
They didn't take it too seriously, but they decided to pick
him up and let him cool off for a while at Fort Gunnybags.
Squad leader Sterling Hopkins was dispatched with several
men to make the arrest.

Maloney took refuge with his friends, Dr. Richard P. Asher
and Judge David S. Terry. Dr. Asher was a physician who
happened also to be a United States naval agent. And Terry,
of course, was the same gun-slinging supreme court justice
referred to earlier in the duel with Judge Belt.

The opposing parties met on the street, all of them armed,

and there was a brief, vigorous scuffle. A shot was fired, but no one was hurt, and Dr. Asher decided that things were getting out of hand. He surrendered his gun.

Judge Terry was of different stripe. He held out his rifle in token of surrender and waited cunningly until Hopkins had reached out both hands to take the weapon. For a moment Hopkins was off balance, and in that instance Terry whipped out a bowie knife and slashed it viciously across the other's throat.

Terry and his friends escaped in the confusion, a bleeding Hopkins was carried back to headquarters, and the fire bell began pealing in ominous summons. Again there was a full show of strength with hundreds of men marching through the street, dragging a cannon behind them. They assembled in front of an arsenal where the opposition was holed up, and Dr. Asher poked his head out to say that the wanted men would give up if their safety was guaranteed.

"There are no conditions," snapped the vigilante officer.

There was also no choice, so Judge Terry, Dr. Asher, and Maloney came out and surrendered.

Soon after a naval officer came rushing around to inquire about Dr. Asher. Luckily, he was not a principal figure, and the vigilantes didn't have to take on the navy. They listed the physician as a material witness, questioned him thoroughly, and turned him loose.

Maloney was only a ward heeler and no one cared much about him. They chased him out of town.

That left Judge Terry as a real embarrassment. The public strength of the vigilantes lay in their incorruptible stance, and they couldn't maintain that position if they permitted privileged killings. On the other hand, hanging a supreme court judge was a step more drastic than they wanted to take.

The only easy out was for the wounded Hopkins to save Terry's neck, and the vigilantes' position, by not dying. That was asking a lot of the man, for his throat was laid open in a great slash; the carotid artery was severed, and the pharynx and larynx were both exposed.

Surgeon-General Cole took personal charge of the case. He reached Hopkins' side a few minutes after the stabbing and found him bleeding profusely; he was in such pain and shock that it was difficult to examine him until he providentially fainted. Dr. Cole packed the wound with cotton, hoping that healing might occur without resort to a desperate operation.

By that evening it was plain that no such simple solution would suffice. Hopkins was hemorrhaging so badly that he seemed unlikely to last the night. Accordingly the Fort Gunnybags hospital was made ready for emergency surgery.

The operation was performed at a twilight hour, a time when it was too dark to receive illumination from the nearby window and yet too light for the guttering candles to be of maximum use. Bad timing that, but there was no help for it; Hopkins had begun sinking all at once, and they couldn't wait.

It was done without anesthetic—chloroform would have imposed additional risks—but the patient "was kept up with brandy and water." Fortunately he was only semiconscious.

There was no asepsis, or even antisepsis. Dr. Cole had not heard of such practice, and when he did hear of it later he never believed in it. For preparation the physician and his assistants merely washed their hands in a basin, dried on a common towel, and then plunged scalpel and fingers into the torn and gaping neck.

If the arrangements were crude, the operation was not, for Cole was a surgeon of marvelous skill. With deft, sure touch he groped through the maze of shattered tissue, found the torn end of a feebly pulsing artery, and tied it off. When the surgeon stepped back from the table Hopkins lay in deep coma, barely breathing, and yet holding on.

The next two weeks was a time of continual crisis. The patient's temperature rose daily to alarming heights and was pushed down each time with quinine. The pulse fluctuated wildly, dropping as low as 85, then racing up to 135. After five days a violent inflammation appeared, and Hopkins had to be packed in ice until it subsided. There was a problem, too, in maintaining nourishment, as only fluids could be used, and much of it leaked out through the still unhealed holes in the neck.

The worst complication of all was the appearance of erysipelas. Dr. Cole fought the skin eruption with applications of silver nitrate, but the infection spread until it covered the entire face and neck. At the same time the stricken man showed signs of what Dr. Cole vaguely described as "cerebral trouble." Hopkins was no doubt delirious, perhaps raving. Dr. Cole poured on more silver nitrate and affixed thirty-six leeches to the site of infection.

It was the silver nitrate that did it. That and the immense hardihood of the patient. After seventy-two hours of acute crisis Hopkins turned the big corner, and within ten days after that he was very clearly on the mend.

The vigilantes were immensely relieved. And so, of course, was Judge Terry. He had spent the entire time under guard, his hopes rising and falling with every report from the sickroom; he had known very well that, high position or not, the condition of his own neck depended very much on that of his victim.

There remained the formalities of a trial. Vigilante punishments were confined to the simplicities of hanging and banishment, and since they couldn't make banishment stick in this case they contented themselves with a vote of censure. Judge Terry was found guilty of assault and turned loose with a stern warning to watch his step.*

* Terry didn't. In a duel three years later he killed United States Senator David Broderick, a development which old vigilantes must have viewed with some mixed feelings. Broderick had been the real power behind San Francisco's political machine.

The Terry affair marked the last big case on the vigilante agenda. On August 18, three months after forming, they massed once more in the streets, but this time it was only a parade and a reminder. Some 8,000 of them tramped through the city and then voluntarily laid down their arms. Three months after that Governor Johnson announced that he had withdrawn his proclamation charging insurrection.

It remained for Dr. Cole to provide a kind of autopsy on the vigilante affair. Being Cole, he did it with a vengeance.

Somehow or other Dr. Cole got hold of the post-mortem findings on King and prepared a paper on the subject for a meeting of the State Medical Society. He named no names— not then—but he stated flatly that it was a case of gross malpractice.

The *Sacramento State Journal* picked it up and gave it a big play, a headline declaring, "James Casey innocent of murder! Death of James King caused by doctors!"

Another paper quoted Dr. Cole as saying that King fell into the hands of ignorant and unprofessional practitioners and that he would have recovered if ordinary skill and prudence had been exercised in the case.

Dr. Cole may or may not have fed the papers those stories. In any event, he was looking for a fight, and he got it.

The exchange that followed was conducted in the form of open letters to the press, Dr. Cole and his opponents having at each other in the columns of the *Alta California*. The first missives were couched in tones of stiff courtesy which barely concealed seething rage on one part and cool insult on the other. The letters:

San Francisco, California, March 2d, 1857.

To Dr. R. Beverly Cole, Sir: We understand that you related a history of the injury and last illness of the late Jas. King of Wm. before the State Medical Convention of California, at its last session, together with comments upon the treatment insti-

tuted in his case. Will you be kind enough to inform us upon
what data, and from whence derived, you founded your knowledge of the case?

> Respectfully,
> Dr. Hammond,
> Dr. Bertody,
> Dr. Toland,
> Dr. Gray.

San Francisco, March 4, 1857.

Gentlemen: Yours of yesterday was received, and in reply I
have only to say, that the information upon which was based
the history of Mr. King's case, as given by me, without comment,
before the State Medical Society, at their last meeting, in Sacramento, was acquired through personal observation and reliable
sources.

> Respectfully,
> Beverly Cole, M.D.

The accused doctors replied with frontal assault, again in
print. Dr. Cole, they asserted, had been a mere bystander and
sickroom watcher; he had never examined the patient or
played any official part. In one instance, they said, he had
been in the room during an examination, but his presence
then had been as inexplicable as it was unexpected and un-
desired. And they added that he had been deliberately excluded because his previous conduct had been such that none
of the others wished to have professional dealings with him.

Dr. Cole replied that he had taken part in one examination,
the first one. As to the others, he wrote, *"I should regret to
acknowledge any participation in them."*

All that was just a preliminary, and while it made interesting reading it was not in itself especially remarkable. Doctors in those days, California doctors particularly, were accustomed to airing their differences in print.

Shortly it took on a new dimension through some leftover
vigilante business. When King was shot it was rumored that

Casey was merely a dupe who had been whipped up to mur-
derous frenzy by the incitement of one Ned McGowan, a San
Francisco police judge of ill repute. The vigilantes had ordered McGowan's arrest; they might well have hanged him
had they caught him then, but he escaped into the back country and hid out for a year. When he felt that things had blown
over he surrendered to the sheriff at Napa and stood court
trial there on a charge of conspiring in the crime.

The evidence against McGowan was thin, but still he was
an unsavory type closely connected with the killer, and his
attorneys naturally wished to deflect attention from that aspect. Accordingly, and in line with good legal practice, they
entered routine denials and then in effect put the doctors on
trial.

The defense simply stated was that McGowan was not involved in the first place, and in the second place, there had
been no murder at all, but only a minor injury which had
led to death through sheer bungling.

The doctors involved were all subpoenaed and put through
the wringer of cross-examination. Dr. Toland bore the chief
burden for the accused medical team, being the most eminent
member, and he stood up to it pretty well. He acknowledged
calmly that they had been wrong about the artery, but he
pointed out that it had been a chancy thing, with risks either
way. When pressed hard, he admitted that ordinarily the
wound would not have caused death, but he insisted that it
was not an ordinary case. King was tubercular, he said, and
in generally poor health, and thus not able to withstand the
shock.

In Dr. Toland's testimony the bite was not in the words
but the manner. He never spoke to Dr. Cole, never acknowledged his presence in the courtroom, but looked through and
past him with an icy contempt.

Dr. Cole in his turn was full of bitter spite. Asked about
Dr. Toland's reputation, he replied, "Among the community

it was quite different from what it was among the profession. I have formed my opinion from seeing a large concourse of people going into his office and judge that his practice is not among the most intelligent and respectable persons in San Francisco. But I do not wish to raise this question and am willing to admit that he is a respectable practitioner." *

Of Drs. Hammond, Bertody, and Gray he said more indulgently, "They have the reputation of being careful practitioners, but it often happens that fatal errors are made by careful men."

As to the wound and its treatment: "In my opinion the wound was not necessarily a mortal one; and the treatment was such as to cause death."

And then he sprang his great surprise. He was not sure that laymen could follow all the medical arguments, and so through arrangement with the attorneys he had set up a demonstration.

Stepping down from the witness stand, Dr. Cole donned a surgical apron and laid out his instruments on a desk. Then the courtroom doors were thrust open to admit a cart draped with a sheet. Dramatically Dr. Cole drew back the sheet to reveal a corpse, indifferently preserved; the body was that of a prisoner who had been executed at the jail the year before.

Dr. Cole had always possessed a great flair for anatomy lectures, and now in the courtroom atmosphere he really warmed to his task. The bullet, he said, had gone in just here and emerged there. The sponge had been inserted so. The artery was placed thus. He sliced into the cadaver as he talked, flopped the body this way and that to afford a better view, and reached into it with dripping hands to illustrate the pertinent anatomical points.

* The facts as to Dr. Toland's qualifications: He had attended the University of Transylvania, graduating first in his class, and then had studied for two years under leading specialists in France. Before emigrating to California he had a successful practice in South Carolina, and he was later to found California's second medical school.

In his enthusiasm he failed to note that for once in his life he had lost his audience. The judge and the jury were still there, because they had to be, but as for spectators, the sight and smell of the thing had cleared the court.

Whether he helped also to clear McGowan is a matter of conjecture. The verdict in any case was not guilty.

CHAPTER 20

———◆———

. . . I quit even.

—Dr. William M'Collum looks
back on a great adventure.

After a while the dust settled. The tumultuous society began
to take on order and form, and California settled down, al-
beit in its own peculiar fashion.

The settling process occurred first in regard to the glittering yellow dust which had lured the adventurers on. They
had suffered at first from the discomforts of the Midas touch,
enjoying a surfeit of gold and a scarcity of everything else,
but that period was brief. The peak of the flush times was
reached in 1852, and by 1855 the pickings for prospectors
were just about gone; long before then the bulk of the population had turned to such mundane occupations as farming
and ranching, business and trade.

The social dust settled, too, though that took longer. The
frontier spirit of rugged individualism lingered on in all its
best and worst aspects, and it was many a year before they
really reconciled themselves to the proposition that men living together had to agree on the rules.

In their rambunctious way the physician participants
served as a civilizing influence. They founded the hospitals
and medical schools, established professional standards, and
helped to codify the laws which shielded people from out-

breaks of disease. They contributed more than soldiers and
sheriffs to taming the West.

Eventually California's doctors even tamed themselves, but
that took the longest of all. Their approach to progress was
well illustrated in the erratic rise and fall of the state's pioneer medical societies. Gold-rush physicians formed innumerable such groups, and within a decade every association had
been disbanded or torn apart. The incurable nomadism of
the members contributed something to that result, and contentious spirit did the rest. Personal quarrels, professional
differences, and political disputes all served to keep the societies in continual turmoil.*

As a typical instance, San Francisco doctors organized their
first society on June 22, 1850. At the initial meeting they
elected officers, adopted a constitution, and raised optimistic
toasts to the good fellowship and professional exchange which
would accrue from the move. At their second meeting they
adopted a fee schedule, amid scenes of violent dispute. Those
who disapproved were soon writing the papers to disassociate
themselves from the highhanded banditry of the thing.
Within four months the group was defunct.

In the next five years three more medical fraternities were
formed in San Francisco. The schisms involved are suggested
by the claims put forward for a particular group, the San
Francisco Medico-Chirurgical Association:

"The Medico-Chirurgical Association is now placed upon
a footing which must make it unobjectionable to all wishing
to belong to a medical society whose objects are to extend the
boundaries of medical knowledge and the sphere of useful-
ness and distinction of the profession. Its president belongs
to no party, clique, or school, and is besides, acknowledged
to be one of the most honorable, intelligent and liberal medical men in this city.

* All over the United States the medical profession was beset by similar
divisions. California physicians were not uniquely quarrelsome; they were
only more so.

"It is very desirable to remove from the character of the medical profession of this city, the disgrace which has been fastened upon it by the ungentlemanly conduct of a few, who, by causing constant discord, have, in times gone by, threatened the very existence of societies for medical advancement."

What statements like that led to, of course, was some more discord about who was causing the discord.

Other professional battles were fought out in the medical journals. The style of dispute was frank and vigorous with no pusillanimous pretense at mere understanding; at times the physician-writers had at each other so brutally that one observer referred to the period as the era of editorial vivisection.

One bitter exchange involved Dr. Elias Samuel Cooper of San Francisco. He was a great surgeon who was also very quarrelsome and vain. His enemies charged that he advertised himself outrageously, using as medium the *Pacific Medical and Surgical Journal* which he helped to found. Then he fell out with the *Journal's* editors and they, too, denounced him as a publicity hound.

The particular quarrel arose from a newspaper story reporting one of Dr. Cooper's operations. The item appeared in the *San Francisco Times* on January 22, 1858, and described the surgeon's skill in terms which the *Journal's* editors felt to be grossly exaggerated. Their reaction:

"With regret, not on our own but on his account, we are compelled to announce that no more of Dr. E. S. Cooper's communications will appear in this Journal. We have long been on terms of friendship with him, and have repeatedly defended him, against even just censure, in reference to his allowing himself to be puffed to repletion in the newspapers. On the 22nd ult., an article appeared in one of the dailies of this city, purporting to be an editorial, redolent with the most noisome flattery, such as no wise man could tolerate to be said concerning himself without disgust. We asked Dr. C.

to deny his complicity in its publication, or allow us to forego his literary aid in future. We do not believe he intended to injure the *Journal,* but still, it would not have been a difficult matter for *him,* to have ignored the fulsome quackish article to which we have alluded."

Dr. Cooper was temporarily deprived of a medium for reply, but that was no hindrance, not so long as there was a letter press in town. Runners were shortly dispatched through the streets to pass out a broadside addressed TO THE MEDICAL PROFESSION. The circular denied that Dr. Cooper had anything to do with planting the newspaper story and went on to give Dr. Cooper's assessment of his jealous detractors:

"I am often amused at the thousand and one ridiculous and inconsistent accusations brought against me by medical men of this city. The last grand crime it is alleged I have committed is, that I gave money to establish the *Pacific Medical and Surgical Journal,* that it was my bantling, and designed alone as a puffing medium.

"How any man of sense could have considered the matter thus, I am unable to see. True, some of my surgical operations were published in the Journal, but that is susceptible of the simplest explanation in the world, viz: *that I had the operations to publish.*

"The snarling quotation, published as editorial in the last number of the Journal, will, I hope, free me from the disgraceful accusation alluded to, by showing that whatever pecuniary sacrifice I was ready to make, and did make, was for the benefit of the profession, as well as for myself.

"The gratitude of the Editors may be best judged of by others. The vindication of their own course I leave to themselves." *

When not occupied in fighting each other California doc-

---

* In Cooper vs. *Pacific Medical and Surgical Journal,* the bone of contention was an ankle operation.

tors were for many years busily engaged in a running battle against quack healers. On the need to curb quacks nearly all were agreed, though, of course, there was some difference of opinion in defining the term.

The rivalries between regulars, homeopaths, and eclectics continued for a long time, but they at least represented medical systems. The more urgent problem lay in asserting some control over the hordes of self-appointed doctors who cluttered the scene.

One of the difficulties was a brisk black market in medical diplomas, both fraudulent and genuine documents being offered for sale. Some quacks bought diplomas from physicians' widows, thereafter assuming the name of the deceased as a professional alias. Then, too, there were mail-order diploma mills which offered certification for a price. As a confusing result, some apprentice-trained doctors in good standing could show no diploma, while others had diplomas but no training at all.

There were some who simply invented such accreditation as seemed required. An ingenious example was provided by a Dr. Barlow Smith; he gave to his clinic quite an air of class by calling it "The Smithsonian Medical and Hygienic Institute."

Still others found the most convincing "diploma" of all to be a newspaper advertisement, pithily phrased. The ads were subject to just one legal restraint—a ban on abortion—and those who practiced in that field found an easy way to evade the restriction. The tip-off on an abortionist was a medication advertised with big black-lettered warning that it was "*Not* for Pregnant Women."

Another favorite field for charlatans was the treatment of "wasting manhood." That covered just about everything from venereal disease to impotence to old age. Often the peddlers of sex nostrums reinforced the lurid ads by outfitting an office with an "Anatomical Museum" which displayed reproductive organs in frightening states of disrepair.

Museum procedures were described by Dr. Henry Gibbons, a San Francisco physician who obtained a frank and, indeed, brazen confession from the proprietor of a typical establishment. The quack's routine, said Dr. Gibbons, went about like this:

"The patient is scarcely sick—does not know whether he is sick or well—has heard a lecture at the 'Anatomical Museum', which is part of the scheme, and which has started some apprehension in his mind. A fee of $5 or $10 secures a hearing. The urine must be examined while the patient waits. If he be a man of consequence in the community, the 'doctor' puts on large airs and keeps him waiting an hour or two, in the style of the Pontiff and Prince Henry. Finally, the strutting finished, and the impatient patient sufficiently impressed with the preliminary demonstrations, the mountebank sits at his side and proceeds solemnly: "Now, Mr. Shivers, you must control your feelings and remain composed. I don't wish to alarm you, sir, but you are in a bad way. Your urine is full of animalcules. The microscope shows them plainly. Be tranquil, sir; your case is not desperate; but your blood is full of spermatozoa. Let me show you the danger, sir. (Here the artist draws on paper two parallel lines to represent a bloodvessel, and pencils a number of eels wriggling along endwise.) Now, sir, as long as the animalcules swim endwise there is no difficulty. They circulate all about the body without injury. But let one of them get crosswise, so. Don't you see the effect—to obstruct the bloodvessel instantly? And then you drop dead, sir! This is one cause of so many sudden deaths. Be calm, sir; I don't wish to alarm you. But if you were to leave my office now, and some one were to come in presently and tell me that a man had fallen dead at the corner of Stockton street, I should know it was you.' "

Ridiculous as the spiel sounds, it had its effect. Dr. Gibbons reported that credulous patients paid as much as $500 for a quick cure to that "sideways" condition.

Reported also by Dr. Gibbons was the whimsical tale of a medical con man who called himself Dr. Young. He operated in the general field, offering wide-ranging cures, and his talents for promotion were such that patients came flocking to his door. However, he was a quack with a conscience. He installed a salaried physician, instructing him to dispense treatments while posing as head of the enterprise. Young himself sat in the receiving room, acting the part of clerk and receptionist, and, incidentally, keeping his eye on the till.

Most of the charlatans were not all that self-effacing. They prescribed freely, conducted examinations without the least hesitation, and inscribed their names on medical reports. Thus in California archives one can find death certificates which attribute the cause of demise to such interesting conditions as "Evil in the Bladder" and "Effects of the Jiggers."

The attempts to curb quack healers seemed at times a hopeless struggle. The medical practitioners were too badly divided to apply effective pressure; the newspapers opposed reforms which would cut off lucrative advertising, and the public viewed with high suspicion any attempt to establish a medical monopoly. Eventually, however, some control was achieved, the first tentative steps being taken when California adopted the Medical Practice Act in 1876.

The law was a patchwork affair which in effect instructed the medical profession to regulate itself. All practitioners were required to obtain licenses, and the state medical societies were assigned the responsibility of setting up Boards of Examiners to act as licensing agents. As to the differing medical systems, the law took a neutral position, the regulars, eclectics, and homeopaths all maintaining separate boards.

For the homeopaths the regulation presented a problem. They were engrossed in internal squabbles at the time and spent two years fighting over which faction would control their board. The regulars had their troubles, too; they were soon plagued by phantom societies which sprang up for the purpose of licensing "regular irregulars." Despite such drawbacks, however, the passage of the law can be taken as marking the Great Divide in California medicine. From that time on the state was committed to official definitions as to who could practice medicine and under what conditions.*

As chance had it, the Medical Practice Act coincided closely with the appearance of the second generation of California physicians. That event occurred in 1874, when Dr. Robert Armisted McLean was graduated from the University of California. He was California's first native son to earn a medical degree from one of the state's own institutions.

Young Dr. McLean represented a full flowering of the pioneer medical tradition. His father, Dr. Samuel Merryweather McLean, had rounded the Horn in 1849 and had wandered all through the gold fields in the role of camp doctor. The boy had been born at Stockton in 1851, the first male child of that community, and was known to the old-timers as "the Stockton baby." After the fashion of old-timers some of them were still calling him that years later when he became dean of the medical faculty at the University of California.

And so an era ended. For long years, however, the atmosphere of it lingered on in the memories of old men and in the legends which clustered around other men who never lived to be old. Among all who shared in it the adventure was an experience which ever afterward set them apart as a special breed.

Some of them acquired such a taste for adventure that they

* With the advent of medical regulation the regulars began to gain ascendancy, though practitioners of the other systems hung on in considerable numbers well into the twentieth century. In 1910 a survey of California's 4,500 doctors revealed a ratio of 77 per cent regulars, 13 per cent homeopaths, 10 per cent eclectics.

went on wandering for the rest of their days. Dr. Palmer, who was San Francisco's first city physician, went on to new exploits in India. And Dr. Middleton drifted to Mexico, dying there as a victim of bandits.

Some stayed in California to pioneer in new ways. Drs. Cooper and Toland became great educators, each founding a medical college.[1]

Many earned high place in their profession, and two were elected president of the American Medical Association. The honor went to men of very different stripes—Sacramento's scholarly, fact-minded Dr. Logan, and San Francisco's colorful and contentious Dr. Cole.

There were still others who played only a minor role in the adventure and yet ever afterward remembered it as the high point of their experience. Dr. M'Collum was one of those. He summed up for many what it was like to be a part of that harsh, wild, questing time when ordinary men lived extraordinary lives.

Dr. M'Collum was middle-aged, comfortably settled in a small-town practice, when he abandoned everything to join the rush. He recorded the crowded, filthy conditions of his steamer, calling it "a glimpse of the elephant," and he endured the rigors of Panama. In California he doctored some and dug a lot; he became one of those erstwhile professional men who roamed the hills ragged, bewhiskered and stinking of sweat. And he found some gold—just enough to pay his passage home when he had had enough of mining.

In his diary he noted the other things that men like himself had sought and found:

"Partaking of the mania of the day, catching a portion of the spirit of enterprise and adventure, I became one of an association who resolved to see, and be, a part of that of which we were hearing so much. For myself, I confess, or rather affirm, that the prospect of mining in that far off region, inviting as it then was—glittering and bright as report had made it—did far less in inviting me into the enterprise, than the novelty of it, the charms and inducements that encountering even perils and hardships sometimes creates.

"I went to see, rather than to acquire. I am not a sufficient devotee of gold to break my neck, or endanger my health and life to obtain it. It was a wild, I may almost acknowledge, a hair brained adventure; and yet it is over and past; a recollection of it is mingled with many pleasant, as well as unpleasant reflections. In looking back there are no regrets, no wishes that it had not been undertaken. With California, and all that is in it, and belongs to it, I quit even."

CHAPTER NOTES

Chapter Notes

CHAPTER 1

1 The word estimate must be written large in all gold-rush migration figures. However, various trail counts and harbor-master reports provide the basis for a reasonable guess.

Conservative figures place the 1849 movement at 30,000 to 35,000 by land, 20,000 to 25,000 by sea. The sea total included a colorful admixture of contingents arriving from Latin America, Asia, Australia, and Europe. Land movements included the California, Santa Fe and Gila Trails.

Figures for the entire gold rush are more difficult to establish, though again there are some base lines. In 1848 California's population was about 15,000. By 1852, with the main surge of the movement behind, it had risen to some 250,000. The movement was even larger than the increase suggests, for one must add the many casualties and the considerable number who stayed for brief periods and then returned home.

2 Casualty estimates are even more speculative than the migration totals. Dr. Stillman underlined that point while observing that his own one-out-of-five figure was on the conservative side.

In a report to the *New York Journal of Medicine,* Dr. Stillman wrote: "The chaotic state in which society was thrown together during the first few months of its existence was very unfavorable for statistical information. It was not until about the beginning of the year 1850 that any attempt was made, even in Sacramento City, by the temporary government, to keep a record of the deaths simply, and that was so imperfect as to be of no value. The opinions of medical men were contradictory; and an unfortunate tendency to exaggerations, and a loose method of generalizing facts, made it difficult to arrive at any conclusions further than were forced upon oneself by his own observations."

3 Lacking medical regulations of its own, California was dependent on the standards of all the states from which it drew its physicians. And that came very close to being no standard at all.

The anarchic state of the profession can be summed up in the fact that fifteen of thirty-one states had abandoned all regulation of medicine by 1851, while eight other states had never had such laws. The abdication of legal responsibility reflected in part the confusion and doubt arising from a scientific revolution that was still a-borning; in part also the trend reflected a kind of populist revolt against "the establishment."

In the process all sorts of weird cults flourished. One of the strangest was phrenology, a system which purported to reveal secrets of the body, mind, and character through interpretation of bumps on the head. It didn't begin as a healing system, but it soon branched out into medicine and indeed into nearly every other aspect of human life. Moreover, its first protagonist in the United States was Dr. Charles Caldwell, a medical instructor at respected Transylvania University in Lexington, Ky.

Some other physicians were also taken in by phrenology. Thus Viennese phrenologist Johann Kaspar Spurzheim was invited to lecture before the medical faculties of Yale and Harvard. Spurzheim made a striking impression at Yale when he illustrated his theories by dissecting a brain. After his death Harvard paid him appropriate homage by enshrining Spurzheim's own pickled brain as an honored exhibit.

Another eloquent spokesman for phrenology was Henry Ward Beecher. He was influenced perhaps by the fact that phrenologists found the Beecher skull to be studded with remarkably prominent Bumps of Eloquence, Benevolence, Power of Thought, and Splendor of Diction.

Phrenology got its final boost from one John Rodes Buchanan, a Kentuckian who was president of the National Eclectic Medical Association in 1848. Buchanan attempted to integrate phrenology, animal magnetism, and medicine in a chaotic system which he variously described as anthropology, neurology, and therapeutic sarcognomy. That, however, was a bit too much. It never caught on.

[4] The theory of heroic remedies originated in Europe but received its most vigorous expression in America. The idea of bold, dramatic treatments just suited the spirit of the country, the West especially.

In the case of bleeding there was a hallowed tradition which traced back to Dr. Benjamin Rush, a signer of the Declaration of Independence, and the so-called founder of American medicine. Dr. Rush believed that up to four-fifths of the blood should be withdrawn in extreme cases. Fortunately he didn't know how much blood the body contained, but even so he drained some patients of more than a gallon at a time.

Another powerful exponent of sanguinary measures was Dr. Daniel Drake of Cincinnati, the founder of the first medical school in Ohio. Dr. Drake was a physician and teacher of great stature; for nearly three decades preceding the gold rush he was a towering influence on frontier medical thought. Generally he used that influence in the service of enlightenment, but when it came to bleeding cholera patients he advised his students thus:

"To bleed a patient who cannot be raised from his pillow without fainting, whose pulse is nearly imperceptible, whose skin is cold, and extremities shrunk up to half their ordinary size, would at first view seem rash and unwarrantable. But experience, which in medicine can grant warrants for any procedure, has sanctioned the use of the lancet even when all these and other symptoms of extreme prostration be present." He added that in patients near death from prostration the blood "generally flows with difficulty and sometimes not at all, though large veins be opened. In every desperate case, recourse should be had to the jugulars."

When Dr. Drake's students came to play their part in gold-rush medicine they sometimes took the old master's advice and sometimes not. The era which spanned the rush was for medicine a time of transition; the orthodox were still stoutly defending the old system, but an increasing number were beginning to ameliorate or discard the most debilitating features. The change cannot be pinned down to an exact period, but generally speaking, bleeding was still very common in the gold rush; ten years later it had virtually disappeared from the scene. There were, however, a few holdouts who kept the idea of bleeding alive almost to the edge of the twentieth century. Thus in Philadelphia in 1878 a prominent professor of medicine was still advising his students to "draw enough to make a profound impression."

5 Calomel, the mercurial salivator and purgative, was the other great stand-by of heroic treatment. In fact, calomel and bleeding were often described together as being the "sheet anchors" of medical practice. One nineteenth-century physician boasted proudly that he had drawn enough blood to float a steamboat and prescribed enough calomel to load it.

Allowing for the hyperbole of the times, it was indeed administered in massive quantities. In 1844 Dr. T. D. Mitchell of Transylvania University charged openly that many physicians were killing their patients with overdoses. Dr. Mitchell cited extreme cases in which calomel was given at a rate of "table spoonful doses every hour, until the patient held, somewhere between the mouth and the rectum, *a pound* of the article." But attacks on such practice were met with furious rebuttal, one defender of calomel calling it "THE MASTEDON IN HARNESS, to do the work of an AGE in a YEAR."

As evidenced by such dispute, calomel also was marked for discard. Its decline, however, was more gradual, reliance on calomel still being widespread as late as the Civil War.

6 Dr. Felix Paul Wierzbicki was a man inclined to sweeping naturalistic views. As a hydropath he saw water as holding the key to all health, and when he turned to prospecting he found earth revealing its secrets through the kind of growth which it supported. Dr. Wierzbicki's formula: "Where there is oak, there is apt to be gold. When oak gives way to pine, quartz pinches out."

Such theories aside—and they were not eccentric views for the time—Dr. Wierzbicki was a shrewd observer of the scene. In his book, *Cali-*

fornia As It Is and As It May Be, or A Guide To The Gold Regions, he left a valuable record of the times. The work is said to be the first English-language book to be printed in California.

[7] Smallpox vaccine was introduced into pre–gold-rush California by one James Ohio Pattie, a trapper and trader who took up medical practice as a way of escaping jail.

Pattie entered Lower California in 1828 in company with his father, Sylvester, and six other Americans. They were promptly arrested and imprisoned by Mexicans, who suspected them of being advance agents for military aggression. Then word came that smallpox was spreading through the Indians. Fortunately the trappers had brought some smallpox vaccine along for purposes of trading. Accordingly Pattie now presented himself as a leading authority on vaccination. He became surgeon-extraordinary to His Excellency the Governor, vaccinating thousands of natives and colonists throughout the territory, and winning in return the parole of his party.

Pattie's father died in the Mexican jail before release was granted, and Pattie himself was much broken in health when he returned to Kentucky in 1830. But when the gold rush began he could not resist another fling at California. He appeared in San Diego sometime after 1850; his subsequent fate is not known.

[8] Quinine began as a witch-doctor remedy. The basic drug was first used by South American tribal healers who extracted it from the bark of the cinchona tree.

According to one account, it was discovered by Western man about 1630, when a native healer cured an ailing Spanish governor by administering a cinchona brew. Later the Jesuits played a leading role in introducing cinchona to Europe, the medication being known at one time as "Jesuit bark."

Great cinchona plantations were ultimately established, but in gold-rush times the supplies of bark still depended on collections made in the jungle. Quinine was correspondingly expensive and often hard to obtain at any price.

CHAPTER 2

[1] Dr. Fourgeaud pioneered in the medical as well as the physical sense. In St. Louis he conducted what was probably the city's first epidemiological study, a statistical survey of the causes and incidence of infant mortality.

He also made his mark at St. Louis as co-editor of the *Medical and Surgical Journal.* It was a vigorous publication, at a time when medical questions were debated as hotly as politics, and Dr. Fourgeaud was soon caught up in such acrimonious dispute that he resigned and went West.

In California he continued to exhibit both a talent for controversy and a show-me approach to medical theory. A typical instance of his inquiring spirit involved a then current dispute as to whether the heart sounds were produced within the organ or by reverberations of the heart against the chest wall. While operating on a wounded sailor in San Francisco, Dr. Fourgeaud settled the question to his own satisfaction by reaching into the thoracic cavity and taking hold of the heart. The sailor survived.

2 The maiden voyage of the Pacific Mail's *California* was in many respects a précis of the misadventures that would befall many another gold-rush vessel.

The first misfortune occurred at Rio de Janeiro where the ship laid up for ten days while Captain Marshall endured a near fatal hemorrhage of the lungs. Though greatly weakened, he insisted on remaining at his post throughout the turbulent events that followed.

The fast-spreading gold rush overtook the ship at Callao, Peru, about a hundred Peruvians getting aboard there when the *California* stopped for supplies. Later, at Panama City, there was a near riot as stranded American adventurers learned that foreigners had pre-empted almost half the berths. Captain Marshall stoutly resisted demands that he put the Peruvians off, but he agreed as a compromise to crowd in an extra American for every foreigner. The *California* left Panama with 365 passengers, or 145 per cent of the registered capacity; the ship as a consequence ran out of food and fuel, and Captain Marshall had to forage his way up the coast, scrounging supplies wherever he could.

An additional crisis developed when the captain fined a stoker who had smuggled a stowaway aboard. The engine-room crew mutinied in support of the seaman, but the insurrection was suppressed when the ringleaders were put ashore at Mazatlán, Mexico.

A further tribulation was a shortage of fuel. In completing the voyage the captain all but dismantled his ship, feeding to the boilers the berths, the spars, even parts of the deck.

When the ship reached San Francisco the entire crew deserted to the mines. It was three months before the *California* was able to resume her Panama run.

CHAPTER 3

1 Cholera was one of the great afflictions of the nineteenth century. To Western man it was a new and mysterious danger.

The ancestral home of the disease was the Ganges delta of India. At least that's where westerners first encountered it. In 1817 a Ganges outbreak killed 9000 British troops. Thereafter recurrent waves of cholera radiated out to envelop huge areas of Asia, Africa, Europe, and the Americas.

The pandemics were part of a pattern in which increased travel and trade served to mingle pools of contagion from all over the world. The diseases thus transmitted often underwent a deadly sea change, striking with added virulence at populations which lacked the immunity acquired through long exposure.

The first American experience with cholera was an outbreak which raged intermittently from 1832 to 1834. It was for many communities a major disaster. New Orleans was so scourged that the city at one point resorted to trench burials for casualties estimated at up to three hundred a week. Chicago was virtually evacuated when the populace took to the woods rather than risk the infection that stalked through the town. Detroit tried vainly to quiet a similar panic by forbidding the tolling of funeral bells while the epidemic raged. The Detroit gesture was peculiarly symbolic of ineffectual resistance; the banning of church bells could scarcely conceal the situation when a disposal cart rumbled day and night through the streets, the driver calling, "Bring out your dead."

After running its course in the 1830s cholera disappeared completely from the American scene until reintroduced at the time of the gold rush. That set off a second, equally deadly, and much more prolonged epidemic wave, outbreaks occurring each year until 1854. The disease then subsided until a last big outbreak in 1866.

Throughout the epidemic years the cause of the cholera remained a mystery. The question was finally resolved in 1883 when German scientist Robert Koch identified the agent as *Vibrio comma,* a motile bacterium which attacks the intestine and is excreted in human waste. The bacterium is transmitted primarily through contaminated drinking water.

[2] In *The Cholera Years* (University of Chicago Press, 1962) Charles E. Rosenberg tabulated medical opinions on the cause of cholera as expressed during the 1849 outbreak. The results illustrate the medical confusion of the period.

The Rosenberg survey covered 146 physicians who wrote about the disease. Among that number 33 stated no clear opinion as to cause. For the rest, 35 favored some general atmospheric influence, 16 specified a miasma, 7 suggested either an excess or a deficiency of electricity in the atmosphere, 4 said an excess of nitrogen or a lack of oxygen, 3 attributed it to an animal poison. There were 5 who blamed tiny, invisible fungoid or animalculae, and 4 guessed microscopic germs.

More than two-thirds of the physicians sampled believed that cholera was noncontagious. That view, however, was decidedly not shared by the general public. In some outbreaks the dead went unburied for days because no one could be induced to touch the bodies, and the announcement that a cholera hospital was being established in a neighborhood was sometimes enough to precipitate a riot.

Looking back, it is not hard to understand why the public considered the disease contagious, while a great many physicians did not. The physicians, after all, had to deal with the thing. It was their duty to expose themselves day and night while treating the victims. For their own peace of mind a good many physicians must have grasped hard at the straws of noncontagious theory.

3 Rosenberg graphically documents the changing medical and social attitudes toward cholera in the period spanning the three great American outbreaks.

In 1832 the prevailing view was both moralistic and fatalistic. Cholera was regarded as God's will, perhaps even his judgment; if it was not a divine curse exactly, it was at least a natural consequence of the depraved and vicious habits ascribed to slum dwellers. So strong was such feeling that the great Cincinnati physician Dr. Daniel Drake felt constrained to apologetics when he found evidence that the disease struck quite impartially at alcoholics and abstainers from liquor. "I expect," wrote Drake, "to be censured for publishing this fact. But I am writing a medical history, not a temperance address. There are obligations to science as well as morality; and they can never, in fact, be incompatible."

Dr. Drake suspected that cholera was caused by invisible animalculae and was one of the first American physicians to urge a cleanup of infested areas. Most communities, however, had to suffer wave after wave of epidemic before the sanitation lesson was finally driven home.

The turning point in control of cholera came with the epidemic of 1866. Medical men were agreed by then that it was contagious, whatever the cause, and that something could be done about it. The effect of such changed attitude was dramatically underlined in New York. The city which had been so casual about quarantine before now fitted out a hospital ship as detention quarters for infected immigrants. And when the contagion got past that guard the board of health was prepared for incisive action. Health inspectors invested with police power patrolled the streets, issuing cleanup orders at the rate of one thousand a week. As cases appeared an alarm was flashed and a disinfectant crew appeared on the scene within the hour; they burned the clothing, utensils, and effects of the victim, doused the building with chloride of lime, spread barrels of coal tar around the area as further disinfectant. There were some howls of outrage at the highhanded methods of sanitation squads, but when it was over a grateful city acknowledged a job well done. New York's cholera deaths that year were only 593, about one-tenth of the loss suffered in the 1849 outbreak.

4 New Orleans in the 1840s was an appalling city even by nineteenth-century standards. Located on swampy ground, it had no proper drainage, no sanitation system worth the name. It lacked a public water supply, the people obtaining their water by catching rain in open

wooden cisterns which became breeding grounds for insects. In such environment cholera was just one more affliction, adding to a casualty rate already swollen by incessant epidemics of malaria, yellow fever, dysentery, and typhoid.

New Orleans was so unconcerned with its health problem that civic officials didn't know what the death rate was. A medical reformer named Dr. John Simonds made that his point of attack when he began agitating for corrective methods. He counted the casualties for a 52-month period, from 1846 to early 1850, and published his findings under the dry but informative title, *On The Sanitary Condition of New Orleans as Illustrated by its Mortuary Statistics.* The tabulation: Out of a mean population of 106,885 the city had suffered 37,785 deaths and 755,700 illnesses.

The Simonds report helped to shock New Orleans into establishing its first permanent board of health. The report was also important as a new approach to medical investigation. The statistical method would later be used to focus even more sharply on specific relationships between environment and illness.

CHAPTER 4

1 The state of native health in Panama was not accurately surveyed until work began on the Panama Canal in 1904. The annual death rate was placed then at 49.94 per 1,000, equivalent to a complete population turnover every twenty years, with yellow fever and malaria the chief killers. There is every reason to suppose that the toll in gold-rush times was at least equally high.

During the canal-building era the isthmus was cleaned up by the great soldier-physician General William Gorgas. By killing the mosquitoes, draining the stagnant pools, and cleaning up the refuse he got rid of yellow fever in seven months; in four history-making years the total death rate on the isthmus was reduced more than half.

Despite the immense sanitation campaign the ten-year canal-building job cost 6,630 lives. It is estimated that without the cleanup effort more than 75,000 would have died.

2 An interesting item in Dr. M'Collum's suggested medicine chest was the Dover's powder, an opium and ipecac compound. It had some villainous connotations both medically and historically.

Originator of the powder was Dr. Thomas Dover, an eighteenth-century buccaneer physician who commanded a raiding ship in a daring expedition against Spain's South American colonies. He may also have sailed as a slaver. In his later years, as a British physician, he concocted his famous powder.

Dr. Dover's original formula called for an ounce each of opium, ipecac, and licorice, plus four ounces each of saltpeter and tartar, the powdered compound being given to the patient in doses of 40 to 70 grains. At such dosages about the best that could be said for it was that the ipecac brought the opium back up, the patient receiving a thunderous shaking as the concoction passed through his system.

A less dramatic version of Dover's powder still survives, the formula being a 10 per cent concentration of opium and ipecac in a lactose compound, given in 5- to 10-grain doses. It is useful in promoting sweating.

CHAPTER 5

1 The fate of the Baker children is not recorded, but doubtlessly some friend or stranger took them in. Somehow or other gold-rush orphans did find homes.

One who became noted for succoring waifs was Dr. David Gould Webber, a Pennsylvania physician who went out via Panama in 1850. An adventurer with a strong civilizing bent, he combined medicine and mining with such other occupations as farming, running a sawmill, constructing roads and buildings, and superintending a school. When his two children died he began to take in homeless youngsters. Ultimately he raised nine orphans, two of whom followed him into medicine.

2 George Blanchard's act in preserving the names of casualties involved something more than sentimental gesture. Many who died were not recorded at all and so vanished like men listed as missing in war. For years after the gold rush California newspapers carried notices from people back East asking for information on relatives who had disappeared.

Of course, there was another side to the disappearance question. Some who vanished meant to.

CHAPTER 6

1 Nicaragua was comparatively healthy by tropic standards, but even so disease at times exerted a decisive role in the country's history.

A major instance occurred in 1780 when British and Spanish forces battled over possession of the same isthmus route that gold rushers would later use. The British were led by Captain Horatio Nelson, then twenty years old and just starting his brilliant military career. Nelson's raiders overran Spanish defenses and seemed on the point of victory when an extremely virulent fever broke out. The epidemic killed nine out of ten in the landing party, and Nelson himself very nearly succumbed; he was ill for many months and suffered for years from the aftereffects.

In the late 1850s, when the gold rush had tapered off into a continu, ing California migration, disease again played a military role on the Nicaraguan isthmus. This time it involved the filbustering invasion led by William Walker. The incredible Walker kept the area in turmoil for five years, from 1856 to 1860, and at one time succeeded in installing himself as Nicaraguan president. His ultimate failure was due to numerous causes, chiefly his own overreaching ambition, but cholera contributed heavily by weakening his troops at a critical moment.

2 A large majority of the gold rushers remained as California settlers, but many thousands returned home after their fling at the mines. The perils of the return trip comprise one of the little-known gold-rush epics.

Documentation is scarce, probably because men homeward bound felt less need to record their experiences in journals and letters. However, such facts as exist indicate that the return was just as hazardous as the original trip.

The epidemic toll among returnees was attested by a big gold-rush graveyard at Kingston, Jamaica, the first port of call for ships leaving Panama for east-coast ports. The death rate on some homeward-bound ships was also recorded. An outstanding case was the steamer *Philadelphia* which lost more than a third of its 155 passengers to cholera during a run up from Chagres in 1852.

A personal glimpse of the return-trip hazard was provided by J. M. Letts. He went out via Panama and returned through Nicaragua, encountering much illness on both routes. In New York Harbor, almost at the end of his round-trip odyssey, Letts wrote in his diary: "As we are nearing the dock, the death of one of the passengers is announced. He was the *last* of a party of six that had embarked for, and I believe the only one of the party who lived to reach California."

CHAPTER 7

1 Gold rushers depended for food preservation on salting, smoking, and drying, all methods which dated back to Neolithic times.

Canning and mechanical refrigeration had been discovered by mid-nineteenth century, but both were still in such imperfect state of development as to be virtually useless to the migrants. In the case of canning there was a persistent problem of contamination by gas-producing bacterium, food putrefying as a result, and the cans exploding. At the time the cause of such spoilage was not known.

Once the nature of the bacterium was understood the canning problem was solved easily enough by processing the food at higher temperatures. Had that simple technique been discovered a little earlier, the hardships of the gold rush would have been immeasurably reduced.

2 Many gold-rush ships carried livestock, and some were almost floating farms. A voyage on an unusually well-stocked vessel was described by Mrs. Elizabeth Gunn who went out with four children in order to join her physician husband, Dr. Lewis Gunn.

Mrs. Gunn sailed in 1851 on an elite clipper, the *Bengal*, bound from Philadelphia for China with a quite incidental way stop at San Francisco. The *Bengal*'s captain declined to jeopardize his primary trading mission by taking on a big passenger list, and only the Gunn family and two other argonauts were privileged to be aboard.

Passengers and crew shared the ship with 120 chickens, 120 ducks, a large flock of geese, and 17 pigs. The ship's larder was well supplied in other respects, too, so that Mrs. Gunn began to worry about getting fat. She left Philadelphia a trim little woman, about ninety-three pounds, and by the time she reached California she was pushing one hundred.

3 Seagoing argonauts encountered some odd bits of lore about the edibility of marine food. One such notion involved the dolphin. The mammal was frequently cooked with a silver dollar in its stomach, the belief being that the dollar would turn black if the meat were poisonous.

The ritual of dollar-in-the-dolphin was often followed blindly without inquiring why. In one instance, however, a captain offered his passengers an explanation. The dolphins foraged on the ocean bottom, the captain said, and in the process picked up quantities of copper. During cooking the copper distilled into the silver dollar, turning it black if a dangerous concentration was present. To gold rushers, newly imbued with metallurgic enthusiasm, the proposition probably seemed reasonable enough.

4 Gold rusher Joseph Kendall reported what may have been another pseudomedical superstition. Or then again, it's just possible that Kendall was the victim of a rather cruel practical joke. In any case, when he sailed through the sweltering tropics he was warned against making his bed on deck.

Wrote Kendall: "It is very dangerous, the captain says, to sleep with the moon shining on one. He says it is as bad as being sun-struck."

After a few nights in the furnace-like hold Kendall decided to take his chances with moonstroke.

CHAPTER 8

1 The Oregon, Mormon, and California Trails were all closely related in geographical terms and shared some common history as well.

The main lines of the Oregon and California Trails were identical for more than half the distance, the common route including the first long stretch that ran from Independence to Fort Laramie and on to South Pass. Beyond South Pass the California Trail split into many branches, but a principal segment of it continued along the Oregon route for nearly 300 miles more. This combined trackway zigzagged through the Rockies, running down to Fort Bridger in southwest Wyoming and up to Fort Hall on the Snake River in Idaho. About two days' march beyond Fort Hall, the two great trails finally parted to go their separate ways.

The Mormon Trail is less important to this story, but still it played a considerable part; it too could be followed more than halfway to California. This one started at Council Bluffs, Iowa. In Nebraska it intersected the Oregon-California route, or, rather, it almost did. The lay of the land was such that across the plains the Mormon path ran along the north bank of the Platte River, while the other route was just a river's width away on the opposite bank. Gold rushers who took the Mormon Trail enjoyed a distinct advantage in that their side of the bank was far less crowded.

At Fort Laramie the Mormon Trail merged with the others, the three routes mingling until Fort Bridger was reached. Then division occurred again, the California-Oregon route swinging north, the Mormon Trail angling southwest. The gold rushers had a choice here; they could stay with the Mormon Trail, pass through Salt Lake City, and rejoin their own route by taking a cutoff. It was advantageous to do so in that Salt Lake City offered an opportunity for resupply. But many chose to bypass the settlement because of the tensions between Mormons and "Gentiles."

Aside from the intertwined routes, the three trails had a good deal of folk history in common. The pathways all emerged in the same period from great mass movements of people.

Until 1840 only a few bold adventurers had moved over any of these routes. The mountain men Jedediah Smith and Joe Walker had led the way to California. The physician-missionary Dr. Marcus Whitman had blazed the trail into Oregon. These men and their companions and followers constituted the tiny handful of Americans who had gone all the way West across this particular span of the continent. And then came the surge.

All through the 1840s the trails were peopled increasingly by pioneers seeking land, by religious outcasts seeking haven, by adventurers seeking excitement and gold. The travelers appeared by the dozens at first, then by the hundreds, then by the thousands and tens of thousands.

In 1841 the first thin sprinkle consisted of 33 people bound for California and about 100 more for Oregon.

By 1843 the Oregon traffic had swollen to 900 people, moving over the trail with a thousand cattle in what was then the greatest wagon train the West had seen.

In 1847 it was the Mormons, 1,800 strong in their first wave.

In 1849 it was the gold rushers, more than 22,000 of them in the first surge, with more than a hundred thousand soon to follow. Thus in a decade three trails West were trampled out.

2 When the first wagon-train survivors staggered into California in 1841 they were half starved and wholly exhausted. But they assumed that their troubles were over when they arrived at the ranch of a fellow American, a physician and entrepreneur known as Dr. Juan Marsh.

The migrants supposed that Dr. Marsh would welcome them with openhanded hospitality. He, however, took it for granted that people so desperate would be glad to pay and pay dearly for whatever they needed. When he found they were nearly penniless he demanded their possessions in exchange for food; he also tried unsuccessfully to charge them a "passport fee" of $5 apiece.

People were always being disillusioned like that by Dr. Marsh.

Before digressing further on this subject the writer will pause to concede that Dr. Marsh didn't take part in the gold rush, that he practiced little if any medicine during the gold-rush period, and that his medical credentials were fraudulent in any case. In fact, there is no reason to remember him here, except that he's too interesting a rascal to be entirely forgotten.

Here, then, in brief aside is the story of Dr. Marsh.

He was born John Marsh in Danvers, Mass., in 1799. He attended Harvard, graduating at twenty-four with a fine education in the classics. Along the way he studied for both the ministry and medicine, but the first profession proved unsuitable to his talents, and the second he didn't quite achieve. Instead, he went to Wisconsin as the first schoolteacher in that territory.

He became a subagent to the Indians, made friends with the Sioux, and devised for them the first alphabet in their language. He also formed a common-law alliance with a part-Indian woman, the marriage producing a son, Charles, who would later become a fearsome frontier character in his own right.

In 1832 Marsh abandoned his post and deserted his family, departing just ahead of a warrant charging him with gunrunning to the Indians. He drifted to Independence, Missouri, ran a saloon there, and failed to prosper. A few years later he went on to California, going by the already established Santa Fe Trail. On the trail he was captured by Indians; he got out of that tight spot by giving medical treatment to an ailing chief.

In Los Angeles (pop. 1,250) Marsh presented himself as a physician, submitting as brash document his teacher's diploma which was written in Latin. The civil authorities in the little Spanish town couldn't read

Latin, so they turned the question over to a panel of priests. The good padres couldn't read Latin either, but they could hardly afford to admit it; they wagged their heads in solemn agreement, and Dr. Juan Marsh hung up his shingle.

He exchanged his medical services for cowhides, acquired a great stack of hides worth $500, and used the money to buy a ranch. That's where the migrants found him in 1841.

If Dr. Marsh did not assist California's travelers much, he did a lot to keep them coming. He became one of California's first boosters, writing to newspapers back in the States to describe the beauty of the land, the allure of the climate, the rich yield from the crops. Clearly he had in mind another kind of rich yield that might accrue to him if the empty regions began to fill up.

Then the gold rushers arrived, and the land did fill up, and the dreams all came true. Dr. Marsh prospered in mining, merchandising, and ranching; he built a splendid stone castle for himself and a new bride; he ruled like a feudal lord over holdings valued at half a million dollars. And the more he prospered the more hardfisted and imperious he became. He developed the bad habit of not paying his Mexican ranch hands for months at a time. Sometimes he dismissed them with the back wages still unpaid. That little quirk was to prove his undoing.

One day in 1856 Dr. Marsh met on a road three men who claimed that he owed them wages. Contemptuously he waved them away. Then in a rage they rushed him, robbed him, hacked him to death.

³ The trail adventures of Dr. John Townsend and his family could fill a volume in itself.

It will be recalled that this wagon train split up at a snow-choked Sierra pass, Dr. Townsend, his wife, and his young brother-in-law all accepting separate assignments. The three were due for some remarkable experiences before they met again.

Dr. Townsend pushed through the pass with the main body, delivered the child born at the Yuba River, then went on to Sutter's Fort. There he joined a revolution against the Mexican governor, marching off as Sutter's aide and company surgeon in the Micheltorena campaign.

Mrs. Townsend, meanwhile, was having some arduous adventures of her own. She had ridden with a group that swung down the flank of the mountains, looking for an alternate pass. They found one finally but not until they had done some rugged exploring; in the process they became the first white people of record ever to stand on the shores of Lake Tahoe.

The physician's brother-in-law, seventeen-year-old Moses Schallenberger, had the roughest time of all. He and two others stayed behind to guard some abandoned wagons and supplies. They built themselves a snug little cabin and counted on shooting game and didn't reckon at all on the severity of Sierra's winter. Presently the snow was up to the eaves of the cabin and game was not to be found. They ripped hickory strips off the wagons then, fashioned some clumsy snowshoes, and tried to mush out. The fine powdered snow was ten feet deep, and after a day's desperate struggle young Schallenberger knew he'd never make it. He waved the others on and turned back to the cabin, fully expecting to die.

At the cabin he pulled himself together for a last try at survival. He found some traps in the wagons and set them out. He caught a coyote which proved revolting fare, and a fox which was delicious. After that he ate foxes and kept coyotes in reserve; in due time eleven frozen coyote carcasses hung outside the cabin as his insurance policy against starvation.

Fear and loneliness were harder to insure against, but the abandoned wagons offered something for that too. Dr. Townsend's luggage yielded some books. The youth pored over them all, even the medical texts, but the volumes that really sustained him were Byron's poems and the letters of Lord Chesterfield.

The lonely trial dragged on for nearly a hundred days. Then one evening Schallenberger stood outside his cabin and heard a wild halloo from up the trail. A comrade had learned of his plight and had come back to help. The other was an expert with snowshoes; he made Schallenberger a good pair, taught him to use them, and they got out easily enough.

It must be noted that Schallenberger might have been rescued a good deal earlier if Dr. Townsend hadn't gone rushing off with that revolution. That, however, was the sort of thing that Dr. Townsend's companions came to expect.

It should be recorded, too, that the abandoned wagons included one loaded with the fine silks that Dr. Townsend had planned on selling to the Spanish ladies. After Schallenberger departed some Indians came along, found the wagon, and bedecked themselves in lovely raiment. Again, typical. Dr. Townsend never had luck with his speculative ventures.

[4] In regard to gold-rush trail casualties, it must be noted again that no statistics exist, and even the most informed estimates vary enormously.

The classic California historian, H. H. Bancroft, estimated that in the 1849 trek cholera alone cost 5,000 lives. That figure is sharply disputed, however, by George R. Stewart's modern, well-documented study, *The California Trail* (McGraw-Hill, 1962). Stewart estimates the cholera deaths in 1849 at about 400—a disparity indeed—and places the total deaths for that year's trek at around 750.

This writer feels that Stewart was overly conservative in regard to the inroads of both cholera and scurvy. Even so, a figure somewhere around one thousand would seem a fairly reasonable guess for the toll of the first year's overland migration.

Whatever the figures, the real point is that the trek was rigorous enough. In fact, if a toll of 5 per cent is accepted as about right, then the danger compared closely with the perils of another, very different mass movement that occurred across the choppy waters and shell-pocked sands of Normandy Beach. In that affair some 100,000 men sailed in the D-day armada, and when the beaches were taken about 5,000 of them were dead or missing.

The analogy is valid, too, in that for both events the statistics had no real relation to individual experience. In the great trek, as in the great battle, all depended on what wave one was in, and where in the wave, and what wild chance of circumstance there occurred. Thus one gold rusher could go through unscathed, and with surprising ease, while not far away another was enduring trials he would never forget.

CHAPTER 9

¹ The gold rush produced an outpouring of tall tales, not the least of which were bogus guidebooks advising travelers on how to make the trip. By the spring of 1849 hack writers had rushed to press with more than two dozen so-called guidebooks, most of them based on rumor and speculation, and some of them wildly imaginative.

Inevitably there appeared also some fraudulent accounts of personal adventures in the gold fields. In fact, the first gold-rush doctor memoir was just such a hoax.

The book in question was *Four Months Among the Gold-Finders in California; Being the Diary of an Expedition from San Francisco to the Gold Districts*, by J. Tyrwhitt Brooks, M.D. It was a neat job in that it offered seemingly knowledgeable details, and it didn't claim too much. Dr. Brooks was presented as an Englishman who chanced to be on hand when the discovery was made. He went to the Bear River, amassed a small fortune from medicine and mining, then lost all when he entrusted his gold dust to a courier who was waylaid and robbed.

Four Months Among the Gold-Finders first appeared in England, Dr. Brooks supposedly having sent the manuscript to his brother there. Subsequently the book enjoyed a very nice sale in English, American, German, Dutch, French, and Swedish editions.

Almost half a century later, in 1893, a popular American writer named Henry Vizetelly published an autobiography in which he confessed that Dr. Brooks was a hoax by his hand. He had intended it as a kind of elaborate practical joke, and he had been delighted, of course, when it proved profitable as well.

The cream of the jest is that Dr. Brooks survived exposure. Vizetelly is a rather obscure figure now, and his confession lies largely ignored in the dusty archives, while in other archives J. Tyrwhitt Brooks lives triumphantly on. In some of the best and most reliable accounts of gold-rush medicine one still finds this quack of quacks pursuing his practice.

2 The gold rush was disastrous for Indians. The Plains tribes suffered greatly, being infected with cholera and other ills, while in California a much more vulnerable Indian population was overwhelmed and all but wiped out by the migration's impact.

The California Indians were generally the most primitive of American tribes. They had little reason to be otherwise; for countless centuries prior to the white man's coming they had lived unmolested in a kind of primordial Garden of Eden. The land was rich enough to supply their needs easily, and they were protected from marauders by the sea and by desert and mountain barriers. In such setting they had developed only the most rudimentary skills.

When the Spanish came many of these primitives were virtually enslaved, their descendants being transformed into abject mission Indians. The rest fled into the hills and to the edge of the desert, there grubbing out the kind of existence which earned them the sobriquet of Digger Indians. And then the gold rush rolled over them. The Diggers put up scattered resistance here and there, but it was both feeble and futile. Outnumbered and outgunned, they were driven from their lands; they were also shattered by disease and debilitated by the vices which their conquerors introduced. As a total consequence the Indian population of California was reduced by an estimated 50,000 between 1849 and 1852.

3 The presence of Cherokee companies on the overland trek represented an ironic full turn in the wheel of history. Earlier the Cherokee Nation had participated in another historic migration, not to a gold rush, but away from one.

The Cherokees were a highly advanced people inhabiting the southeastern Appalachian country, notably Georgia and the Carolinas. In the 1830s they were dispossessed by a small-scale gold rush to their territory. The eviction was accomplished in the usual ways, by a dubious treaty; the United States Supreme Court upheld the Cherokee protest, but President Jackson in effect overruled the court. In 1838 the Cherokees were rounded up by the United States Army and conducted to the Indian Territory (Oklahoma) in human herd drives. Of some 13,000 thus transported about one-third perished on what the Cherokees called "The Trail of Tears."

CHAPTER 10

[1] Mountain fever has been recorded in countless gold-rush annals, but the designation remained vague until 1942 when historical diagnosis was offered by Georgia Willis Read, then an assistant editor at Columbia University Press. Working in collaboration with Dr. R. R. Parker, director of the Rocky Mountain Laboratory at Hamilton, Montana, Miss Read offered the theory that the conditions most frequently involved were probably Rocky Mountain spotted fever and Colorado tick fever, especially the latter. The analysis was based both on symptoms reported by the adventurers and on the endemic patterns of the area.

Miss Read should be credited also as the first to document a general pattern in which cholera, mountain fever, and scurvy appeared by turn in well-defined geographical stages of the trek. An outline of the evidence is found in her article, "Diseases, Drugs, and Doctors on the Oregon-California Trail in the Gold Rush Years," *Missouri Historical Review,* April, 1944, Vol. XXXVIII, No. 3, pp. 260–76.

[2] Another important contribution to medical chronicles of the era was Dr. Anthony J. Lorenzo's "Scurvy in the Gold Rush," *Journal of the History of Medicine,* October, 1957, pages 473–510. Dr. Lorenzo pointed out that gold rushers who suffered scurvy on the desert were surrounded all the time by cactus plants containing juices which could relieve the condition.

The plant in question was the prickly pear, or Opuntia. It was first used as an antiscorbutic by the Spanish explorer Sebastian Vizcaino in his California expedition of 1603. By gold-rush times the plant's medicinal properties had been forgotten, but the secret was rediscovered only a decade later by an army surgeon, Dr. E. W. Johns, at Fort Laramie. Dr. Johns's pharmacologic method was to broil the cactus leaves over a fire, then steep them in water to extract a thick greenish-brown mucilaginous residue; the antiscorbutic prescription called for a tumblerful of cactus juice in two ounces of whisky, with essence of lemon for flavoring.

CHAPTER 11

[1] When P. F. Castleman's party took a short cut through the Idaho mountains they were following a route known as Hudspeth's Cutoff. It was a new track which had been laid down only a few weeks earlier by a Missouri train led by Benoni Hudspeth and his scout, J. J. Myers. Hudspeth and Myers were veteran frontiersmen who shared an inclination to gamble. They were leading their company along the Bear River, following an established route which looped north, and they

noted terrain which seemed to offer some chance for a straight run to the west. On sheer speculation, and thinking that they could always retrace their steps if it didn't work out, they swung off to explore.

The venture succeeded; through luck and skill they were able to find a way for the wagons through what soon became a tangled mass of steep inclines and tortuous canyons. At the Raft River they got out of it and rejoined the main trail. Their success was most fortunate, for meantime they were being followed by thousands of others who assumed that men like Hudspeth and Myers knew where they were going. If the migration had been forced to turn around in those tight passages, a disastrous traffic jam could well have resulted.

One who refused to be lured by Hudspeth's Cutoff was J. Goldsborough Bruff. When he came to the turnoff point his company wanted to chance it, but he was skeptical. The question was resolved in the form of a wager, Bruff and a few companions taking the regular trail and betting the others that they would beat them to the point where the two routes linked up. Bruff arranged also to measure the comparative distances, and it turned out that he was essentially right. The cutoff seemed shorter from the evidence of the map, but the apparent advantage was nullified by a series of twists and turns, and the going was much rougher. The comparative distances as reported by Bruff: 132½ miles by the cutoff, 134 miles by the regular route.

2 Another supposed short cut—taken by Castleman, Bruff, and many others—was the ill-famed Lassen's Route. This was the path which branched off from the Humboldt River, swung north almost to Oregon, and then doubled back to Sutter's Fort. It, too, was a trail tramped out by sheer chance, and it proved to be an entire mistake.

The route was named for Peter Lassen, a blacksmith turned explorer and rancher. He got the westering urge early, going to Oregon by land in 1839 and to California by sea in 1840. In 1844 he established a lonely little ranch in northern California. Then ambition bit him and he decided that he could become, like Sutter, the ruler of a wilderness fief. Accordingly in 1848 he returned to the East, collected a party of emigrants, and led them off in the general direction of his ranch.

Despite all his years in the West Lassen knew little of exploring, and his 1848 expedition has passed into folklore as an adventure of legendary incompetence. It is said that he guided by one mountain one day and another the next, not knowing the difference between them. There is a story, too, that at one point his followers threatened to hang him. Other tales are told in the same vein, all of them adding up to the fact that Lassen got lost. Eventually, however, he stumbled through to his ranch, having left behind him a haphazard path.

A year later the gold rushers came along, and great numbers of them branched off to follow Lassen's Route. The mistake does not require much explanation; they arrived at a fork where they had to decide, and some made the wrong choice. The error was largely confined to the first year's migration, because after that the word went back that Lassen's Route was strewn with trouble.

Of Lassen's Route, and of all other dubious short cuts, it can be said that despite their individual defects they did possess some collective merit. The hardships attendant to overcrowding would have been magnified many fold if the adventurers had all followed a single track.

³ The problems presented by the branch paths afford a wry side light on human nature. The adventurers quite often decided that whatever route they were on represented about the worst possible choice. Usually, too, they had a tendency to blame the predicament on the bad judgment of others.

As typical instance, here is Castleman explaining how his group wound up on Lassen's Route:

"We had quite an argument about the way we should go; some saying that they would go by the old road any how, but finally we put it to the vote (which was) so equally divided that it was a tie but as C. Churchill and H. Buckner were boath on the side in favour of going the neare way to the mines, as it was called, the opposing party yielded to their judgment, which was much regretted by all the company long before we reached the settlements."

Even the straightforward Bruff felt need for alibi after choosing Lassen's Route. When the question arose he called his company together, presented cogent reasons for the course as he understood it, and secured a unanimous vote of approval. Six months later he was recalling that he had favored a northern route but "not this long crooked *Lassin's* part of it."

And then there was William Manly of the Death Valley party. Reading his memoirs, one could easily conclude that he was a man of solid judgment who journeyed with rash companions.

Of course, there's nothing surprising in such retroactive reassessment. Presidents and generals have been known to edit their memories to very similar effect.

CHAPTER 13

¹ One index of San Francisco health conditions is provided in a report submitted by State Marine Hospital to the California Legislature. The period covered is from May 1 to mid-December, 1850. The tabulation:

Number admitted	1200
Discharged as cured	912
Remaining in hospital	139
Deaths	149

Diagnosis on Admission		*Deaths*	
Diarrhea	262	Diarrhea	32
Dysentery	204	Dysentery	26
Intermittent Fever	93	Typhus	16
Typhus Fever	37	Colic	3
Erysipelas	13	Fistula	4
Colic	24	Paralysis	3
Hepatitis	23	Cholera Morbus	7
Gonorrhea	40	Phthysis Pulmonis	3
Fistula	15	Delirium Tremens	2
Fracture	25	Bronchitis	3
Paralysis	13	Laryngitis	2
Cholera Morbus	5	Pneumonia	5
Phthysis Pulmonis	29	Hemorrhoids	4
Asthma	23	Hemiplegia	3
Delirium Tremens	9	Scurvy	14
Bronchitis	28	Cholera	2
Laryngitis	3	Jaundice	2
Pneumonia	26	Secondary Syphilis	5
Contusions	17	Mania	2
Orchitis	4	Dropsy	3
Acute Rheumatism	113	Cystitis	2
Chronic "	47	Wounds Punctured	2
Hemorrhoids	7		
Hemiplegia	1		
Debility	14		
Scurvy	46		
Cholera	9		
Jaundice	15		
Secondary Syphilis	16		

[2] Another hospital report yields a random sample as to age, group, sex, and nativity of California patients. The listing appeared in the July 1856 issue of the *California State Medical Journal* and covered a period of approximately twelve months in a Sacramento hospital operated by Dr. W. G. Proctor and his partner, a Dr. Price. Patient breakdown was as follows:

Sex

Males	615
Females	7
	622

Age Group

Children	12
Adults	610
	622

Nativity

Ireland	189
Germany	82
England	21
Scotland	16
France	48
California	14
Mexico	21
South America	10
Sandwich Islands	3
United States	218
	622

(Ed. Note: One observes the disproportionate number of Irish. It was the time of the potato famine in Ireland, and large numbers of Irish were choosing the hopeful hardships of California in preference to the dead-end miseries of their native land.)

[3] The medical statistician Dr. Thomas M. Logan compiled the following records on average age of death in Sacramento over a two-year period. The findings were published in the *California State Medical Journal* for October 1856.

Ages for 1852 and 1853

	1852	1853
Under 1 Year	17	18
From 1 to 5	32	23
" 5 to 10	8	4
" 10 to 20	21	15
" 20 to 30	214	87
" 30 to 40	126	70
" 40 to 50	79	43
50 and over	40	24
Unknown	106	49
Total	643	338

[4] The October 1856 issue of the *California State Medical Journal* also carried Dr. Logan's findings on the reported causes of death in Sacramento for the years 1851 to 1853. The three-year total was 1,251 with a breakdown as follows:

Table of Mortality

	1851	1852	1853
Diarrhoea and Dysentery	60	84 / 31	46 / 16

Table of Mortality (Cont.)

	1851	1852	1853
Fevers	59	140	63
Phthisis	19	27	32
Erysipelas	15	1	1
Pneumonia	13	—	—
Dropsy	7	13	9
Enteritis	6	19	16
Mania a Potu	5	—	—
Infl. and Con. of Brain	9	27	12
Hydrothorax	4	—	—
Disease of the Heart	2	2	4
Bronchitis	2	9	—
Ptyalism	—	1	—
Worms	—	1	—
Disease of Kidneys	—	—	1
Bilious Cholic	—	—	1
Rheumatism	3	—	—
Liver Complaint	1	3	5
Intem. and Exposure	1	15	8
Gastritis	1	—	—
Debility	1	7	9
Tonsilitis	1	—	—
Scorbutus	1	2	4
Spinal Disease	1	—	—
Pertussis	1	—	—
Influenza	1	—	—
Pleuritis	1	—	—
Still-born	—	—	3
Abdominal Abscess	1	1	—
Ulceration of Bowels	2	—	—
Jaundice	1	—	5
Croup	—	1	—
Dentition	—	1	6
Cystitis	—	—	1
Cancrum Oris	—	—	1
Parturition	—	—	1
Convulsions	1	—	3
Wounds and Accidents	9	19	7
Drowned	8	11	11
Executed	4	—	3
Poisoned	1	—	—
Unknown	29	58	27
Diseased Lungs	—	11	17
Smallpox	—	19	16

Table of Mortality (Cont.)

	1851	1852	1853
Epilepsy	—	1	1
Rubeola	—	3	—
Paralysis	—	1	—
Hip-joint Disease	—	1	—
White Swelling	—	1	—
Cholera Morbus	—	15	—
Cholera	—	102	—
Burned	—	6	—
Suicide	—	8	1
Fungus Hematodes	—	—	1
Cholera Infantum	—	—	1
Murder	—	—	4

CHAPTER 14

[1] In denouncing the exorbitant prices charged by physicians **Dr.** Logan cited a suggested fee-bill adopted by the Medical Society of San Francisco in October of 1850. Some representative items:

For a single visit, or advice in a case in which no further visits are required ..... $		32.00
For each visit in which the physician is in regular attendance, or for advice at his office		16.00
When detained for one hour		32.00
For a written opinion or advice to a patient	50.00 to	100.00
For a night visit	30.00 to	50.00
For a visit as consulting physician during the night ..		100.00
For vaccination		32.00
For a post-mortem examination, in the case of legal investigation		200.00
For a case of ordinary labor, in accouchement		200.00
For the operation of turning, in accouchement		500.00
For the operation of a cataract		1000.00
For trephining		1000.00
For the operation of strangulated hernia		1000.00

The fee-bill inspired the *Alta California* to an editorial blasting the physicians as follows: "The Medical Society of California, doubtless composed of most learned gentlemen, well skilled in the healing art, has existed for a few months in our city. We question not their ability, we doubt not their science—we will acknowledge each and every member a most excellent 'leech.' Their recent acts have entitled them to such a reputation."

2 The Independent Order of Odd Fellows at Sacramento was the first of many volunteer groups to attempt public-health service in the gold fields, with Dr. John F. Morse being a prime mover in launching the organization's program. The Odd Fellows began by visiting the sick in their tents and providing coffins for the dead; they then joined with the Masons in opening the charity hospital managed initially by Dr. W. Grove Deal.

Throughout the gold fields other benevolent enterprises sprang up; they were sponsored by Protestant, Catholic, and Jewish groups and by emigrant societies representing the French, Germans, Italians, Swiss, Scandinavians, and Chinese. The volunteer organizations were variously active in underwriting health-insurance programs and founding hospitals.

The most notable charity hospital was developed by the Sisters of Mercy, an order of Catholic nuns. The first contingent of sisters arrived in San Francisco from Ireland in 1854; their appearance coincided with the height of the Know-Nothing frenzy and they were greeted with scurrilous abuse by such newspapers as the *Herald, Sun, Evening Bulletin,* and *Christian Advocate.* However, they stuck it out and won respect on the town's own terms, performing valiantly when a cholera epidemic broke out the same year. The *Sun* then apologized handsomely for its earlier remarks, and when the *Evening Bulletin* persisted in calling them "unfit and unable" the sisters demanded and got exoneration through a public inquiry.

In 1857 the sisters took over the defunct State Marine Hospital, renaming it the Hospital of the Sisters of Mercy and later Saint Mary's. By the early 1860s they were operating San Francisco's finest hospital.

A particular touch at Saint Mary's was the installation of a plumbing system which provided hot and cold water baths on every floor. That, at the time, was about the ultimate in first-rate facilities.

CHAPTER 20

1 Dr. Cooper founded California's first medical school, the Medical Department of the University of the Pacific, at San Francisco in 1859. It was a tiny little college meeting in temporary quarters, impoverished in money and equipment, but rich in talent. Six of the city's leading physicians served as instructors to a student body of ten.

After Dr. Cooper's death his school closed for lack of funds, but a successor institution was established by his nephew, Dr. Levi Cooper Lane. Meantime Dr. Toland had founded the Toland Medical College at San Francisco. Ultimately the Toland institution was incorporated into the University of California, while the Cooper-Lane school became a part of Stanford University.

The rival schools engaged in fierce competition for funds and prestige, and that led to ironic development. In 1870, in order to buttress his position, Dr. Toland installed his old enemy, Dr. Cole, as dean of the faculty. Thereafter Dr. Cole fought for Dr. Toland with the same highhanded tactics he had previously employed against him.

ACKNOWLEDGMENTS
AND
BIBLIOGRAPHY

Acknowledgments and Bibliography

Many people have contributed generously to the preparation of this book. I am indebted to:

My wife, Lynn, who has helped enormously in researching, consulting and, inevitably, retyping.

Marion Burdick, Susan Cora Schneider, Katherine Thanas, and Elizabeth Wing, for their extensive research assistance.

Helen Smith, for translating the rare and valuable *Voyage médical en Californie*, by the French physician Dr. Pierre Garnier.

The always helpful and courteous staffs of the Bancroft Library at the University of California; the Western Americana Collection of the Bienecke Library at Yale University; the California State Library at Sacramento; the New York Academy of Medicine Library; the New York City Public Library; and the Sacramento city and county libraries.

Dr. C. Albert Shumate of San Francisco, president of the California Historical Society, for his numerous suggestions on source materials.

Others who volunteered very useful leads included Dorothy Berger, co-editor of *Diary of America*, Archibald Hanna, curator of Western Americana at Yale, J. R. K. Kantor of Bancroft Library, Helen Mayden of Sacramento City Library, Dr. Dwight L. Wilbur of San Francisco, and the rare-book firms of Edward Eberstadt & Sons, New York City, and John Howell, San Francisco.

The author gratefully acknowledges permission to reproduce material from the following sources:

Gold Rush, The Journals, Drawings, and Other Papers of J. Goldsborough Bruff, April 2, 1849–July 20, 1851, edited by Georgia Willis Read and Ruth Gaines, by permission of Columbia University Press; *The Cholera Years: The United States in 1832, 1849, and 1866* by Charles E. Rosenberg, by permission of The University of Chicago Press (copyright © 1962 by The University of Chicago); *A Frontier Lady: Recollections of the Gold Fields and Early California Life,* by Sarah Royce, edited by R. H. Gabriel, by permission of Yale University Press.

321

"Diary of a Journey from Missouri to California in 1849," by Bennett C. Clark, *Missouri Historical Review*, Oct. 1928, by permission of The State Historical Society of Missouri; "The Gold Rush and a Hospital," by Frances Tomlinson Gardner, *Bulletin of the History of Medicine*, April, 1942, by permission of the *Bulletin*; "Scurvy in the Gold Rush," by Anthony J. Lorenzo, *Journal of the History of Medicine and Allied Sciences*, Oct., 1957, by permission of the *Journal*; "Diseases, Drugs and Doctors on the Oregon-California Trail in the Gold Rush Years," by Georgia Willis Read, *Missouri Historical Review*, April, 1944, by permission of The State Historical Society of Missouri.

Diaries, letters and manuscripts as listed in the bibliography, by permission of the Bancroft Library of the University of California, the California State Library at Sacramento, and the Western Americana Collection of Yale University Library.

––––––––––––

The literature of the gold rush and of pioneer medicine are both enormous. I would like to make particular mention of three references which I have found especially useful for the purposes of this book:

Scalpel Under Three Flags in California, by Dr. George D. Lyman. San Francisco: A. H. Clark Co., 1925. Dr. Lyman's account was published under the same title by the *California Historical Society Quarterly*, Vol. 4, No. 2, June, 1925, pp. 142–206.

California's Medical Story, by Dr. Henry Harris, introduction by Charles Singer. San Francisco: Grabhorn Press for J. W. Stacey, 1932.

Memories, Men and Medicine: A History of Medicine in Sacramento, California, by Dr. J. Roy Jones. Sacramento: The Sacramento Society for Medical Improvement, 1950.

Among the brief accounts a few should be cited for unusual value— John E. Bauer's "The Health Factor in the Gold Rush"; Francis Tomlinson Gardner's "The Gold Rush and a Hospital"; Dr. Anthony J. Lorenzo's "Scurvy in the Gold Rush"; Georgia Willis Read's "Diseases, Drugs, and Doctors on the Oregon-California Trail in the Gold Rush Years," and the MD Medical Newsmagazine article, "Gold Rush Medicine." Taken together, these articles comprise almost a short history of the subject. Publication details will be found in the section under Periodicals.

Special mention should also be given to *The Midwest Pioneer, his ills, cures & doctors*, by Madge E. Pickard and Roscoe Carlyle Buley. R. E. Banta, Crawfordsville, Ind., 1945. The work does not deal directly with the gold rush, but I have found it indispensable as background to nineteenth-century American medicine.

In addition I have drawn on my own extensive experience as a magazine writer in the general field of medical history, and I have tried to base the book as much as possible on the reports of those who took part in the gold-rush adventure. The principal sources:

MANUSCRIPTS

Adams, Frank, and others. Parcel of seven letters. Hardships culminate in an account of death and burial on the trail. (Yale)

Barber, P. J. Diary. Panama tribulations. (Bancroft)

Blanchard, George B. Letter. Vivid description of an epidemic at sea. (Yale)

Blennerhasset, Horatio. Letter. Topsy-turvy conditions in San Francisco. (Yale)

Castleman, P. F. Diary. Laconic but well-detailed account of a difficult trek. (Yale)

Chelton, James. Letter-journal. Epidemic at sea. (Yale)

Collier, James. Letter. An official offers unheeded advice. (Bancroft)

Cornell, George. Diary. Hunger and disease on the Nicaragua route. (Yale)

Davis, Dr. George W. Letter. Illiterate but revealing report from a gold-rush physician. (Yale)

Eastman, Sophia A. Letters. A nurse at Dr. Peter Smith's hospital. (Bancroft)

Gordon, Betsy. Letter. A feminine gold rusher who placed scant faith in doctors. (Yale)

Handerstein, Arthur. Letter. Cholera on the trail. (Yale)

Johnson, John A. Diary. Trail hardships, including cholera and crowding. (Yale)

King, John Nevin. Diary. Death and burial on the trail. (Yale)

Middleton, Dr. Joseph. Diary. General observations. (Yale)

Moxley, Charles G. Letter. Ordeal by hunger. (Yale)

Ness, Richard. Diary. Trail hardships. (Yale)

Paden, Melvin. Five letters. Life and death in the mines. (Yale)

Perkins, Isaac. Three letters. Sacramento epidemic. (California State Library, Sacramento)

Sargent, Lorenzo D. Diary. Around the Horn with an exuberant gold rusher. (Yale)

Schaeffer, Dr. Luther Melanchthon. Diary. A physician describes California and comments on his fellow practitioners. (Yale)

Sherman, William Tecumseh. Two letters. Mining camp conditions. (Yale)

Shuart, Jesse H. Some fifty letters. Voluminous comments on camp life. (Yale)

Tasheira, Anthony L. and Eliza. Two letters. A wife waits out an epidemic. (California State Library, Sacramento)

T——, (Dr. T.). Diary of a trek. (Bancroft)

Wells, Dr. Albert C. Letters from Panama. (New York Historical Society Library)

Windeler, Adolphus, and Christendorf, Charles. Diaries. Camp life described by two picaresque adventurers who were inseparable companions. (Yale)

MEMOIRS

Borthwick, J. D. *Two Years in California.* Edinburgh and London: William Blackwood and Sons, 1857.

Bruff, J. Goldsborough. *Gold Rush, The Journals, Drawings, and Other Papers of J. Goldsborough Bruff, April 2, 1849–July 20, 1851.* Edited by George Willis Read and Ruth Gaines, with a foreword by F. W. Hodge. California centennial edition. Columbia University Press, 1959.

Buffum, Edward Gould. *The gold rush: an account of six months in the California diggings.* Preface by Oscar Lewis. London: Folio Society, 1959.

Clappe, Louise. *The Shirley Letters from the California Mines, 1851–52.* With an introduction and notes by Carl I. Wheat. New York: Knopf, 1961.

Delano, Alonzo. *Across the plains and among the diggings; being scenes and adventures of an overland journey to California.* Foreword and epilogue by R. R. Wilson. New York: Wilson-Erickson, Inc., 1936. Original edition in 1854.

Ferguson, Dr. Charles D. *California Gold Fields.* Oakland: Brobooks, 1948.

Garnier, Dr. Pierre. *"Voyage médical en Californie,"* French-American *Review,* July–Sept., 1949; reissued by the Washington, D. C., Institut Français de Washington with a foreword by Gilbert Chinard. Original edition, Paris, 1854. Translated for author by Helen Smith.

Gibbons, Henry. *Introductory Lecture to the eighth session of the Medical Department of the University of the Pacific; delivered July 5, 1870.* San Francisco: J. H. Carmany & Co., 1870; also appears in a supplement to the *Pacific Medical and Surgical Journal,* Vol. IV, No. 39, Aug., 1870.

Goldsmith, Oliver. *Overland in forty-nine. The recollections of a wolverine ranger after a lapse of forty-seven years.* Privately printed, Detroit, 1896.

Griswold, Dr. Chauncey D. *The Isthmus of Panama, and What I saw There.* New York: Dewitt and Davenport, 1852.

Gunn, Elizabeth LaBreton. *Records of a California Family.* Edited by Anna Lee Marston. San Diego, Calif., privately printed, undated.

Letts, J. M. *A Pictorial View of California.* New York: Henry Bill, 1853.

Lloyd, Benjamin E. *Lights and Shades in San Francisco.* San Francisco: A. L. Bancroft & Co., 1876.

Manly, William Lewis. *Death Valley in '49*, with a foreword by John Steven McGroarty. New York and Santa Barbara: W. Habberd, 1929.

Marryat, Frank. *Mountains and Molehills*. New York: Harper and Brothers, 1855.

M'Collum, Dr. William. *California As I Saw It*. Edited by Dale L. Morgan. Los Gatos, Calif.: The Talisman Press, 1960. Original edition, 1850.

Morse, Dr. John F. *Illustrated Historical Sketches of California, Including References to its Discovery, Early Missions, Revolutions and Settlement by the United States; together with a More Ample History of Sacramento Valley and City*, 1853. Reprinted by Sacramento Book Collectors' Club as *First History of Sacramento City*, 1954.

Otis, Dr. F. N. *Illustrated History of the Panama Railroad*. New York: Harper and Brothers, 1862.

Palmer, Dr. John Williamson. *The New and the Old, or California and India in romantic aspects*. New York: Rudd & Carleton, 1859.

Praslow, Dr. J. *Der Staat Californien, in medizinischer, geographischer Hinsicht*, Goettingen, 1857; English translation by F. C. Cordes, *The State of California: a Medico-Geographical Account*, San Francisco: John J. Newbegin, 1939.

Read, Dr. George Willis. *A Pioneer of 1850*. Edited by Georgia Willis Read. Boston: Little Brown, 1927.

Royce, Sarah. *A Frontier Lady: Recollections of the Gold Rush and Early California*. Edited by R. H. Gabriel. New Haven: Yale University Press, 1932.

Stillman, Dr. J. D. B. *Seeking the Golden Fleece*. San Francisco: A. Roman and Co., 1877.

Taylor, Bayard. *Eldorado, or, Adventures in the path of empire; comprising a voyage to California via Panama, life in San Francisco and Monterey, pictures of the gold region, and experiences of Mexican travel*. With introduction by Robert Glass Cleland. New York: Knopf, 1949. Original edition, New York: Putnam, 1850.

Taylor, Rev. William. *California Life Illustrated*. London: Jackson, Walford and Hadder, 1882. Original edition, 1858.

Tyson, Dr. James Lawrence. *Diary of a physician in California; being the results of actual experience, including notes of the journey by land and water, and observations on the climate, soil, resources of the country, etc.*, New York: D. Appleton & Co., Philadelphia: G. S. Appleton, 1850.

Wierzbicki, Dr. Felix Paul. *California As It Is and As It May Be*. San Francisco: Grabhorn Press, 1933.

BOOKS, GENERAL

Adams, James Truslow, ed. *Album of American History*. New York: Charles Scribner's Sons, 1945.

Berger, Josef and Dorothy, ed. *Diary of America*. New York: Simon and Schuster, 1957.

Caughey, John W. *Gold Is the Cornerstone*. Berkeley, Calif.: University of California Press, 1948.

Cleland, Robert Glass. *From Wilderness to Empire; A History of California, 1542–1900*. New York: Knopf, 1947.

Commager, Henry Steele, and Nevins, Allan, eds. *The Heritage of America*. Boston: Little Brown and Co., 1939.

Davis, Winfield J. *An Illustrated History of Sacramento*. Chicago: The Lewis Pub. Co., 1890.

Lewis, Lloyd. *Captain Sam Grant*. Boston: Little Brown and Co., 1950.

Lewis, Oscar. *Sea Routes to the Gold Fields; the Migration by Water to California in 1849–52*. New York: Knopf, 1949.

Lyman, Dr. George D. *John Marsh, Pioneer*. New York: Scribner's, 1930.

———. *The Book and the Doctor*. San Francisco: Grabhorn Press, 1933.

Minter, John E. *The Chagres; River of the Westward Passages*. New York: Rinehart, 1948.

Morgan, Sister Mary Evangelist. *Mercy, Generation to Generation; History of the First Century of the Sisters of Mercy, Diocese of Sacramento, Calif*. San Francisco: Fearon Publishers, 1957.

Read, J. Marion. *History of the California Academy of Medicine*. San Francisco: Grabhorn Press, 1930.

Rosenberg, Charles. *The Cholera Years*. Chicago: University of Chicago Press, 1962.

Stewart, George R. *The California Trail*. New York, Toronto, London: McGraw-Hill, 1962.

Stewart, George R. *Committee of Vigilance*. Boston: Houghton Mifflin, 1964.

Valentine, Alan. *Vigilante Justice*. Reynal and Co., 1956.

Walsh, Father Henry L. *Hallowed Were the Gold Dust Trails*. Santa Clara, Calif.: University of Santa Clara Press, 1946.

Weyman, Walker D., ed. *California Emigrant Letters*. New York: Bookman Associates, 1952.

Wiltsee, Ernest A. *Gold Rush Steamers of the Pacific*. San Francisco: Grabhorn Press, 1938.

Woodward, W. E. *The Way Our People Lived*. New York: E. P. Dutton & Co., Inc., 1944.

DOCUMENTS

Cross, Major Osborne. "A Report in the Form of a Journal to the Quartermaster General of the March of the Regiment of the

Mounted Riflemen to Oregon from May 18 to Oct. 5, 1849." Report of the Quartermaster General, Part II, A, 1850.

Resolution of the Legislature of California, recommending "The payment of a debt incurred by the city of Sacramento, in providing for the sick and the burial of deceased emigrants to that city." Passed April 28, 1851, by the Sacramento assembly and senate; listed as Miscellaneous No. 23, Thirty-second Congress, First Session, in proceedings of the United States Senate.

Smith, General Persifor. "The correspondence of General Persifor Smith, including reports by his assistants, John Peoples and Maj. Daniel Rucker." Senate Executive Documents, Thirty-first Congress, First Session, No. 52.

PERIODICALS

Andrist, Ralph K. "Gold!" *American Heritage,* Vol. XIV, No. 1, Dec., 1962, pp. 6–27, 90–1.

Baldwin, Roger S. "Tarrying in Nicaragua," *Century Magazine,* Vol. XLII, New Series XX, Oct., 1891, pp. 911–31.

Bauer, John E. "The Health Factor in the Gold Rush Era," *Pacific Historical Review,* Vol. XVIII, No. 1, Feb., 1949, pp. 97–108.

Berman, Alex. "The Heroic Approach in 19th Century Therapeutica," *Bulletin of the American Society of Hospital Pharmacists,* Sept.–Oct., 1954, pp. 321–7.

Bieber, Ralph P., ed. "Diary of a Journey from Missouri to California in 1849," by Bennett C. Clark, *Missouri Historical Review,* Vol. 23, Oct., 1928.

Bryant, Dr. Berryman. "Reminiscences of California 1849–52," *California Historical Society Quarterly,* Vol. XL, No. 1, March, 1932, pp. 35–9.

Gardner, Francis Tomlinson. "John Townsend—The Peripatetic Pioneer," *California and Western Medicine,* Sept., Oct., Nov., 1939.

——. "King Cole of California," *Annals of Medical History,* Third Series, Vol. II, No. 3, pp. 245–58; No. 4, pp. 319–47; No. 5, pp. 432–40; May, July, Sept., 1940. Published as *King Cole of California.* New York: Paul B. Hoeber, Inc., 1940.

——. "The Gold Rush and a Hospital," *Bulletin of the History of Medicine,* Vol. XI, No. 4, April, 1942, pp. 371–88.

Groh, George. "Doctors of the Frontier," *American Heritage,* Vol. XIV, No. 3, April, 1963, pp. 10–11, 87–91.

Harwood, John. "A General Practitioner in California," *Once a Week,* Feb. 9, 1861.

Jones, Guy P. "Early Public Health in California," *California's Health,* Vol. II, No. 13, Jan. 15, 1945, pp. 100–1.

Logan, Dr. Thomas M. "Letters from California," *New York Journal of Medicine,* March–May, 1851.

Lorenzo, Dr. Anthony J. "Scurvy in the Gold Rush," *Journal of the History of Medicine,* Vol. XII, No. 4, Oct., 1957, pp. 473–510.

Lyman, Dr. George D. "The Beginnings of California's Medical History," *California and Western Medicine,* May, 1925, pp. 561–576.

——. "The Sponge," *Annals of Medical History,* Oct. 10, 1928, pp. 460–479.

McDermitt, James Francis. "Two Fourgeaud Letters," *California Historical Society Quarterly,* Vol. XX, No. 2, June, 1942, pp. 117–25.

MD Medical Newsmagazine, Anon., "Gold Rush Medicine," Vol. II, No. 6, June, 1958, pp. 106–9.

——, Anon., "Frontier Medicine," Vol. III, No. 1, Jan. 1959, pp. 90–2.

Nagel, Charles E. "Sacramento Cholera Epidemic of 1850," *Golden Notes,* pub. by Sacramento County Historical Society, Vol. IV, No. 1, Oct., 1957, pp. 1–8. Nagel's extended paper on the same subject is available at the California State Library, Sacramento.

Read, Georgia Willis. "Diseases, Drugs, and Doctors on the Oregon-California Trail in the Gold Rush Years," *Missouri Historical Review,* April, 1944, Vol. XXXVIII, No. 3, pp. 260–76.

——. "The Chagres River Route to California in 1851," *California Historical Society Quarterly,* Vol. VIII, No. 1, March, 1929, pp. 3–16. Privately printed under same title, San Francisco, 1929.

Read, J. Marion. "California's First Medical Historian, Victor Jean Fourgeaud," *California and Western Medicine,* Feb.–March, 1931.

Sawyer, Dr. Albert F. "On the Vital Statistics and the Causes of Mortality in San Francisco," *The Boston Medical and Surgical Journal,* Vol. LV, Oct. 16, 1856.

Stewart, George R. "The Smart Ones Got Through," *American Heritage,* June, 1955, pp. 60–3, 108.

Stillman, Dr. J. D. B. "Observations on the Medical Topography and Diseases of the Sacramento Valley, California," *New York Journal of Medicine and the Collateral Sciences,* Nov., 1851, pp. 289–307.

Taylor, Dr. W. W. Excerpts from diary, *California's Health,* Vol. II, No. 19, April 15, 1945, pp. 146–9.

Waite, E. G. "Pioneer Mining in California," *Century Magazine,* Vol. XLII, New Series XX, May, 1891, pp. 127–41.

Warren, L. V. "Medical Quacks and Heroes of Early California," *Historical Society of Southern California Quarterly,* June, 1959, pp. 101–6.

NEWSPAPERS

In New York, the *Herald,* the *Tribune.*

In Sacramento, the *Placer-Times, Settlers and Miners Tribune, State Journal, Transcript, Union.*

In San Francisco, the *Alta California, Daily Evening Bulletin.*

INDEX

INDEX

Abby Baker (bark), 219
abortionists, 285
Acapulco, 43, 50-51, 62
accidents, 174-75, 233, 239
accommodations, 33-34, 167-68, 170, 230-31. *See also* construction; specific types
Adams, Frank, 107-8
advertisements, 285, 287
Africa, 65
age, 174; of hospital patients, 313
Aiken, Dr. Cyrus D., 254, 255
albatrosses, 66
alcohol. *See* liquor and drinking
Alexander (slave), 96
Alta California, 43-44, 62-63, 173, 184, 276-77; and cholera, 208-10, 212, 213, 214-15; on physicians' fees, 316
American Medical Association, 289
American River, 195, 233
amputation, 239
Anderson, Father Augustin P., 221
anesthesia, 11
animalculae, 10
animals, 110, 124, 125, 133. *See also* meat; overland routes; specific traveling parties
Antarctic Circle, 69
apples, 169
Arcane, J. B., and family, 137, 139
arms. *See* weapons
army, 16-17, 52-54, 271, 309; relief parties, 151-64
arson, 203
ascorbic acid shortage. *See* scurvy
Asher, Dr. Richard P., 272-73
autopsies, 255-56

Bailey, Nancy Ann, 240n

Baker, John R., and family, 46
Baldwin, Roger, 55, 57-59
Ball, Dr. Albert, 43-44
Bancroft, H. H., 307
banishment, 245
Barber, P. J., 46-47
Barnum, P. T., 29
Batchelder, Dr. Amos, 92
Bauer, John E., 12
Beale, Edward Fitzgerald, 18, 19
beans, 118, 237
Bear River, 310-11
Beecher, Henry Ward, 294
Belt, Judge G. C., 257, 258
Benard de Russailh, Albert, 204-5
Bengal (clipper), 303
Benicia, Calif., 17
Bennett, Asabel and Sarah, and family, 137, 139
Berger, Josef and Dorothy, 133n
Bertody, Dr., 266, 277, 278
Bidwell, John, 79, 82-84
Bidwell's Bar, 82n, 127
Bigelow, Hardin, 202
Bigler, John, 221
Black Hills, 81, 109, 110
Blanchard, George, 45, 47-49
bleeding, 7
Blennerhasset, Horatio, 5
blistering, 8
Blue Wing Saloon, 262
Board of Health, 213, 214
Boards of Examiners, medical, 287-88
Bolinas Bay, 62
Bonne Adele (bark), 70-72
books, fraudulent account of adventures in, 308-9
Borthwick, J. D., 41-42, 245
Boston, Mass., 73-74

Boston and California Joint Mining and Trading Company, 74
botanics, 9, 180, 182n
Bradford, Dr., 126
brandy, as medicine, 41, 223
Brannan, Sam, 15
Brannan and Company, 18
bread, 116, 169
Brier, Rev. James, and family, 136, 137, 139
British, the, 301-2. *See also* England
Broderick, David, 275n
Brooklyn (ship), 68-70
Brooks, Dr. J. Tyrwhitt, 308-9
Brother Jonathan (ship), 60
Brown, David (or William), 246-48
Bruff, J. Goldsborough, 90, 105-7, 119, 311, 312; on cemeteries, 215-16; John Peoples and aid for, 158, 159-60; starves in Sierras, 140-49
Bryant, Dr. Beeryman, 182-84
Buchanan, John Rodes, 294
Buckner, Dr. H., 95, 96, 122-23, 312
buffalo chips, 118
Buffum, Edward Gould, 236-37
burial; graves, 3, 91-92, 98, 99, 107, 108, 170, 212n, 215-16 (*See also* specific parties); alive, as scurvy remedy, 239; in flood, 197, 199, 200; Indian, 97, 102, 103-4; mining-company funeral, 240; in Panama City, 38
burnings to death, 175
bush cabins, 230

cactus, 119
Caldwell, Dr. Charles, 294
California, State of, 167-290, 293 (*See also* specific places); admitted to union, 211; Indian population, 309; militia mustered, against vigilantes, 270-71; and relief parties, 152-53; travel to (*See* overland routes; sea routes); U.S. claims from Mexico, 14
California (ship), 19
California, University of, 317
California As It Is . . . , 295-96
California State Medical Journal, 173n, 313-14

California State Medical Society, 276, 277
California Trail, 79-87ff.
California Trail, The (Stewart), 307
Callao, Peru, 297
calomel, 8, 123, 223
camphor, 221, 223
cannibalism, 85-86, 147-48
canning of food, 302-3
Cannon (murdered miner), 253
Cape Horn, 4, 29, 64-75
Carolina (ship), 209-10
Carson River, 114, 160, 163, 164n
Casey, James P, 263-64, 267, 269-70, 276, 278
Castle Rock, 97
Castleman, P. F., 93-98, 110, 122-27, 312
cauterizing, 8
cemeteries, 38, 215-16, 240
Chagres, 32-33, 34, 36, 39
Chagres fever. *See* malaria
Chagres River, 33, 36
Chapin, Dr. Edward B., 192-93
charity and the poor, 185, 186-87. *See also* hospitals
Chelton, James, 47
Cherokee, the, 104
Cheyenne, the, 102
Chicago, Ill., 298
children, 60, 61, 174, 196 (*See also* specific routes, travelers); abandoned boy, Bruff and, 141, 142, 143-44; orphans, 46, 301
Chile, 69, 71-72
China, 24, 169
chloroform, 11, 233
cholera, 24-29, 174, 207-26; in Panama, 35-36, 38-39, 51-52; at sea, 52-54; 60, 61; on the trail, 87, 89-111, 118, 122, 151, 307
cholera morbus, 211
Cholera Years, The, 298-99
Christendorf, Carl, 230
Christiana (brig), 219
Churchill, C., 74, 126, 312
cinchona, 296
Cincinnati *Gazette,* 92
Clam, Paul, 259-60

Clappe, Dr. Fayette, 239, 241, 249, 251, 252
Clappe, Mrs. Fayette (Louise), 230-31, 239-40, 241, 243-44; and Brown's execution, 246, 247-48; and riots, 249, 250, 251, 252
Clark, Bennett C., 129-33
Clark, Bennett Champ, 133n
Clark, James B., 133n
Clay Street (San Francisco), 168
climate, 34, 60, 65. *See also* weather; specific areas
Clough, Warren, 142-43, 144-45
Code Napoleon, 178
coffee, 34
coffins, 173, 197, 198
Cole, Dr. R. Beverly, 51-54, 264-67, 268, 272, 289, 318; feud with confreres, 276-80; saves man with throat cut, 274-75
Coleman, William, 268
Collier, James, 90, 151
Coloma, Calif., 223, 229
Colón, 33n
Colorado River, 134
Colorado tick fever, 115
Colton, Walter, 13, 16-17
Columbia (sailing ship), 54
Commercial Wharf (San Francisco), 179
Congress, U.S., 153
construction, 167, 169, 205, 230. *See also* accommodations; specific places
Cook, Henry, 251-52
Cooper, Dr. Elias Samuel, 283-84, 289
co-operative ventures, 73
Cora, Charles, 261-63, 267, 269-70
Cornell, George, 42, 229
Cortes (ship), 61
Corum, Alfred, 130
Council Bluffs, Iowa, 304
coyoting, 228-29, 233, 239
cradle, mining, 228
Cragin, Dr. Charles, 184
Crescent City (side-wheeler), 29-30
crime and violence, 175, 242-80
Cross, Osborne, 90, 91
crow, 129
Cruces, 33, 38, 53n

dandy funk, 66

Davis, Dr. George, 92-93
D-day, 308
Deal, Dr. W. Grove, 176-77, 184-85, 317
Death Valley, 136-39
deaths, death rate, 3, 5, 170, 171, 173, 174-75 (*See also* burial; specific causes); cost of 1st year's migration, 87
Delano, Alonzo, 108, 109
Detroit, 298
diarrhea, 92, 93, 118, 171, 174, 199-200
Diary of America, 133n
Digger Indians, 309
diplomas, 285
disease, sickness, 3-11, 170-74 (*See also* doctors; hospitals; specific diseases); on Cape Horn route, 64, 65; in mining camps, 233-39; in Nicaragua route, 60-61; on Panama route, 31, 35-54; on trail, 87, 115-21 (*See also* cholera; specific traveling parties)
doctors (physicians), 6-11, 40-44, 172-173, 176-81, 214, 217, 281-89 (*See also* hospitals; specific doctors, traveling parties); fees, 178, 180; in mining camps, 233-34, 255-60, 266-67, 276-80
dolphins, 66
Domingo (miner), 249-50
Donner party, 85-86
Dover, Dr. Thomas, 300
Dover's powder, 223, 300-1
Downieville, 253-55
Drake, Dr. Daniel, 294-95, 299
drinking. *See* liquor and drinking
drownings, 175
druggists, drugstores, 178, 179
drugs. *See* medicine
duels, 252, 256-60
dysentery, 170-71, 174, 188, 233, 235

ear cropping, 245
eclectics, 9, 287, 288n
Edward Everett (ship), 73-75
eggs, 169
Eichelroth, Dr. William B., 256
emanations ("miasma"), 25, 207-8
Emily (bark), 47-49
enemas, 223n
England, 24. *See also* British, the

entertainment, mining-camp, 240-41
epidemics. *See* disease, sickness
erysipelas, 275
ether, 11
Europe (ship), 67
Evans, George W. B., 218-19
Everett, Edward, 73-74
executions, 175. *See also* hangings

Falcon (ship), 19-20, 23
families, 154n. *See also* children;
    women; specific parties, routes
Farragut, David G., 271
Feather River, 223, 244
fees, doctors', 178, 180
Ferguson, Charles, 237-39, 257
fevers, 170, 174. *See also* specific dis-
    ases
filth. *See* sanitation
fires, 191, 203-6, 214, 216
First History of Sacramento City
    (Morse), 185n
fish, 66
Fisher, Charles, 109
flogging, 245, 250, 251
floods, 195-203
flour, 116, 121
food and food shortages, 83, 110, 116-
    19, 120-21, 137-38, 143-44, 172, 229
    (*See also* relief parties; specific foods,
    travelers); hospital, 183-84, 189;
    prices, 169, 229; San Francisco
    corpse dead of starvation, 173; and
    scurvy (*See* scurvy); on ships, 30-31,
    47, 48, 49, 57-59, 66, 67-68, 70-71,
    73, 74-75
Fort Bidwell, 82n
Fort Bridger, Wyoming, 304
Fort Gunnybags, 267, 269, 270, 272,
    274
Fort Hall, Idaho, 84, 304
Fort Kearney, Nebraska, 86
Fort Laramie, 81, 91, 109-10, 161, 304
Fort Leavenworth, 89-90
Forty-Mile Desert, 113-14, 132-33
*Four Months Among the Gold-Find-
    ers . . .*, 308-9
Fourgeaud, Dr. Victor Jean, 15
Fourth Infantry, 53n
France, 24; French medical system,
    178

fruit, 116, 117, 229. *See also* specific
    fruits
funerals, 31, 239-40. *See also* burial

Ganges River, 24
garbage, 4-5, 26, 109-10, 208
Garnier, Dr. Pierre, 178-79, 255-56
Geddes, Paul, 83
Germany, Germans, 24, 26, 27
Gerry, Dr. S. Russell, 209
Gibbons, Dr. Henry, 286-87
Golden Gate (steamer), 52-54
Goldsmith, Oliver, 98-102, 111, 118,
    155-57, 232; has festering boil, 234;
    has scurvy, 236
Gordon, Mrs. Betsy, 42
Gordon, George, 55-56
Gordon Passenger Line, 56
Gorgas, General William, 300
Gorgona, 33, 39
Grant, Ulysses S., 52-53
graves. *See* burial
Gray, Dr. H. M., 265, 266, 268, 277,
    278
Great Divide, 112, 134
Great Salt Lake, 83
Green, Talbot, 82-83
Green River, 134
Griffin, Dr. John S., 269
Griswold, Dr. Chauncey, 36-37
Guadalupe Hidalgo, Treaty of, 14
guidebooks, 308
Gulf of California, 134
Gunn, Elizabeth, 303
Gunn, Dr. Lewis, 303

Half-Way House, 33-34
Hammond, Dr., 265, 266, 277, 278
hangings, 245-48, 251, 254-55, 270
"Happy Valley," 168, 171
Harte, Bret, 240n
Harvard University, 294
Haun, Catherine Margaret, 117
Hawaii, 17
health insurance, 193-94
heart sound, 297
Hebe (bark), 73
Henstis, George, 70
homeopaths, 8-9, 287-88
Hone, Philip, 28
Honolulu, 17, 169

Hopkins, Sterling, 272-75
hospitals, 174, 177, 181-94, 197, 198-200, 312-14; Panama City, 38; special, for cholera, 213-14, 216
hotels, 33-34
housing. *See* accommodations
Hudspeth, Benoni, 310-11
Hudspeth's Cutoff, 123, 310-11
Hullings, Dr., 258-60
Humboldt Desert, 160, 161
Humboldt Hotel, 231
Humboldt River, 113, 115, 119, 124
Humboldt Sink, 113, 132
Hunt, Jefferson, 134-36, 140
Hushamagrundy, 74
Hutchinson, Robert, 28
hydropaths, 9, 10

ice, 52, 66
ice cream, 117
Illinois, 150n
Independence, Mo., 81, 88-89, 98, 304, 305
Independence (ship), 62
India, 24
Indian Bar, 231, 248-53
Indian Territory, 309
Indians, 87, 89, 94, 125-26, 158; and cholera, 97, 102-4, 223-24
insanity, 243
insurance, health, 193-94
Iowa, 90. *See also* specific places
ipecac, 8
Ireland, 314

Jackson, Andrew, 309
jails, lack of, 244. *See also* crime and violence
jalap, 7
Jamestown, Calif., 223
Jayhawkers, the, 136
Jefferson City, Mo., 94
Jesuits, 296
Johns, Dr. E. W., 310
Johnson, J. Neely, 268, 270, 276
Juanita (murderess), 253-55
justice. *See* crime and violence

Kanakas, 17
Kansas, 99, 104
Kearney St. (San Francisco), 168

Kelsey, Nancy, 83
Kendall, Joseph, 67
Kentucky, 94
Kibbe, Dr., 254, 255
killings. *See* crime and violence
King, John Nevin, 108
King of William, James, 262-70, 276-80
Kingston, Jamaica, 302
Kingston (ship), 43
Koch, Robert, 298

Lake Nicaragua, 55
Lake Tahoe, 306
Lambkin (fleeing father), 141
Lambkin, William (child), 141, 142, 143-44
lancets, 7
land, city, 169, 191-92
land routes, 4, 79-164
Lane, Dr. Levi Cooper, 317
Lassen, Peter, 153, 311
Lassen's Route, 124-27, 128-29, 153-54, 159, 311-12
laudanum, 180
laundry, 169
Laura Ann (brigantine), 57-58
Law and Order Party, 268, 272
leeches, 7
Leggett, Billy, 252
Letts, J. M., 36, 302
lettuce, 189
levee, Sacramento, 201, 202-3
Lewis (ship), 61, 62-63
licenses, medical, 287
lights, 168
Lincoln, Abraham, 82n
liquor and drinking, 87, 231-32, 272, 299; as medicine, 41, 74, 223; and violence (*See* crime and violence)
livestock. *See* animals
lobscouse, 66
Logan, Dr. Thomas M., 173-74, 179-80, 211, 215, 314; president of AMA, 289
long tom (mining tool), 228
Loomis, Leander V., 167, 169
Lorenzo, Dr. Anthony J., 310
Los Angeles, 17, 135, 140, 305-6
Luck of Roaring Camp, The, 240n
Lynchburg, Va., 157

lynching. *See* hangings
Lyon (cholera victim), 99, 100

M'Collum. Dr. William, 29-30, 34-35, 40-41, 289-90
McGowan, Ned, 278-80
McLean, Dr. Robert Armisted, 288
McLean, Dr. Samuel Merryweather, 288
mail, 19
malaria, 11, 171, 208n, 233, 300; pernicious, 36-38
Maloney, Rube, 272
"manhood, wasting," 285-86
Manly, William, 133-39, 312
Marryat, Frank, 49-51
Marsh, Charles, 305
Marsh, Dr. Juan, 84
Marshall (ship captain), 297
Marshall, James, 13, 14
Mary (brig), 56
Marysville, Calif., 223
Masons, 185, 317
Massachusetts, 73n
Mathews, Dr. Samuel, 107-8
measles, 46-47
meat, 66 (*See also* food); taken from animals which died, 121, 142-43, 145, 155-56
Medical and Surgical Journal, 296
medical journals, 283-84
Medical Practice Act, 287-88
medical societies, associations, 282-83
medicine, 8-9, 11, 28, 40-41, 143, 223-24 (*See also* doctors; specific diseases); and doctors' fees, 180
Medico-Chirurgical Academy (Sacramento), 217
Medico-Chirurgical Association (San Francisco, 282-83
Melhado, Dr., 187-90
Meredith, William, 151
Mexico and Mexicans, 13, 17, 48, 62 (*See also* specific places); Mexican War, 14
"miasma." *See* emanations
Micheltorena campaign, 306
Michigan, 98
Middleton, Dr. Joseph, 4-5, 91, 205-6, 289
militia, state, 270-71

Miller's Point, 170
mining, mining camps, 227-41ff.
Mississippi Boys, the, 136
Mississippi River, 89
Missouri. *See* land routes; specific places
Missouri Historical Review, 310
Missouri Republican, 116
Missouri River, 81, 86, 88, 89-90, 94-95, 128. *See also* specific towns
Mitchell, Dr. T. D., 295
Mojave Desert, 138
Montague (schooner), 219
Monterey, 13, 16-17
More, Preston, 97
Mormon Trail, 81, 304
Mormons, 86, 134, 150, 225, 304, 305
Morse, Edwin, 235-36
Morse, Dr. John Frederick, 43, 172, 185, 186, 202-3, 216; and flood, 196, 197-98, 199, 200, 201-2; and Odd Fellows program, 317
mosquitoes, 36
mountain fever, 115, 123, 158, 233
mountain men, 82, 84, 304
Moxley, Charles, 127-29
Mulligan, Billy, 262-63
Mundos, John, 212-13
murders, 175. *See also* crime and violence
Murphy, Elizabeth Yuba, 85
"museum, anatomical," 286-87
mustard, 223
mutinies, 70-72, 297
Myers, J. J., 310-11

Napa, 278-80
nativity of hospital patients, 314
navy, 271. *See also* sailors
Nebraska, 86, 304. *See also* specific places
Ned Red (slave), 95, 96
Nelson, Horatio, Viscount, 301-2
Ness, Richard, 235
Nevada, 82, 128, 131. *See also* specific places
Nevada City, 257
New Orleans, 19, 27, 35, 36, 89, 207, 298, 299-300

New York, 169, 208, 225-26; cholera in, 25-27, 299; ship service from (*See* sea routes)
New York (packet), 23-24, 26
New York Herald, 25
New York Journal of Medicine, 293
New York Tribune, 38
Nicaragua, 55-63
Nolan's Inn, 88
Normandy Beach, 308
nursing, 188
Nuttall, Dr. J. K., 264, 266

Odd Fellows, 185, 317
Oklahoma, 104, 309
opium, 223
Opuntia (prickly pear), 310
Oregon, 17, 304-5
Oregon Trail, 81, 128
orphans, 46, 301
Otis, Dr. F. N., 37-38
overland routes, 4, 79-164

Pacific (ship), 60
Pacific, University of the, 317-18
Pacific Mail, 19
Pacific Medical and Surgical Journal, 283-84
Paden, Melvin, 5, 232-33
Palmer, Dr. J. W., 176, 180-81, 289
Panama, Panama route, 4, 19-20, 29-54, 61, 207
Panama City, 20, 34-35, 36, 40, 52, 53, 297; American hospital, cemetery, 38
Panama fever. *See* yellow fever
Panama Railroad, 37-38, 61
Panamint Mountains, 138
panning, 227-28
Parke, Dr. Charles R., 117
Parker, Dr. R. R., 310
Patagonia, 68, 71
Pattie, James Ohio, 296
Pawnee, the, 102
pears, 221
Peoples, John, 153, 157-60
"people's courts," 244
pepper, 223
Perkins, Isaac, 221-22
petroleum, 223n
Phelan, Dr. Gregory, 216

Philadelphia, 51
Philadelphia (steamer), 302
Phillips, Hugh, 232
phrenology, phrenologists, 6, 294
Physiomedicals, 182n
pigs, 25
Pioneer Line, 120
Pizarro, Señor, 252
Placerville, Calif., 223, 258-60
Platte River, 81, 96, 102, 130, 304
pleasures, mining-camp, 240-41
Plymouth, Mass., 23
pneumonia, 233
Polk, James J., 19
Pond, Dr. Horace R., 245
porpoises, 66
potatoes, 69, 238
Poyle, William, 142-43, 144, 148-49
Praslow, Dr. J., 68, 69, 70
Pratt, Captain Timothy, and family, 219
Price, Dr., 313
prices, 167-68, 169, 187, 194, 229; of medicine, 11, 180
prickly pear, 310
Proctor, Dr. W. G., 313
property: city, 191-92; prices of, 169
purging, 8, 41-42, 70. *See also* specific diseases

quacks, quackery, 177-179, 214, 233-34, 257-58, 285-88. *See also* doctors
quarantine, 26, 180, 208-9, 210, 213, 299
quinine, 11, 37, 40, 180. *See also* malaria

Raft River, 311
rains, 168, 172, 193. *See also* floods
rats, 168
Read, Georgia Willis, 310
real estate, 169, 191-92
Reed, Dr. Isaac, 30-31
Reformed Botanics, 182n
regulars (doctors), 7, 8, 9, 10, 287, 288. *See also* doctors
relief parties, 151-64
rents, 168, 180
rheumatism, 171, 233
rice, 116
Rich Bar, 240, 246-53

Richardson, Mr. and Mrs. W. H., 261-62
rickettsia, 115
Rio de Janiero, 67, 297
robbery (theft), 243, 244-45
Rocky Mountain spotted fever, 115
Rocky Mountains, 97-98, 111-15ff., 161 (See also mountain men; specific areas, travelers); South Pass, 81, 87, 112, 304
Rogers, John, 137, 138, 139
Root, John, 156-57
Rosenberg, Charles E., 298, 299
Royce, Mr. and Mrs. Josiah, and family, 150, 160-64
Royce, Josiah (son—philosopher), 164n
Rucker, Major D. H., 153-55, 158, 159
Rush, Dr. Benjamin, 294
Russia, 24
Ryan, Arabella (Belle), 261-62, 270

Sacramento, 3, 17-18, 169-70, 173-75, 208 (See also Sutter's Fort); cholera epidemic, 208, 211-12, 215-23; first hospitals, 182-87; floods, 195-203
Sacramento Placer-Times, 186, 211-12
Sacramento River, 195
Sacramento Settlers and Miners Tribune. See Settlers and Miners Tribune
Sacramento State Journal, 276
Sacramento Transcript, 207, 215, 216, 217, 218, 223
sailors, 193. See also navy; sea routes
St. Joseph, Mo., 86, 89, 90, 95
Saint Mary's Hospital, 317
salads, 117
saloon-clinic, 179
"salt horse," 66
Salt Lake City, 86, 134-35, 161, 304
salt pork, 116
San Blas, Mexico, 48
San Diego, Calif., 17
San Francisco, 3, 4-5, 11, 12, 60, 167-71, 173, 175, 176-81; cholera in, 202, 208-11 212-15; contributions to relief parties, 153; crime, violence in, 261-80; Dr. Ball recommended to citizens of, 43-44; fires, 203-6; first hospitals, 187-94; learns of gold 14-16; voyage to (See sea routes)

San Francisco Alta California. See Alta California
San Francisco Bay, 83
San Francisco Evening Bulletin, 262-63, 317
San Francisco Sun, 317
San Francisco Times, 283-84
San Jose, Calif., 17, 233, 244
San Juan River, 55, 156
San Juan del Sur, 61
Sand Walking Company, 135-90, 161
sanitation, 4-5, 25-26, 34-35, 168, 208, 299-300. (See also specific diseases, places); Board of Health and, 213; doctors and, 10 (See also doctors); fires and, 205
Santa Barbara, Calif., 17
Santa Cruz, Calif., 17
Santa Fe Trail, 305
Sargent, Lorenzo, 12
Scannell, Sheriff, 269
Schaeffer, Dr. Luther M., 10
Schallenberger, Moses, 306-7
schools and training, medical, 9, 285, 289. See also doctors
Scofield, H. A., 70-71, 72
Scroggins, John, 154
scurvy and scorbutics, 66, 68-70, 75, 115-21, 171, 183-84; in mining camps, 229, 236-39
sea routes, 4, 19-23, 29-75
Seeking the Golden Fleece (Stillman), 185n
service berries, 117
Settlers and Miners Tribune, 215, 223
sex: of hospital patients, 174, 313; "wasting manhood," 285-86
shark, 66
Shaw, Reuben, 75
Sherman, William Tecumseh, 18, 270-71
ships, 64-65 (See also sea routes); abandoned, 167
Shirley, Dame. See Clappe, Mrs. Fayette (Louise)
Shuart, Jesse, 244
sickness. See disease, sickness
Sierra Nevada (ship), 61
Sierra Nevadas, 83-86, 114-15ff., 125, 140-49, 155-57ff., 306-7. See also specific routes, travelers

silver nitrate, 275
Simonds, Dr. John, 300
Sioux, 102, 103
Sisters of Mercy, 317
slaves, 94, 95-96
smallpox, 11
Smith, Dr. Barlow, 285
Smith, Jedediah, 82, 304
Smith, General Persifor, 152-53
Smith, Dr. Peter, 190, 191, 214
Snake River, 304
snakeroot, 143
soldiers. *See* army
Soledad Canyon, 138
Somers, Tom, 249
Sonoma, Calif., 17
South Pass, 81, 87, 112, 304
Southern California, 58
Spain and the Spanish, 32, 249-51
Spaulding, Dr. Volney, 211, 217
Splendid (clipper), 219-20
spruce tea, 238
Spurzheim, Johann Kaspar, 294
Stanbury, Captain Howard, 103, 104
Stanford University, 317
starvation. *See* food and food shortages
State Marine Hospital, 171, 193-94, 317
Staten Island, 27
steam baths, 238
Stewart, George P., 307
Stillman, Dr. J. D. B., 5, 171, 172-73, 185, 186, 239, 293; in flood, 198-99, 200
Stillman-Morse hospital, 185-86, 198-200
stowaways, 70
Strait of Magellan, 65, 73
Strangers' Friends Society, 190
streets, 168. *See also* sanitation
suicides, 175, 252, 271-72
Sullivan, James "Yankee," 271-72
sulphur pills, 214, 223
surgery, 11, 239, 274-75
Sutter, John Augustus, 14, 169
Sutter's Fort, 14, 18, 81, 116, 124, 169, 184, 306
sweating, 7-8
Sweetwater River, 81

tacks, 168
Tasheira, Mrs. and Mrs. Anthony Lewis, 225-26
tax, commutation, 193
Taylor, Bayard, 32, 38-40, 127
Taylor, Dr. W. W., 220
Taylor, Rev. William, 188-89, 192
Terry, David S., 258, 272-75
Thayer (lawyer), 254
"Theodor," 230, 234
Thompson, Dr. Jeter L., 104
Thomson, Dr. Samuel, 182
Thomsonians, 9, 182
ticks, 115
Toland, Dr. Hugh H., 265, 266, 268, 277, 278, 289
Toland Medical College, 317-18
Townsend, Dr. John, 15-16, 84-85, 224
Townsend, Mrs. John, 85, 306
training, medical. *See* schools and training, medical
Truckee River, 114, 133, 160
True Thomsonians, 182n
Tucker (injured man), 126
Tuolumne County, 225
Twain, Mark, 60
typhoid, 171, 233
typhus, 171, 172
Tyson, Dr. James, 7

Uncle Sam (ship), 61
United States Mail line, 19

vaccination, 11
Valparaiso, 71-72
Vanderbilt, Cornelius, 59
Vanderbilt Line, 59-63
vegetables, 229. *See also* specific kinds
Venice, 208
Vibrio comma, 298
vigilantes, 244, 250, 251, 261, 267-76, 278
violence. *See* crime and violence
Vizcaino, Sebastian, 310
Vizetelly, Henry, 308-9
Voyage Médical en Californie, 178
vultures, 35

wages, 168
wagon trains. *See* overland routes
Walker, Joe, 82, 304

Walker, William, 302
"Walkers' Train," 115
Ware, Joseph E., 108-9
water, 93, 113-14, 128, 161-62, 208; alkali in, 110; and disease (*See* disease, sickness; specific illnesses); hydropaths and, 9, 10; at sea, 48, 57, 58-59, 66-67, 70, 71
weapons, 89, 244. *See also* crime and violence
Webber, Dr. David Gould, 301
Weberville, Calif., 223
Webster, Kimball, 91
Wells Fargo Express, 258
Whitehall (N.Y.) *Whitehaller*, 72
Whitman, Dr. Marcus, 304
Wierzbicki, Dr. Felix Paul, 9-10, 71
Willis, Dr. Edward, 258-60
Windeler, Adolphus, 230, 234, 236, 241; and Brown's execution, 246-47

wing dams, 228
Wolf, Lawrence, 219
wolves, 92
women, 30, 60, 61, 67 (*See also* specific people, routes, traveling parties); in flood, 96-97; sex of hospital patients, 174, 313
Wood, Rev. James, 64, 67-68
Woolley, Dr. G. W., 215
Wyandot Indians, 104
Wyoming, 81. *See also* specific places

Yale University, 294
yeast, 116
yellow fever, 36, 46, 47, 60, 61, 300
Yeomans, Captain ("Dr. Roberts"), 257-58
Young, Dr., 287
Yuba River, 85